About the author

An American nurse-midwife, Laura Fitzgerald has worked in direct client care and in public health programs domestically and overseas for twenty years, serving extended posts in Malawi, Tanzania, Eswatini and Pakistan. Laura now lives with her husband and two daughters in southeast Asia. *Those Who Eat Like Crocodiles* is her first book.

Those Who Eat Like Crocodiles

Those Who Eat Like Crocodiles

Laura Fitzgerald

unbound

This edition first published in 2020

Unbound
6th Floor Mutual House, 70 Conduit Street, London W1S 2GF
www.unbound.com
All rights reserved

ISBN (eBook): 978-1-78965-070-9
ISBN (Paperback): 978-1-78965-069-3

Cover design by Mecob

Printed and bound in Great Britain by Clays Ltd, Elcograf S.p.A.

MIX
Paper from
responsible sources
FSC® C018072

For Abraham

Super Patrons

Jessica Aaker
Sohail Agha
Carolyn Alesbury
Sheldon Allen
Mike Arvelo
Kait Atkins
Becca Beaumont Talcott
Jeanette Begany
Sara Bellamy
Meg Bertram
Jennifer Breads
Megan Bridges
Kerry & Thom Bruce
Cal Bruns
Kathryn Carmichael
Mary Carmody
Catherine Carr
Elaine Charurat
Megan Christofield
Anne Condon
Meghan Constantino
Kelly Cure
Kelly Curran
Ronnene & Cooper Dawson
Dogmatix
Kate Earle Jensen
Leah Elliott
Cherrie Evans
Mae Fayer
Toby Fitzgerald

Jill Fitzgerald
Anne Fitzgerald
Ed Fitzgerald
Maureen Flood
Linda Fogarty
Bob Forrester
Jeane Garcia Davis
Katie Alice Gibson Overby
Meredith Goff
Meghan Greeley
Ashley Gresh
J.C. Hallman
Leah Hart
Leilani Hastings
Courtney Hilbert
Sara Hougan
Richard Hughes
Allison Jane
Peter Johnson
Dan Kieran
Maryjane Lacoste
Joseph Lanning
Eva Lathrop
Nicole Leigh
Jodi Lis
Linda and Paul Loffler
Frances Longley
Khanya Lue
Tiffany Lundern
Kirsten Lyerly

Scott MacEachern
Liz Mallas
Christina Maly
Cristin Marona
Melody McCoy
Anna McCrerey
Owen Ryan & Trevor McLaren
Mary Laird McNeel
Maureen Mersmann
John Mitchinson
Susan Moffson
Jennifer Nelson
Annelie Nilsson
Anne O'Hara
Jennifer Page-Osman
Katie Peel
Bernice Pelea
Cindy Pfitzenmaier
Anne Pfitzer
Theresa Piorr
Marya Plotkin
Hazel Plunkett
Justin Pollard
Martha Purdy

Jason Reed
Stephanie Reinhardt
Maureen Ries
Benjamin Rinehart
Mike Rizk
Rost Rost
Jean Sack
Sarah-Jane Savage
CeCe & Mark Sieffert
Karen Smack
J.R. Smeaton
Kira Smith
Galina Stolarsky
Amy Styles
Meghan Swor
Hannah Tappis
Alena Troxel
Alison Trump
Meredith Turner
Charlotte Warren
David Watts
Gwynneth Wong
Megan Wysong
Susi Wyss

1

At 2.15 p.m. on a Friday afternoon, a sedated pregnant woman lying alone in a dark room off the maternity ward nearly died. Earlier that day she had arrived at Kibo Hospital having what looked like an epileptic seizure. Saliva bubbled at the corners of her mouth. Her movements were exaggerated, jerky and unnatural. Her eyes rolled deep into the back of her head, like glass doll eyes. Mid-convulsion, she wet herself.

I watched the whole thing unfold in slow motion. Here it was: textbook eclampsia, a life-threatening disorder of pregnancy marked by high blood pressure, progressive organ damage and seizures. I knew that much, even though the only eclamptic patient I'd ever cared for directly was a smart, ponytailed classmate faking a fit in the Yale School of Nursing's clinical skills lab two years earlier.

After the pregnant woman came to, still lying on the concrete floor, one of my fellow midwives gave her a hit of Valium and admitted her into that dark side room. She'd been quiet back there for the better part of the afternoon until a nurse went in to check vitals and couldn't find her

1

baby's heartbeat. Initially, this didn't overly worry the nurse. Sometimes babies hid, played games with you. But the nurse didn't have time for games. The maternity ward was packed. Impatient to locate the horse-hoof gallop of the baby's heart, the nurse pressed the wide bell of a fetoscope deep into the sleepy woman's abdomen. When the pressure caused the groggy patient to shriek, the nurse pulled back, startled. She then watched in horror as a wadded cloth tucked underneath the woman's pelvis bloomed with successive rushes of red-black blood.

The nurse came running into the chaos of the maternity ward, calling for Julia, a Kibo midwife who'd just been hovering at my side throughout an uneventful delivery. I understood the nurse's impulse; in her shoes, I'd want Julia to take over too. Julia was like my mom, an in-control woman unflustered by medical crises. I, meanwhile, felt the air prick with the electric charge of emergency and stood deer-in-the-headlights frozen.

A few minutes later, two skinny men in black rubber boots swooped into the ward with a rusted gurney, hoisted the pregnant woman onto it and disappeared down a corridor. When they were gone, the senior midwife sat down at the ward's only desk and spooned three scoops of white sugar into a mug of milky tea. She swirled the sweet liquid around and around.

'Will she be okay? Is there a doctor on duty for surgery?' I asked her.

I rarely spoke to the senior midwives. This was because, as a visitor and a white American, my overall goal at Kibo was to keep a low profile. Well, that and the fact that they could be an intimidating bunch.

The in-charge, unmoved, looked at me. She blew on her tea. 'Yes, the surgeon is here. It is in God's hands now, my dear.'

Maybe it's a cliché, one that does a disservice to too many African friends and colleagues, to paint my experience in a Tanzanian hospital this way: the sickness, the chaos. But that doesn't make it any less true. This six-month stint at Kibo was not my first rodeo; it followed a couple of Peace Corps years in Malawi teaching community health, a few weeks at a bare-bones midwifery school and associated hospital in Haiti, and a month in a rural South African hospital during a news-making outbreak of multidrug-resistant tuberculosis. But, somehow, Kibo was different. And by different, I mean worse.

Kibo was a referral hospital, a depot for the sickest of the sick. When you entered Kibo's maternity ward, the smell hit you first – ammonia, metallic blood, paraffin, cleaning chemicals. Orderlies wearing enormous army-green gumboots dumped bucketloads of water directly onto the floor and shooed laboring women out of the way as they swept amniotic fluid, urine, or vomit into a grated drain on the side of the room. IV stands ricocheted off gurneys with banging noises. Placenta-filled kidney dishes piled up next to a single washbasin. Mothers and sisters, nieces and cousins bustled in with fresh clothes and roasted corn. Laboring women beat fists into thighs in a silent attempt to discharge the pain.

I pulled off plastic gloves soiled with blood and sticky white vernix and made a quick note in my patient's file: 'Normal spontaneous vaginal delivery. Estimated blood loss 250 ml. No lacerations. Mother and baby doing well.'

Then, I excused myself.

I managed to keep it together until I was safely behind the closed door of the staff toilet, where a voice in my head screamed: *Get me out of here!* I was so ashamed of this. I was a certified nurse-midwife, thoroughly and expensively trained to handle environments and situations like these. So why, exactly, did I find it all so unbearable? Every day, why did I experience this place as such a terrible, disintegrating assault on my body and spirit and psyche? What was wrong with me?

Throughout the three years of my midwifery program, instructors had commented on how level-headed I was in a crisis. Kept my wits about me, kept my voice steady and calm. During that clinical rotation in South Africa, a professor gave me the highest praise a seasoned midwife can offer a young apprentice: 'If I were going to have another baby, I'd want you by my side.' It should have set me aglow with pride. Instead, I felt like the worst kind of fake.

Because the instructors didn't see me bawling in bathrooms the world over. They didn't know about my recurring nightmares – phantom babies stuck halfway out, babies dropped on the floor, babies stashed in dresser drawers and forgotten. My instructors didn't know how I sat in navy-blue scrubs in a parked car on York Street, anticipating disaster, summoning the strength to open the door, approach the elevator and pass into Yale New Haven Hospital's Labor and Birth unit. They didn't know I ruminated for days after a first catheter insertion made my patient claw at my arms, were unaware of the gut-punch I felt when a laboring teen who sucked her thumb through each contraction barked at me to shut the fuck up.

They didn't know these things because I didn't tell them. I'd grown up in leafy Fairfield County, Connecticut, a peace-making middle child pegged since kindergarten as conscientious and easily wounded. But by my twenties, I'd learned how to work around these supposed weaknesses, disguised them behind a steady flow of achievements. I mastered the art of sizing up instructors' expectations and delivering my work carefully tailored to meet them.

But here's the thing: it turns out this way of working couldn't be further from the functioning of human physiology.

Or of real life. The ability to sit alone with a keyboard and crank out a prize-winning essay, or slog through a 26.2-mile race, or hang out for two years in an East African village as an underworked Peace Corps volunteer, bore no relationship whatsoever to the capacity to witness another's astonishing pain, or to respond with cool composure to rivers of blood pumping from unrecognizable, mangled vaginal tissue. My achievements meant nothing to the women at Kibo who looked at me with pleading eyes and sliced the sides of their hands across their bulging abdomens. Some who knew English begged, 'Please, madam, *cut me.*'

I'd been a fool to think that the fears I'd experienced in high-tech American hospitals would subside in Tanzania. Still, there was at least an approximation of logic behind why I'd applied for, and accepted, the US-funded position to support Kibo healthcare workers to deliver services that prevented the transmission of HIV from women to babies around the time of birth. A year after passing my licensure exam, I theorized that my problem with midwifery was that I had entered a medical field in the US so marked by fear and litigation – in one final-semester 'professional issues' class, we were told that, statistically, we should expect to be sued within the first seven years of practice – that it was divorced from the heart of the work. In Tanzania, I knew I'd face a substantial workload but figured I'd be buoyed by my recent, evidence-based education and driven by a clear sense of purpose. After all, the reason I became a midwife was what I'd seen as a Peace Corps volunteer in Malawi: the particularly insidious effect poverty, gender inequity and insufficient healthcare resources exert on women's reproductive lives. I thought returning to Africa would solidify my commitment to midwifery. I had wanted to get on an airplane and leave behind the internal voices of guilt (*why don't you love delivering babies?*) and inadequacy (*because you just can't hack it!*).

But it hadn't quite worked out that way. The maternity unit at Kibo was tougher than anything I'd ever known. Like an animal who instinctively seeks a dark corner to give birth, I'd sweated and struggled in that hard place, trying to force a metamorphosis. Several months in, I just felt battered and stupid and heartsick.

Safe behind the closed door of the staff toilet, I pushed the heels of my hands against my tear ducts and fanned my splotchy cheeks in front of a narrow window grate. Then I pulled my phone out of the saggy pocket of my scrub bottoms and texted Rachel, a Tanzanian nurse-midwife who was also thirty-one years old, and my best friend at Kibo Hospital. *I need to get out of the maternity ward. Are you in the antenatal clinic?*

Petals of sweet-smelling frangipani glistened wet above my head as I marched one foot in front of the other along an open-air corridor. Backed up against the wall, dozens of pregnant women in early labor waited in unmoving queues. Their heads turned as I passed. Continuing along a worn brick pathway to meet Rachel, I got real with myself. Inside my head, what felt to be both a very true and deeply sad statement came to me: 'Your last-ditch effort to become a real midwife is failing.'

The only person I'd ever explained this to with any kind of clarity had been a New Haven therapist. 'I love the idea of midwifery, but I don't think I actually like being a midwife,' I'd told her. The therapist looked like quite a few midwives I knew: no makeup, middle part, Dansko clogs. When she asked me what I thought the problem was, I babbled something about blood, vomit, adrenaline, medical egos, the constant beeping of machinery, 2 a.m. emergencies, mistakes, the terrible life-and-death consequences of those mistakes. 'I think

I've just spent tens of thousands of dollars on an education I regret,' I told her.

Up to that point in my life, all three full decades of it, I'd never met anyone who went to the extreme effort and expense of earning a professional degree from a prestigious institution before choosing not to use it. How would one would go forth into the world and explain such a baffling decision?

'Knowing what you don't want to do is sometimes as valuable as knowing what you do,' the therapist responded, which I found too saccharine, too a-day-late-and-a-dollar-short to be either helpful or comforting. But her next question got me thinking: 'Are there any aspects of the work that you do enjoy?'

Oh, yes. A thousand times, yes. I loved listening to women. I loved their stories, their personalities. I loved being able to give good news, validate normalcy. I loved contributing to a happy outcome.

So, for over a year after graduation I had continued to work at a New Haven community women's health clinic. I dealt with abortion clients, mostly, and spent much of my workday counseling and consoling. But the thought of doing that for a lifetime – being a technician of termination – did not appeal. Given the uninsured and mostly undocumented population we worked with, there were not enough happy outcomes. I took a pair of mental binoculars and looked out across the expanse of the next thirty years and didn't like what I saw – a greying, emotionally spent, politically frustrated and intellectually under-stimulated woman.

Which was not who I wanted to be. Despite the blushing introversion, the hypersensitivity and the people-pleasing, I desperately wanted a sweeping, storybook, swashbuckling life: to be Hana from *The English Patient*, equal parts tragedy and romance, conducting an intrepid, care-giving life in polka-dotted summer dresses and rubber-soled tennis shoes. What to do with that self-awareness? How to square my deep wish for the unconventional with my exposure-averse temperament?

Rachel was wrapping up with the day's pregnant clients when I arrived at the Reproductive Health Unit. Before shifting to the maternity ward, I'd worked side by side with her there. Early on we developed a tradition of debriefing at the end of the day – Rachel in the clinician's chair and I sitting atop an old examining table – while we sipped cold Coca-Colas from glass bottles. I'd pester her with a dozen nosy questions: *How do you get schoolgirls to come for HIV testing? Do they have sugar daddies? Did you? Will our clients use the condoms we give them? What about traditional healers? Are our clients seeing them, too? Why isn't she taking her medications? Why is she delaying her baby's treatment?* She'd gather up the questions over the course of a day and then answer them all at once through tales crafted in wide, looping circles as we finished our paperwork and fanned ourselves with faded green client charts. 'You Americans,' Rachel would say, 'speak too directly. Listen. I will teach you how to be clever with your words.'

That day – after the convulsing woman, after my meltdown in the staff toilet – I needed her wisdom. I needed her unfailing competence, her companionship.

'What's the problem, *buzi*?' she asked as soon as she saw me, using a slang Kiswahili word for a casual lover that had somehow morphed into an affectionate, platonic nickname that we used for each other.

'Ah, Rachel. I had to conduct another delivery today.'

'And what happened?' she asked.

'It's the maternity ward, I just... well, I can't do it. I think a woman might have died today.'

'*Buzi*, no one likes it in there,' Rachel declared, disingenuously, in my defense.

How silly, how self-absorbed I must sound to Rachel; to any of the midwives at Kibo. They didn't dither. They didn't hesitate. They did their jobs. And half the time, they did their jobs without basic supplies. One blood pressure cuff serviced the entire maternity ward. I mean, really, could I not just suck it up? Just trust myself? Just do what I'd been trained to do?

No, I could not. That's just it, I simply could not. I would not solve this one with fierce determination, could not rely on the old ninety-percent-perspiration rule. I couldn't outsmart, out-analyze this. I was done giving myself endless do-gooder, pull-yourself-up-by-your-bootstraps, grandiose lectures about how disadvantaged women needed me. No one needed a Nervous Nelly midwife.

'Sometimes I think I am not well suited to this work, Rachel,' I said, rubbing my temples with my fingertips.

I paused. Maybe I just didn't want to get into this. To get into my crisis of confidence would be to launch headlong into territory I tried my best to avoid: class, privilege, choice. Such discussions would, in my mind, highlight just how different our worlds were. I was afraid they would distance us. 'I'm not like you,' I said instead. 'You handle stressful situations so well.'

'I will tell you... Even for me, it's not easy. You are not always sure if you have done the proper thing. It's true, sometimes babies die, and sometimes mothers die. Sometimes we make mistakes,' Rachel said. 'We are learning through our mistakes... even you! Remember when you arrived? You were making so many mistakes!' she teased, then softened. '*Buzi*, today you need to enjoy. It is Friday. Today we will forget our problems. Let's go to town and drink some cold Tuskers!'

Then it was my turn to tease. 'Hey, maybe tonight I can finally meet your Big Raila?'

After a few weeks of working together counseling pregnant women about HIV – testing them once in the first trimester and again in the third, caring for those who tested positive and pricking the heels of their newborns to check for the virus – Rachel began to talk to me of the two men who wanted to marry her. We called each of these would-be boyfriends 'Raila.' The etymology had something to do with the botched Kenyan presidential election between Raila Odinga and Mwai Kibaki, an event that coincided with my arrival in Tanzania. Raila had become part of our invented language, one of the co-opted words that articulated our friendship.

A man we dubbed Small Raila called her cell phone several times a day and interrupted her patient visits to deliver gifts of perfume or jewelry. Rachel teased him just enough to keep him around, strung him along for recreation. The situation with Big Raila, however, a university lecturer who lived in Dar es Salaam, drove his own car, traveled to international conferences and had a not-quite-ex-wife and a couple of kids somewhere in the southern part of the country, was quite different from the comedy of Small Raila. Rachel's usual take-charge self-assurance faltered when she spoke of Big Raila. It was obvious that this Raila held her heart.

At my suggestion of inviting Big Raila for a night of drinking, Rachel hesitated. But then she punched a message into her flip phone and sent the text through.

'You will be a detective tonight, *buzi*,' she said to me. 'You will ask him the important questions.'

'Of course,' I agreed.

I had taught Rachel three new English words, all of which she employed often: gossip, stalker and detective. According to Rachel, most women were the first, most men were the second and she was the third.

We left Kibo and went straight to the tin-roofed house

where she rented a room. The scent of frying fish spiked the air. A TV in one of the front rooms pounded out hip-hop, matching our footsteps beat for beat. Rachel led the way toward her bedroom, where she began arranging fat batik-covered pillows – turquoise, purple and zebra-print – at the head of her bed. It was the first time I'd seen where she lived. 'It looks just like my room!' I said. This was true. The foam mattress underneath a mosquito net and the clothing strewn over a few haphazard pieces of furniture had identical twins back in my $25-a-night room in a nearby guesthouse.

While I perched on her bed, Rachel stepped into flowing brown pants and dropped a matching top, embroidered with whorls of gold thread, over her head, pulling the fabric down her long arms. She applied burgundy lipstick from a beveled tube.

'You remember the questions, right?' she asked.

'I remember,' I told her.

In order to assess Big Raila's worthiness and his intentions, I would ask him how long he had known Rachel. Then, when he answered the honest six years, I was to follow up with this kicker: 'Well, after six years, what exactly are you expecting?'

I think the idea was to catch him off guard and corner him into verbalizing a desire to marry her. But I knew, even during our rehearsals, that I would chicken out. In any case, I doubted the usefulness of my interference, although I understood her situation perfectly. Despite the dissimilarities in our life circumstances, Rachel and I were passengers aboard the same boat. We craved wavering men and cared for pregnant women while doing our best to ignore the biological clocks that buzzed like maddening mosquitoes within us.

'What does he do? Does he have a good job?' Rachel had asked when she learned of my own ambivalent Raila, an Irishman with an insatiable wanderlust.

'He's a teacher,' I told her.

'Does he want to marry you?' she had probed.

'No.'

'Is he married already?'

'No.'

'Then what?'

I could have said that we were both too stubborn and too independent and too cerebral, but I didn't. 'He just doesn't want to.'

'But how long have you been with him?'

'On and off for six years. The same as you.'

Rachel dropped her hands softly onto my shoulders. 'You may need to consider that your Raila has another girlfriend,' she said, as if delivering a difficult diagnosis. I nodded. In Tanzania, popular wisdom held that everyone, if he or she could afford the upkeep, maintained an extra lover or two.

Big Raila, when he arrived to pick us up, was thin, almost slight next to my muscular friend. He wore glasses and a hearing aid. His face was pleasingly soft and lined, his smile kind and his manner gentle. Rachel left me alone with him in one of the front rooms as she retreated back down the hallway to gather her handbag. The TV still blasted Kiswahili MTV, where near-naked women writhed atop shiny cars and shinier, gold-chained men. Five-year-old Lukia, the daughter of one of Rachel's neighbors, sat next to me on the crimson velour couch, sliding small fingers along the inside of my wrist, tormented by two competing fascinations – the thick blue of my blood vessels, visible through pink skin, and the TV. I wrapped an arm around her tiny waist.

Then, remembering my assignment, I trained my attention on Big Raila and asked him back-to-back questions in English. *Where did you grow up? How many are in your family? Tell me about your university. Tell me about your students.* I was nearly yelling over the TV. His eyes drifted repeatedly to the long-haired Kenyan dancers on the screen. I worked harder, pressed further, a steady stream of questions that did not include those I had been charged with asking. I sensed Big Raila was a decent man. I sensed he cared about my friend. Their situation, like mine, was probably complicated by factors that would be difficult for anyone else to fully understand.

Lukia waved from the front porch as we got into Big Raila's car, a beat-up grey sedan. We were headed to one of his favorite haunts: 'Somewhere you can hear real African music,' he said. 'You will love it. It's a real mix-up.' We drove away from Kibo and toward Dar es Salaam, about an hour away.

We started out with plates of noodles at a Chinese restaurant. Several cold beers all around. By the time we got to Q Bar, my head was spinning. Rachel held my hand and led me through the crowd while Big Raila secured more drinks. Indeed, it was a real mix-up: paunchy, aging white men nuzzled against eye-shadowed, belly-baring, high-heeled African teenagers. An Asian woman circled the room, whirling a silken curtain of waist-length hair.

I sat at a wooden picnic table. Rachel planted a bottle of cold Tusker beer in front of me and leaned into my ear, shouting over the music. 'This place is HIV,' she said. 'These people are all drunkards. There will be no protection in the guesthouses tonight!'

I did not want to think about the virus. I just wanted to be carried into carefree oblivion by the thrum of the speakers and the unfolding panorama of easy, democratic couplings, to silence my daily lectures about choices, about restraint. As if to help me achieve this, a lanky man with a tousled mop of blonde hair motioned to the empty spot by my other side. I told him in Kiswahili that he was welcome to it.

'Where are you from?' he asked, settling onto the bench.

'The US,' I replied. 'You?' Based on the swagger, he could be a hero-type, I decided. Or a safari guide. Or another Kilimanjaro-bound tourist.

'The Netherlands. I am a pilot with the UN. We're dropping emergency food supplies into the Sudan.'

Ah, yes. Here he was. I had met so many versions of him. Part humanitarian, part danger junkie. The hard drinking. The intense blue eyes. Fingernails bitten to the quick. Strings of faded beads and worn rope around the wrist. Tattoos. Squinting up at a face that was darker but less handsome than my Irish Raila's, I realized that I could do whatever I wanted about this situation. I was at Q Bar in Dar es Salaam, Tanzania, getting wasted.

Rachel sat quietly sipping her beer as I chatted with the pilot. Her clinical intuition often astonished me, and I wondered what she was thinking as I cocked my head and bent it toward him so I could hear what he was saying. The Dutch pilot was angry with our president, George W. Bush. He was pretty direct in his condemnations of Americans in general, actually, which took guts considering that he was hitting on one.

Eventually, Rachel stood up. Then Big Raila, who had joined our table, followed suit. Rachel said, 'Laura, it is late. I'm sorry, my friend, but now it is time to go home.'

Obediently, I rose from the bench, wobbling as I straightened my legs, arms braced against the plastic tablecloth. I apologized to the pilot for our hasty exit and trailed Rachel and Big Raila to the parking lot.

We didn't talk much on the drive. I stared out the window at the sleeping city. Honking vehicles, swerving minibuses and aggressive peddlers had long packed it in for the night. Humid air, filtering in through the crack in the rear window, smelled of the ocean.

Rachel suggested that I spend the night at her house to avoid

14

the gossip that would follow an indecently late and inebriated arrival at my guesthouse. It was nearly three o'clock in the morning when Big Raila pulled up to Rachel's front steps. He wished us both a good night and then executed a tight turn in the space between a water pump and the porch.

Alone with Rachel in her bedroom, I worried. 'I can't sleep next to you. I've been drinking beer all night. My breath will suffocate you!'

She waved this away. 'Now I am also a drunkard. Nothing will disturb me.'

Rachel unknotted the mosquito net from above her bed as I stepped through a door to a bathroom, planted my bare feet on a pair of cement footprints and looked down at the black hole in the floor between them. Facing me, lining a tiled wall, bottles of skin-lightening cream and spray deodorant sat under a freestanding faucet.

When I returned to the bedroom, sadness descended. How nice it had been to get away from Kibo, from women desperate to keep their unborn children from contracting the virus, from the nightmare of the maternity ward. Rachel lay prostrate on her mattress, arms at forty-five-degree angles from her torso, hands arranged with pale palms facing up, feet splayed apart and eyelids lowered. 'Good night, *buzi*,' she mumbled.

I flipped onto my side, a curved spine facing my sleeping friend – how much I loved her, how her unthinking generosity humbled me – and drew my bare knees up to the hem of my T-shirt. Rachel snored. A soft breeze puffed in through the window. I planned the optimistic reassurances I would offer Rachel about the future she longed for. Meanwhile, when I considered my own uncertain future, defeat and pessimism bubbled back.

The next morning, Rachel was up with the roosters and the pre-dawn call to prayer from a nearby minaret. 'I have an appointment at the hair salon,' she explained, her tone breezy, her manner rested and cheerful. 'What are you going to do today, *buzi*?'

'The *mzungus* invited me to the Yacht Club,' I told her, still horizontal on a sweaty, twisted sheet. 'I promised them I would go.' I used the local term for white foreigners as a way to align myself with her, wanting her to believe that I would rather spend the weekend in the village with her, even though the truth was that every Saturday I could not get out of the village fast enough.

A claptrap minibus took me back to my guesthouse where I would shower and pack a few things for a night in Dar es Salaam. Even at 7 a.m., the heat was insufferable. Wedged into a window seat, I stared out the cracked window and remembered the woman with eclampsia from the day before. I never found out what happened to her.

I climbed down from the minibus at the main market of my village, Mile One. The conductor slid open the side door and a whoosh of red dust and heat spilled inside as we ducked our heads and piled out. A clutch of Rasta boys congregated next to the bus stop, straddling their motorcycles, bored.

'Eh, sister Flora!' they said in high-pitched voices. 'How are you? Eh, Flora! Good morning!' They collapsed with the weight of stoned laughter. I seethed in silence.

Tanzania was a place of predictable routines, my daily encounters with the bike boys just one reliable element. Another: the two fresh chapatis bought from the same market woman each morning, after making a beeline from the minibus. She fried the bread right there on the steps of her house while her toddler, naked from the waist down, played contentedly in the dirt next to the burner. She lifted the greasy circles from the searing heat with nerve-deadened fingers, wrapped them in a sheet of newspaper and handed them over with a full-faced smile.

Walking up the hill to the guesthouse, I nibbled on torn strips of hot chapati and sweated. The back of my lungs ached. There was a new soreness when I inhaled. Too much smoke at Q Bar. And Rachel's mattress was hard. The mattress at my guesthouse was also hard. So were the pillows. Somehow, my bones felt too close to the surface. Tanzania was adding creaks and tweaky pains, the red dirt destroying shoes, clothes and bags. But wasn't this what I had wanted? To be refined, sanded down, toughened up? Forced to override the uncooperative, too-easily-hurt mess of me?

Just as I had in Malawi, I patted myself on the back for my attempts at virtue and authenticity, for the rivers of sweat that stung my eyes and tasted salty on my lips, for my efforts to speak Kiswahili, for living and working side by side with Tanzanians. Yet I also cursed the shower that stank of rot, and was incensed to learn that the expansive pool of water and sludge that sat stagnant next to my guesthouse was an outpouring of raw sewage.

To cope, I moved from moment to moment, hour to hour, day to day, from one hit of pleasure to the next. A life lived in constant jumping-bean propulsion toward the next sugary treat, the next email from home, the next good book, the next hour of real TV, the next bit of shade, the next cool breeze, the next long-distance reunion, the next cold drink, hot drink, alcoholic drink, the next annihilating hit of relief.

And so, as always, I was eager to get back on the road to Dar, where a whole host of escapist comforts awaited me, not least of which was the promise of easy, unthinking communication – the halting tumble of curses and tangents and 'you knows?' of other English-speaking expats. People who would never need to know of my failures.

2

Barbara, a vivacious, middle-aged American who'd spent a career in development, invited me to the members-only Yacht Club after she'd decided that, firstly, I needed to have more fun, and, secondly, I needed to network. She told me to get to the club by five, time enough for a swim and a one-on-one cocktail before meeting other expats for an all-ladies dinner.

The organization that had hired me to work at Kibo maintained a staff house in a Dar neighborhood called Upanga. The spacious ground-floor apartment had two en-suite bedrooms and a big kitchen. Our landlady, who lived upstairs, worked for the World Food Program. Apparently, feeding Tanzania's poor paid well: each apartment rented for close to $2,000 per month. Ours accommodated a Dar-based Ugandan social worker full-time and any of the other six of us short-termers whenever we were passing through.

I hung out at the apartment for a few zoned-out hours, watching BBC under the blasting aircon. Then there was just enough time for a quick pre-club jog beside the Indian Ocean. I pulled on a pair of loose jogging shorts (to expose my knees – a modest but thrilling liberation I allowed myself only in the city) and arranged headphones over my ears. Soon my feet fell into a pounding rhythm through sand-swept Upanga side streets. Past a bicycle equipped with an ice-cream freezer and churning out a music-box version of 'Oh My Darling, Clementine', past a tall, lean man in long braids and red tartan wraps who gave me a thumbs-up from his seat at the Scout Bar, to the beach on Ocean Road.

Eventually, instead of turning back to Upanga, I crossed a noisy, chaotic T-junction toward the ritzy Peninsula. Peddlers walked right out into the middle of the madness to hawk newspapers, cheap sunglasses and cell phone chargers. A shop on the left side of the road sold reed furniture, beanbag chairs and hammocks. The shrubby patch to the right led down to a littered, scrabbly oceanfront populated by a small colony of homeless men, several of whom were albino.

Soon the posh Peninsula revealed itself as the manicured, septic-tanked, razor-wired realm of the well-to-do. I followed a dirt path along picture-perfect estates, took in circular drives and guarded fences, terraces and wrought-iron lawn furniture. This was the antithesis of the ascetic life I professed to live in Mile One. It was material beauty, unabashed excess. The fantasy of it called to me – just a brief respite, to value style over substance, to glide along the surface.

Battling this constant tension consumed much of my energy. I loved Rachel, felt closer to her than to anyone during my four months in Tanzania. And I deeply valued the work of the midwives in Kibo. After a high-stress week on the job, they spent their weekends cooking for their families, washing laundry by hand and readying their kids for church. They supported aging parents, cared for sick siblings and paid school expenses for nieces and nephews. They regularly – without recognition or drama – pulled bills out of their own pockets to fund clients' transport, laboratory test fees, or telephone airtime. But I would never be one of them. Nor could I truly stomach the idea of being a full-time insider in the eye-candy mansions here, where landscaping alone cost more than Rachel earned in a year, and where tinted car windows kept Kibo Hospital's uncomfortable reality out of view.

I turned to running, in part, because I could not reconcile these things. I found solace in the straightforward industry of the body, in the scenic back roads, zoning out through my headphones as my feet pounded the ground. The tunes I'd cued up for that Saturday were sent by my Raila, the Irish teacher with an encyclopedic knowledge of indie music. I liked to think his compilations held hidden meaning, that he chose lyrics to say things he couldn't.

My twenties had been unusually peripatetic, and the Irish teacher, tall and green-eyed, was the highlight of the decade. It had been months since the six-day trip to the west coast of Ireland when we last saw each other. Tucked away in a nearly empty bed-and-breakfast, the wind and rain battering at the windowpanes, we'd crawled back into bed in the early afternoons. The Irishman drew constellations between moles on my back with long, freckled fingers. He named them: Andromeda, Cassiopeia and Pegasus.

'What do you think of when you think of me?' I had asked him.

'Your perfect handwriting. Your letters,' he'd replied. Then he asked me to stay, which was nice, but not entirely convincing.

'I can't. I'm going to Tanzania, remember?'

Nevertheless, when I suggested meeting up after my assignment at Kibo ended, he swept my hair to the side and kissed his agreement onto the back of my neck. Sometimes he called my cheap Tanzanian mobile late at night, drunk and sweet. He would tell me he missed me in his singing Irish accent, and I convinced myself that by missed, he meant loved.

For six years, I'd been waiting. Drunken sweetness, whirlwind trips and long-distance theatrics had more or less sustained me during graduate school and the soul-searching months that followed. But here I was, in Tanzania, feeling increasingly lost in my life. I wanted him here to help me sort it out – yet another ache I attempted to release while feet pounded pavement, while hot air squeezed through sore lungs.

That afternoon, after my run, a driver dropped me at the edge of a palm-treed parking lot overlooking a low tidal flat. It didn't take much effort to pretend that I was somewhere familiar – maybe Cape Cod, where I'd spent every summer as a child and where it was perfectly normal to be surrounded by white people and cocktails and sparkling fiberglass boats. I wished I could loll in the salty water or catch an afternoon nap on a chaise longue. But Barbara had summoned me to the club to meet people, specifically to meet other American women in a position to offer me a job.

Barbara waved enthusiastically from a shaded table on a patio next to the lower bar. She was impossible to miss in an enormous straw hat. I was unsurprised to learn later that, during a posting in Uganda, she had landed a moment as an extra in a Leonardo DiCaprio film. Barbara was just that kind of woman – always around when things got interesting. When I first met her, she worked as a consultant for the same NGO that funded my placement at Kibo. With cropped gray hair and a loose jumper, she had struck me as a safe, motherly type, like those midwives who call grown women 'hon' and bake from-scratch brownies for hospital staff rooms. Then, like now, Barbara gave me a bright, unmistakably American smile. 'Laura! Up here!' We hugged. She smelled of lavender.

'How are things going at Kibo?' she asked.

'Not great,' I said honestly as we settled into our deck chairs.

'Hold on… I want to hear all about everything, but first – snacks and drinks!'

She ordered grilled shrimp marinated in Zanzibar spices and a round of Kilimanjaro lagers. We clinked bottles. After our first meeting a few months earlier, Barbara had given me this advice about my job: 'Organization!' she had said. 'That's where you can help. Other than that? Listen. Disappear into the background. Focus on the big picture. Ask tons of questions. Let them teach you. Let them tell you what they want and need. You're here for only six months? Relax. It may be that all you can do in that time frame is demonstrate to people that you care. Learn. Don't expect too much.'

I'd been trying to follow her advice. On good days, I could manage the chilled-out Zen approach. However, on the bad days, I felt as though I had no skin; like every irritation, discomfort, visual/auditory/olfactory offense projected itself directly and deeply into my flesh.

'Okay,' Barbara said, settling into her wicker chair. 'Talk to me. What's the latest?'

'Well, the situation is not exactly improving. I've shifted from the antenatal clinic to the maternity ward. I've got to tell you what I discovered last week.'

'Oh God… what?' Her eyes widened.

'Okay, so after babies are born, they are left in a separate nursery. It's not staffed all the time, nurses just go in every so often to check on the babies. Last week I was sitting next to the nursery door and I could hear a baby crying and smacking his fists against his mouth, trying to suck them. So I went in to see if I could bring him to his mother for a feeding. When I walked in, I saw that there was a bundle of a baby wrapped in cloth next to the fussy baby. The quiet baby's face was covered. My heart started to race. It wasn't moving at all. I peered in for a closer look. That was when I saw a piece of tape stuck to the inside of the tiny crib. There was a name written on it, the name of a woman who'd been rushed to surgery. The baby in that crib was dead. The body was just lying there in the nursery with the live babies.'

'That's intense.' Barbara shook her head empathetically. 'It's a tough place. That environment would be stressful for anyone. Just imagine what's it's like for the patients, or for the people who work there and don't get to leave after six months.'

'I know… But here's the thing, Barbara… I'm finding it so hard. I just don't want to be there.'

'Yeah, it's hard,' she said, 'that's why you're here. But you were a Peace Corps volunteer. And you are a midwife. Stick it out until the end of your contract, and then one of these NGOs should snatch you up. See what you can do tonight. I'll put in a good word.' Her eyes were equal parts kindness and mischief.

A couple of hours (and beers) later, the small crew of expat ladies arrived. One of them was the head of my NGO. What she self-deprecatingly called her 'cheerleader hair', the great sweep of thick gold that swished down around her elbows, was held off her face, headband-style, with a pair of oversized black sunglasses. She had the familiar look of certain French-manicured moms from my New England hometown; women who, during my high-school years, praised my way with kids when booking me for a Saturday night, asked about my nonexistent love life in warm whispers, pulled frozen pizzas out of stainless steel freezers, and came teetering home at midnight, urging corporate husbands to drive me home because they, wink-wink, were over the legal limit. Silently studying the gaggle of them at the Yacht Club, I was aware that, in all likelihood, these women were my future – the women my NPR-listening, yoga-practicing, book-clubbing friends and I would become. To find them so well represented in Tanzania? Now that surprised me.

Barbara expertly managed a round of introductions, and the women – who were a well-formed social circle already – fell into musical conversation. One of them, who did not look much older than me, kicked off flip-flops, stretched bare feet across patio tiles and asked me what had brought me to Dar. 'I'm working with a team of nurses on their prevention of mother-to-child transmission of HIV program in a hospital about an hour from here.'

We got to talking. She worked at a US-government office downtown, three floors of a white building flanked by shoe-shiners and chippie stands, where she attended back-to-back meetings, wrestled budgets and waded through project proposals. She was a donor, I realized, meaning she held the purse strings for projects like mine. I, on the other hand, held women's hoe-calloused hands and pricked sharp needles into babies' tiny feet. It was a trade-off. Her position comfortably financed a lakeside summer home in the States and covered private school for her daughter – but I had the hands-on street cred.

This donor, her face so open and interested, wanted to know exactly what it was like at Kibo. I looked over at Barbara, who had so generously orchestrated this meet-and-greet. I considered how to describe it. On one hand, if this donor was funding these programs, she should know the reality. On the other hand, I wanted to be diplomatic and measured, because, well, ultimately, I wanted a permanent job.

'It is a tough place,' I began. 'The conditions… how women are treated…'

So much for measured. And once I'd started, I couldn't stop.

'My first day on the ward, I saw a placental abruption. I'd never seen one before, only learned about it in midwifery school. But nurses here say it happens all the time.'

24

'What's a placental abruption?' the donor asked, her expression neutral.

'It's when the placenta detaches from the wall of the uterus during labor. Untreated, women can bleed to death and babies are cut off from their oxygen supply.'

'What causes it?'

'Well, in the States, it's usually drugs. Here? High blood pressure, diabetes, trauma to the abdomen – I'm not sure,' I answered.

We were quiet for a moment.

A Tanzanian woman approached the table with a sleeping infant nuzzled against her neck – a nanny with her charge. She handed the child to one of the other women, who mouthed 'thank you' and draped the bendy infant over her lap.

The donor picked up where we left off. 'So, what does it look like, the maternity ward?'

And suddenly I was telling the dead baby story again. 'There is a tiny room, off to the side of the triage unit that is supposed to house babies who need extra attention.' In my mind, I saw the nursery door, the handwritten sign that listed the steps in newborn resuscitation on a piece of torn flipchart paper. 'You know, they put the premature babies in there, or the babies who are discolored at birth.' I had seen plenty of them myself, some blue from a lack of oxygen, others yellow from the herbs women took to hurry labor. Then I told her about the lifeless baby, so carefully wrapped and labeled.

'When I asked about it, my friend Rachel told me about an incident that happened a couple of years ago – when two babies died on the same day. They were brought to the morgue unlabeled, and the staff gave the families the wrong babies. So after that, she said that they started keeping the babies' bodies, marked, in the nursery – to avoid confusion.'

Dear God, who talks about dead babies over chilled beer on

a Saturday night at an exclusive club to a group of *mothers*? I hoped the twilight disguised the red rising in my cheeks. I had to turn away from the women. My gaze shifted to a military procession of black ants crossing the patio. They moved in such a proud, certain motion, unbothered by the smoke wafting from a smoldering mosquito coil. Though their hard bodies would crunch loudly under a boot bottom, together they could bring down a gazelle, bite by bite.

I started to apologize when a third woman pulled up a chair. She carried a plate of spicy prawns and a tossed green salad in one hand and a Serengeti beer in the other. After she'd set the plate on the chair, she turned toward the beach and shouted, 'Hey, stop horsing around on the hammock. It's not made for that!' and let out an exaggerated sigh. 'I'm Karen,' she said and smiled kindly at me. It turned out that Karen was employed by an NGO that also worked in maternal health.

'Laura was just telling us,' the donor said, with unspoken encouragement, 'about her work in the maternity ward at a local hospital.'

Karen asked, 'Oh cool! What's your impression, generally speaking, of the quality of nursing care here?'

'Well, there are definitely some cultural differences.'

Karen set her plate of prawns on the porch's concrete floor. 'Yeah, that's not surprising, I guess. I'm curious to hear how you would describe the differences?'

'Well, at my hospital, there just simply aren't enough staff. Cleaners help out with deliveries on the busy days.' *Why can't I just shut up?* I wanted to send a telepathic SOS to my mentor Barbara, but when I turned in her direction, she was gone, just her wide-brimmed hat sitting on the chair. But then all three women nodded in understanding. 'There are no pain meds, you know?' I continued. 'No epidurals, no analgesics, nothing like that. So women are really... well, they are in pain and nobody has time to really deal with them.'

'I'm actually working on national nurse training programs,' Karen said, pushing her hair behind her shoulder. 'And, I wonder sometimes... well, I just think it's hard to blame the nurses. I mean, their pay is terrible, right? They don't have the tools they need to do their jobs. They're overburdened with high-need patients. They have sick family members at home. They're scared of getting HIV or they already have it. I can't even imagine.'

My cheeks burned. I wasn't getting the tone right. I could not manage the smoothness these women managed when talking about difficult topics; didn't yet possess their ability to take in the hard stuff with equanimity.

The woman with the sleeping baby chimed in: 'I had him' – she pointed to her lap with her chin – 'naturally. It was one of the best experiences of my life. I mean, I know that every woman is different, but I don't believe all women need pain meds.'

It was the donor's turn now. 'Yeah, I actually had my daughter in Uganda at a government hospital. For me, it was the ultimate cross-cultural experience. But I totally agree, every woman needs to decide for herself. It's deeply unjust that so many women aren't given the choice.'

A boy raced across the patio in dripping-wet Hawaiian shorts and with a chest so thin that you could see every bone outlined in his ribcage as it heaved. 'Jonathan kicked me. In the stomach! Mommy! It hurts!' Karen pulled him close, made shushing noises into his crew cut. She looked over his head and rolled her eyes.

The donor glanced at her watch. 'We should probably head home soon,' she said.

There was a commotion of plates and glasses and tubes of

sunscreen. I rose from my chair to help the women gather their things. A couple of husbands appeared, men who played golf and raced catamarans around the harbor while their wives won the bread. I did not know if I envied or pitied a day-to-day existence that fell somewhere between the unending vacation of an early retiree and the boredom of a housewife rendered useless by nannies, cooks and gardeners.

I found Barbara standing at the beach, lifting the hem of a tasseled wrap and poking her toes in the salty water. I let her know I was taking off.

'How did it go?' she asked.

'Oh, fine,' I said. 'Thanks for everything.'

When I got back to the Upanga apartment, I binged on peanut butter and jelly sandwiches. I thought the evening had been a complete disaster until the next day, when I learned something amazing. After I'd left the Yacht Club, as a cool breeze blew in off the Indian Ocean and a live band played New Orleans jazz, and boozy expats tapped strappy shoes across the ceramic tiled patio, Barbara – my global health fairy godmother – had, in fact, secured me a ticket out of Kibo's maternity ward and into an international NGO's American headquarters. It turned out that Karen, the maternal health expert, thought my training and experience were just the right fit for her organization.

Two months later, as I was wrapping up my contract in Tanzania, the organization emailed me requesting an interview. It was all I could do not to tell the directors that I would be honored to scrub the office toilets if it meant that I could get my foot in the door. A couple of months after that, when I was offered a salary that was substantially more than I'd earned as a clinician in New Haven, and learned that I'd even be flying around the world on their dime, I felt like I'd won the lottery. I vowed that if things worked out and I found myself in a position like Karen's someday, I would be as generous to up-and-comers as she had been to me.

And then I started to study.

The directors explained that I would be supporting a new initiative: the nascent Male Circumcision for HIV Prevention program. It was the first I had ever heard the words 'Male Circumcision for HIV Prevention,' so I googled it. The images that popped up were either pornographic or uncomfortably surgical.

I can do this, I said to myself. I can make the professional shift from vaginas to penises, a small price to pay for a professional second chance. This was it, my godsend of a Plan B, a way to exit the bloody birthing business with my professional reputation intact. I tried to convince myself that landing a job with a well-respected NGO meant that I wasn't a failure. I needed to excel straight out of the gate. This time there could be no question that I had what it took.

3

BALTIMORE

Job offer in hand, that autumn I moved to a narrow railcar apartment situated upstairs from Kooper's, a lively pub that boasted the best burgers in Baltimore. Along Kooper's walls hung yard sale photos of Ireland in the fifties and sixties. When I brought my dad there during an early moving-in trip, he immediately spotted a faded close-up of a distant second cousin, a County Kerry rugby star with the famous Fitzgerald cleft chin. I took this as a sign that the changes – new job, new city, new life – were sanctioned by the cosmos. He took it as a sign that he should spend more time in Baltimore, relieved that I seemed to be settling into a stable job stateside.

But I felt uneasy. In terms of public health, I was a complete newbie. I'd never before managed a project budget or drafted a work plan. Each working day, I battled an unending stream of acronyms. I learned the lingo of aid: that I would *face challenges* (not problems), avoid *reinventing the wheel* and *look for synchronicities*. I would not *duplicate efforts*; I would *harmonize* them. I'd *get on the same page*, *touch base*, *follow up*, *facilitate*, *support*, *share*, *reach out*, and *build consensus*. I'd also *build capacity*. Hell, we were a well-known training organization; we built all kinds of crazy capacity.

Sure, by that point in my life I could hold my own in places most Americans don't venture, but rural Africa was more my comfort zone than a corporate office in Baltimore, Maryland. The East Coast's 'Charm City', known for local crabs and the unique character and community spirit of its distinct neighborhoods, was made famous several years earlier by the gritty cop show *The Wire,* which had confronted its deep economic and racial divisions. My new office was in a beautiful building just down the street from my new apartment. I was routinely so disoriented on my way to meetings that I'd have to ask strangers in the carpeted hallways for directions. Other staff, seated in particleboard cubicles, had laptops docked below big viewing monitors and an assortment of work-issued gadgets. It shouldn't have surprised me, but it did. How did this make sense? We were working in the poorest areas on earth, writing winning proposals to improve healthcare in places where it was dangerous to give birth and to be born. I'd just come from such a place. So... what was up with the fancy automated coffee machines?

That first week at my new NGO job, I was invited to attend a two-day meeting in Washington D.C. to kick off a multi-partner, global project. The program's funding ceiling was in the hundreds of millions. Before the meeting, I printed out a copy of the project proposal and studied the lengthy document as if it was a medical text, marking up the important bits with a neon highlighter. I brought the fat printout with me on the train from Baltimore to D.C., but spent the ride chatting with new workmates rather than rereading it. My colleagues, experienced midwives in the last chapters of their careers, made inquisitive small talk and educated me about expense reporting. They reminded me of Barbara, inclusive and care-taking.

I experienced so many competing emotions at this stage, not the least of which was exhaustion, a heavy fatigue born of an inability to slot this polished, expenses-paid NGO reality against the Kibo reality I had just left. I'd seen unforgettable things in the places I'd worked, images still front and center in my mind: wailing women throwing themselves atop corpses outside my rudimentary office at the district hospital in Malawi; white-capped nurses weighing babies on grain scales; dozens of scrubbed latex gloves fluttering on the clothesline next to the Nutritional Rehabilitation Unit, like fifty little white hands waving in the wind.

Now, I sat cross-legged in a hotel meeting room in Washington D.C. with thirty public health professionals sipping bottled water, nibbling on pastries and listening as an external facilitator divided us into small groups and instructed us to draft elevator speeches summarizing the new project. We would pitch these to potential partners, donors and beneficiary governments.

My small group talked about reducing the maternal mortality ratio and addressing the leading causes of newborn death. It was a whole new world where the individual – my patients at the public health clinic on State Street, or my nurse friends at Kibo Hospital – was subsumed by the collective, the science of public health being about populations rather than specific people. A young, vibrant woman in my group, a West African pediatrician who worked for a partnering NGO, informed us that her role in the new project would be spearheading an initiative called Kangaroo Mother Care, a low-tech, low-cost intervention that involved keeping premature babies snugly attached in skin-to-skin contact with their mothers for the first few weeks of life. I looked at her and thought, with your obvious intelligence, with everything you have been trained to manage as a clinician, that's all you do now? You left the bedside where you'd cared for countless kids in need – each one possessing a complex and unique set of family and environmental circumstances, physical symptoms and lab results that you had to interpret – to sit in board rooms and talk about just this one, relatively simple thing? Then the obvious follow-up... Wasn't that exactly what I was doing?

In that moment, I realized something. This kind of work would require a completely new perspective. I would need to learn to focus on the collective good, not on individuals. I would have to work with the law of averages, rather than singular particulars, with issues rather than people.

About a week later, Erin, my new supervisor, set up a meeting with me. I steadied myself as I opened an office door papered with crayon drawings and family photos. Ever a sponge for other people's energetic weather patterns, I found myself slightly vibrating as I sat in a chair in front of her desk. Everything about Erin operated at top speed: her brain processed information so quickly, it seemed, that her words struggled to keep pace.

As she spoke, I focused on the contrast of fair skin against sweeps of red lipstick. Her hair brushed in thick dark waves against her shoulders. I quickly learned that Erin's imposing intellect and statement-making color choices accompanied a genuine warmth. I got the feeling, right off the bat, that she wanted me to learn and she wanted me to succeed, and that she would do her best to help me achieve both, despite being the youngest and only female member of the NGO's directorship team, juggling three young kids at home and traveling internationally more than half the time. She was the first, but definitely not the last, of my new colleagues to model a special breed of overachieving workaholism that left me both inspired and forewarned.

'Okay, Laura, here's what you need to know,' Erin said. 'A

private foundation is fronting a substantial amount of money over a five-year period to bring MC' – this was public health shorthand for male circumcision – 'to scale in two focus countries: Zambia and Swaziland. We are short-staffed with project managers, so I'm thinking that you should backstop this new award. It would give you some great management and field experience.'

'Sure.' I made a mental note to text my Peace Corps friend Gene, now in a global health graduate program, to ask for a quick definition of backstopping. I'd been calling him a lot lately.

'And we're going to have to get you out there pretty quickly,' Erin continued, 'to get a handle on things. Another NGO is priming the award. Oh, sorry – I keep forgetting, you'll get the lingo soon, don't worry. The prime is the lead organization. We are one of several sub-organizations. We're responsible for the clinical training and assuring the quality of the clinical circumcision services. The prime is going to expect us to marshal our resources – human and otherwise – quickly. But it will be fine. You can do this.'

Erin was speaking so fast that I started to slip into a minor trance.

'Zambia's in decent shape,' she continued. 'We have an established in-country office and the management infrastructure there to take on more work, but we don't have a presence yet in Swaziland. Have you been to the travel office yet? Or the travel clinic? We'll want to prep you ASAP to get into the field.'

'Great!' I blinked and gave her my best you-can-count-on-me face.

'Maybe you should just plan to stay in southern Africa after the project kick-off meeting in Zambia in a few weeks. Meet everybody. Get to know the donors. You'll have to pack some nice stuff. We may be invited to the embassies. Do you have a suit?'

I shook my head no.

'I'm listing that as one of your annual performance objectives, then,' she joked. 'You're going to need to get one.'

I left Erin's office and realized I had no idea where the travel office was. I stopped the first approachable-looking person in the hallway, a tall man in glasses and a bright tunic.

'Sorry,' I asked him, 'could you point me in the direction of the travel office? I think I'm going into the field ASAP.' I cringed while saying the last part, the going into the field part, because who did I think I was, Margaret Mead? Was I really supposed to talk like this with a straight face? And was I really supposed to buy business suits for nonprofit work?

The man pointed down an adjacent corridor. When he spoke, his English was tinged with French. 'Just ask for the travel coordinator,' he said. 'Actually, I'm going that way, I'll go with you.' Then he looked me in the eye and held out his hand. 'I'm Remi. Are you Laura, by any chance?'

I nodded, surprised.

'I work on Erin's team too. We're thrilled you're here.'

Well, fancy that, I thought, I was known! I was wanted in this impressive place by these impressive people!

The travel coordinator took my photo to save for future visas and handed me a checklist with all the preparations I'd need to make for my first trip to Swaziland – everything from submitting a travel query to book my flights and registering with various databases that issue travel warnings to organizing a cash advance and ensuring I had the requisite immunizations. But once I started lining up my paperwork for that first trip, I began to discover something strange: it was almost as if the world didn't seem to want to acknowledge Swaziland's existence.

First, my younger brother misheard me on the phone. I got an email from him afterward that said something along the lines of, 'Wow, Switzerland... that's a step up from the places you usually go. Send us some chocolate.' Later, a bunch of documents, mostly official ones required for my work permit – clearance from the police department in Baltimore, my graduate school transcript from New Haven, various licenses and certificates, things that were a serious pain in the ass to acquire notarized copies of – got waylaid in Geneva. Even FedEx, it seemed, could not keep the two countries straight.

To be honest, at that point, I probably couldn't have located the Kingdom of Swaziland on a map either. I probably knew it was one of those small 'island' countries in the middle of South Africa, but I couldn't have said whether Swaziland or Lesotho was the mountainous kingdom on the eastern side (Swaziland) or the one on the western side (Lesotho). I also couldn't have told you which one was famous for horseback riding in the snow-covered mountains (Lesotho) and which one built a reputation in the eighties and early nineties for its legal casinos and apartheid-free, no-holds-barred nightlife (Swaziland).

It was winter in Baltimore, a slushy, windy, grey time of year, when I departed for my first trip to Swaziland. From the back of my closet, I pulled out long cotton skirts and lightweight tees, the stuff I wore in Tanzania. Toenails that had not seen the light of day in two months were painted an understated merlot. I shoved in my carry-on an expired blister pack of antibiotics and a baggie of those face wipes that make you feel like a million bucks after a sixteen-hour flight. Then, with my taxi to Dulles International Airport waiting, I purchased a variety box of Bigelow herbal tea from the Fells Point Whole Foods. Kristi Forrest, the prime's project director in Swaziland, had sent me a last-minute email asking if I would mind bringing her some. 'Of course!' I'd replied from my Blackberry, already in the back seat of the taxi – because, firstly, how well I knew the particular joy of a tiny comfort in a difficult place, and, secondly, Kristi was a technical director for my biggest project. I wanted her to like me. I wanted us to get off on the right foot. This was, after all, what Erin called the relationship-building phase. I may have been clueless with the program management stuff, but damn, I could still channel my people-pleasing, prom-queen past to charm and disarm. Fake it 'til you make it. That, I knew how to do.

4

A few words on this male circumcision business. For those outside of the global health or HIV/AIDS communities, I get that this surgical intervention may sound a bit off-the-wall. Nevertheless, try to imagine the original giddy 'aha' moment when the lightbulb first went on.

It was back in the late 1990s, when AIDS was rapidly making a name as a modern-day global plague. A handful of anthropologists and epidemiologists had observed something intriguing: the vast majority of men living in the countries most devastated by the HIV virus – Zimbabwe, Botswana, Namibia, Zambia, Swaziland, Malawi, Mozambique and Rwanda – were uncircumcised. The scientists asked themselves this: was there a relationship between a country's HIV prevalence and its circumcision habits?

To arrive at a possible answer, they did what scientists do. They took a closer look. They mapped it all out, geographically superimposing circumcision rates on top of HIV rates. And, sure enough, what they found was impossible to dismiss. Where more men were circumcised, HIV rates were lower. Significantly lower.

Thus, a theory was born. Circumcision protected against

HIV transmission. Maybe circumcision did, as the ancients argued, confer medical benefits after all. However, any scientist is quick to point out that correlation does not equal causation. So, in short order, three research trials were launched to test the theory. The trials – in Uganda, South Africa and Kenya – pitted a group of HIV-negative uncircumcised males against an HIV-negative circumcised group and tracked the number from both who became infected over time. When the South Africa trial team reported out in July of 2005, it was clear that something major was happening. A year and a half later, review boards halted the Uganda and Kenya trials early: the evidence was beyond compelling. Denying circumcision to the control groups was deemed unethical.

International health organizations took immediate note, and in 2007, the World Health Organization and the Joint United Nations Program on HIV/AIDS convened to review the data, declaring, 'The efficacy [of male circumcision to partially prevent HIV transmission] is proven beyond a reasonable doubt.'

By reducing the risk of female-to-male heterosexual HIV transmission by roughly 60 percent, male circumcision was boldly likened by some to an HIV vaccine for men. In fact, the trials demonstrated circumcision to be more effective in preventing (heterosexual, female-to-male) HIV transmission than the flu shot is in keeping people sneeze-free during flu season. Put another way, 2009 modeling studies suggested that between five and fifteen circumcisions, depending on the HIV incidence in a particular country, could prevent one new HIV infection. This electrifying 'discovery' sent off a charge within a field beset by a decade of disappointment.

In response to the new research, HIV scientists and global health experts embarked on a spirited advocacy campaign for the new intervention. Voices joined in from multiple sectors of the international aid community. Circumcision, it seemed, could truly help stem the tsunami of HIV. Not a silver bullet, they cautioned, but a wise investment. Fewer infected men meant fewer HIV-infected men, women and children who would eventually require a lifetime of antiretroviral therapy. Long-term, the promotion of circumcision would be life-saving (well into the millions) as well as cost-saving (modelers calculated ten-figure dollar amounts). Empirically, economically, epidemiologically – it was hard to argue with these kinds of numbers.

The mantra: eradicate foreskins. Don't give HIV a place to hide. Articulated pleas opened the Capitol Hill coffers. Philanthropists and vocal journalists hitched their hopes to the circumcision wagon. Finally, after nearly thirty years, it seemed that the international health community had the knowledge, the skills, and – perhaps most importantly – the cash to turn the tide against a devastating pandemic.

5

'Madam, may I offer you a lift?'

The voice came from the driver-side window of a white ten-seater van parked next to the chain-link fence surrounding Matsapha International Airport. Alone on the pavement with a plastic-wrapped suitcase, I squinted in the sunshine, confused. Was he speaking to me?

Honestly, I had been confused since touchdown. Clutching my carry-on and wobbling down the flimsy staircase onto Matsapha's landing strip, an explosion of tall swaying grasses greeted me. Such greenness, in the middle of an African summer, seemed wrong. Sloping hillsides in all directions boasted vibrant vegetation. Knotted pine trees kissed a clear blue horizon. A rainbow display of wildflowers and succulents marked the perimeter of the tiny airstrip.

Where was the dust? The sun-scorched brush? The city sprawl? Where were the peddlers pushing vegetables and cheap trinkets? Where were the eager hands reaching for my bags? In other words, where was the Africa that I'd come to know over the near decade I'd spent as a Peace Corps volunteer, a nomad, a graduate student and a disillusioned newly minted midwife?

Eventually, I walked over and peered into the van. The

driver did not seem too eager for business, his head buried in the *Times of Swaziland* and his feet kicked up on the dash. Still, he smiled in my direction, flashing a set of impressively even white teeth.

'I'm James,' he said. 'Like in the Bible.'

We shook hands. 'I'm Laura,' I told him. 'I have a brother named James.'

'Ah, my sister! Madam, please consider me your Swazi brother! Wherever you need to go, I can take you.'

James threw my luggage on one of the back benches, urged me into the back seat and pulled out onto a two-lane country road with banana trees lining both sides. He asked if I would like to take the direct route to Mbabane on the new road or if I wanted to take the scenic route on the old road. I opted for the old road when James told me that it offered a close-up view of a cliff face creepily named Executioner's Rock.

As we drove off, I took in a view of distant hills shrouded in puffy cloud cover. James swerved around a fat, lazy cow, its ear pierced with a plastic tag, which was walking down the middle of the airport road. We passed a collection of identical squat, block-shaped white houses with matching blue doors and tin roofs. These were the government-issued homes of the Royal Swazi Police Force, James said. Then he lifted a hand from the steering wheel and pointed through the windshield. 'And those are the Mdzimba Mountains. The old kings are buried in the caves there.' I couldn't tell if this was historical fact or if I'd signed up for some kind of Disney fantasy ride, a sort of southern African *Pirates of the Caribbean*.

Then he indicated right, and we merged onto a busier road, although not what I would call a proper highway. James told me that this was the industrial area, where the bulk of the country's sugar and wood pulp manufacturing took place. We passed windowless warehouses of bright orange and green, and then crossed a bridge over a full-flowing, clear-watered stream. Concrete gave way to farmland and a scattering of wooden roadside stands selling tomatoes, onions and greens. We traveled past great fields of sugar cane topped with feathery cattails, then pineapple. A young-looking guy faced the field of fruit, in full view of traffic, relieving himself onto the dark soil. We continued on, surrounded on three sides by impressive shrubby mountainside. A green sign directed traffic toward Mlilwane Game Park. Then we were in a place called Ludzidzini.

'This is the king's sacred grounds,' James told me as he pointed to what looked like a football field with multicolored bleachers and streamers in yellow, blue and red strung like Buddhist prayer flags from the bordering telephone poles.

James did not need to tell me when we had arrived at Executioner's Rock. It was exactly as he'd described it – a triangular jutting precipice of granite that stretched like a gangplank hundreds of feet above the road. 'This is where the old kings punished criminals. In fact, this is where anyone who spoke evil of the king was punished. It was a dangerous job to escort criminals to the rock. Often those soldiers were also pulled over the edge.'

Shaka Zulu, the murderous, bloodthirsty king of the neighboring Zulu tribe, James explained, had waged a campaign for control of Swazi people and land during the nineteenth century. The Swazis, James's ancestors, managed to avoid Shaka's wrath by hiding in the thousands of caves hidden among the lush, rocky Swazi mountains. And through the special *muti* of their kings.

'*Muti*?' I asked.

'Swazi traditional medicine. You might call it magic.'

I had just learned my first siSwati word.

I nodded from the back of the van, still not quite sure if I was playing along with a mutually agreed-upon conceit or if what James was telling me was factual truth. I'd been in Swaziland for just an hour, and, so far, the presence of the monarchy was the cornerstone supporting all things, the reference point for both language and geography.

Speaking of the monarchy, chances are if you know anything about Swaziland, you know that it is the last absolute monarchy in Africa, then ruled by a forty-four-year-old king with fourteen wives. But there was another claim to fame that placed this tiny country squarely on the world map, the reason I had come to this overlooked dot on the vast expanse of the African continent. A tragic and dubious distinction, Swaziland's HIV epidemic was the worst on the planet.

I knew the numbers that charted this crisis in human terms. Over a quarter of all Swazi adults lived with the virus and its attendant miseries – tuberculosis chief among them. At forty-nine years, Swaziland's average life expectancy was the fifth lowest in the world, and almost half of all kids under the age of eighteen were legally considered orphaned or vulnerable. In Swaziland, 70 percent of sex workers were infected, the highest prevalence for this group anywhere in the world. And, finally, the statistic that kicked me hard in the gut: in the two decades between my first year of high school and my arrival in Swaziland, the percentage of HIV-positive pregnant women in Swaziland had multiplied ten times over, leaping from 4 percent to a staggering 41 percent. It was difficult to wrap one's mind around the scale of such a disaster, particularly in the face of apparent peacefulness and spectacular natural beauty.

A few minutes later, we began a steep ascent. 'This is the Malagwane,' James told me. I tried to minimize the terror I felt at sitting inside a minivan creeping around hairpin turns with nothing but a heavily dented guardrail to separate us from a careering free fall. This was like the Peace Corps all over again, when I'd had no choice but to travel in and out of my isolated village through a mountain pass on decrepit lorries whose rusted flatbeds gave me a full view of the graveled gullies and ditches below. James downshifted and we continued our twisting ascent of what I later learned was 2,000 feet over a ten-mile stretch.

'It seems sort of dangerous,' I said.

'Oh, yes.' James nodded. 'This hill is famous. We are in your book. You know it, that famous book for records?'

'*The Guinness Book of World Records?*'

'*Yebo!* Yes, madam! *The Guinness Book*. Our Malagwane Hill had the highest number of motor vehicle accidents per year anywhere.'

It was a relief to enter Mbabane, Swaziland's capital city, although I would never have known if James had not announced it. I scanned the scene. This was the capital? And a city? As far as I could tell it was three covered bus stops with benches, a red light and a couple of billboards – one for Domino's Pizza and one for Build It, Swaziland's apparent answer to Home Depot.

I was jetlagged and wired, but this just didn't seem right. Home to 60,000 residents, this place continued to be so different from the Africa that I knew. In contrast to Nairobi or Addis Ababa or Dar es Salaam, there was next to no bustle. We drove through two more red lights, and things started to pick up a little. The liveliness of the *kombis* – the minibuses hooting for customers and jockeying for position amongst each other in a bus rank the modest size of my hometown library's parking lot, seemed about as rowdy as it got. The few main streets undulated and curved and, plentiful potholes aside, were paved and sidewalked. People milled about in no particular hurry: women in bright colors with babies secured to their backs by double-knotted terrycloth towels, men in business suits, officials in snappy government uniforms and people of all ages in square cloths of red-printed fabric, knotted at the waist or at the shoulder. Just about everyone chatting away on cell phones, herded into waiting clumps at the traffic lights James called robots.

Through the van window, I watched the frequency and familiarity with which people greeted each other, the flashes of wide smiles and outstretched hands, the embracing, the ripple of recognition's happy giggles and shouts. Even before I knew a single Swazi, as I made my way along Gwamile Street in James's van on a Monday afternoon, I picked up a social tone somewhat reminiscent of a school reunion. I couldn't help but find it quaint, a welcome whiff of a bygone era where human connectedness was an ever-present, easily accessible thing.

With just over one million inhabitants – half of Paris, a quarter of Johannesburg – on a land mass the size of New Jersey, it seemed to me that the entire country possessed a distinctly small-town vibe. I let my shoulders relax by a fraction of an inch and absently released a tired, audible exhalation. When I did so, my driver James glanced up to his rear-view mirror to check on me. He smiled reassuringly – that brilliant white-toothed smile. Already, I loved this place.

6

James dropped me at the Mountain Inn, where Kristi Forrest, the American project director with a taste for herbal tea, had reserved a room for me. It felt immediately familiar. With wall-to-wall carpets, folksy paintings of southern Africa signed by British-sounding names and a continuous loop of Celtic folk music, it held on to the vibe of colonial-era Africa. I checked into a clean, simple room and looked out the window onto a bowl-shaped valley almost artificially green.

That was when I formally acknowledged to myself how embarrassingly little I knew about Swaziland. Like, I knew next to nothing about its history, culture, or religion. Hadn't a clue about the national economy or government structure beyond the polygamous king. My self-designed homework for the trip had focused on the health indicators of the landlocked kingdom and on my personal objectives for the trip: to meet Kristi and her team as well as our Ministry of Health counterparts, to hire at least one staff member of our own to provide local support for our project activities and to establish my NGO as a legal entity in Swaziland.

But now that I was actually here, I had a sudden desire to educate myself. I had planned to nap after the long flight but found I could not. I pulled out the pristine copy of the 2008 *Lonely Planet* for *South Africa, Lesotho & Swaziland* I'd ordered on Amazon. A quick skim and I learned a few more things. Like the fact that each year this country, the smallest in the Southern Hemisphere, claimed the most lightning strikes per person of anywhere in the world; that it was home to Sibebe, the planet's largest unbroken granite dome; and that it possessed the oldest iron ore mine on earth.

I also learned that the present-day Swazi people, a grouping comprised of some sixty or so clans, originated from the Nguni, southern African pastoralists who measured their wealth in numbers of cattle and wives. As Nguni people, the Ndebele of Zimbabwe, the Zulu and Xhosa in South Africa and the Swazi share a common history going back some one thousand to two thousand years when they traveled southward together from Eastern and Central Africa. Now, the tribes were still linked by similar languages, telltale click sounds in all of them, and various cultural identifiers including a system of chief headmen or kings.

From what I was reading, it sounded as though traditional culture was uniquely preserved in Swaziland. While Christian missionaries were mostly successful in converting the kingdom at the end of the nineteenth and early twentieth centuries, indigenous spiritual and cultural practices managed to continue right alongside incoming Western ideas without apparent contradiction or bloody conflict. My guidebook suggested that Swaziland's two famous cultural events, the *Umhlanga* and *Incwala* ceremonies, were still practiced in almost the same form that they were celebrated hundreds, if not thousands, of years ago. In fact, Swaziland had never actually been militarily conquered by those – the Zulus, the English and the South African Boers – who wanted Swazi land or Swazi minerals or propriety rights to the Swazi route from the interior to the

Indian Ocean. The Lonely Planet guide also briefly mentioned that traditional medicine, what foreigners termed witchcraft and my driver James called *muti*, was also alive and well in Swaziland.

Appetite whetted, I exited my room, followed an outdoor walkway to Mountain Inn's check-in area, where I purchased a Wi-Fi voucher from a pleasant receptionist and then started googling. Sure enough, an alleged eight thousand traditional healers practiced their craft in Swaziland, about fifty times the number of medical doctors caring for the same population. Somehow, the practice of magic – or traditional medicine – was tied to a continued engagement with ancestors, with the spirit world, and seemed to be wielded by and for the powerful royal family. It sounded complicated and mysterious.

However, in spite of its old-world leanings, the absolute monarchy was also surprisingly open-minded. Owing partly to its geographic location, and partly to its tendency to look the other way, the Kingdom had served as a safe haven for refugees seeking peace from numerous violent conflicts on the continent. Although whites, black Swazis and 'colored' lived in separate communities, in 1964, Swaziland opened the first desegregated school in the African region.

Which is not to say that Swaziland was a Shangri-la of interracial harmony. According to Swazi lore, King Sobhuza I, who ruled from 1815 to 1836, had had a prophetic dream shortly before his death. In it, he saw fair-skinned people with hair like cows' tails arriving in Swaziland with two types of objects: books and round pieces of metal. He urged his people to accept the former and avoid the latter. Still, when the *mlungu* missionaries and prospectors arrived in the mid-1800s, as predicted, a timeworn tale of exploitation and bitterness ensued. The monarchy slowly granted fertile Swazi land and mineral rights in concessions to white settlers. By 1900, over

50 percent of the country, which had previously been held in trust by the king and shared by all, was private farmland owned by Europeans. A new phrase cropped up to describe the English – 'those who eat like crocodiles.' For when the English grabbed land, much like the way a crocodile snatched its prey and disappeared with it into the waters below, it was gone forever.

My eyes starting to tear with fatigue, I glanced once more through my glass patio doors to grassy meadows peppered across a lush, concave mountain valley. It was as if the Enchanted Forest game I had played as a kid, a plastic-pine treed board with a Brothers Grimm premise, had come to life. A silver stream and crystal waterfall were perfectly placed at the center of the boulder-and-leaf valley. Only a smattering of simple homesteads interrupted Nature's masterwork. It was not difficult to see just why visitors arrived, settled in and sought to grab pieces of this fairytale Kingdom for themselves.

7

When I walked into her office the next day, Kristi Forrest was all business. After a quick hug, she showed me to an office marked Technical Services Director. 'Could you wait here for a minute?' she asked, 'I'm just wrapping up another meeting.'

I could hear her voice, a speedy East Coast clip punctuated with West Coast uptalk, coming from the shared workspace outside her office. Apparently, the production of some promotional materials was too slow and the final quality was, in her estimation, unsatisfactory. I crossed and uncrossed my legs, eavesdropping on the tense exchange, and asked myself why I was wearing heels and a pencil skirt when Kristi was in jeans and flip-flops.

'Sorry about that,' she said, as she returned to her office, closed the door and slid into the chair behind the desk. 'Okay, where do you want to start?'

Huh? I was supposed to set the agenda? I thought we were just going to make some get-to-know-each-other small talk and maybe take a tour of the office. I mean, I was the sub to her prime, and I was brand new to this whole public health meets male genitalia thing. Kristi, on the other hand, was the Swazi MC Program Director. She was, you know, in charge.

She saw my frozen look. 'Well, Erin and I have been in touch about the scope of your work during this visit,' she said. 'And I'm glad you're here. I think you'll see that, given the way things work in Swaziland, you cannot implement this program from afar. Everything requires close and frequent follow-up. In person.'

At that point, I didn't know much about Kristi. What little I knew came from Erin, who'd gotten to know Kristi during the writing of the original project proposal. From Erin, I had learned that Kristi was about my age, if not younger, and had been doing this type of project management stuff for a while, both in D.C. and elsewhere. There was a beachy, freckled prettiness about her, the sort of woman who considered lip balm makeup. She led with a double-whammy of brains and confidence. She knew the lingo, the US government funding rules and regs, and the global players in MC. I found her bottom-line directness abrasive, particularly in this part of the world, as well as professionally intimidating. She also fascinated me: how had this young woman ended up in the Kingdom of Swaziland running a circumcision project? More to the point, how the hell had I?

Like me, pretty much everyone who works in development has some personal connection to the work. There are plenty of easier, more lucrative ways to earn a living – especially in the beginning, when you spent your weekends crossing the Atlantic in economy-class middle seats, writing cookie-cutter reports and puking into hotel toilets, desperately regretting the salad you ate because you just could not stomach the thought of more fried meat and refined carbohydrates. Sure, we all wanted to 'make a difference,' but you needed experience to do that; good aid workers do not emerge fully formed from Masters in Public Health programs at age twenty-five. We are honed, humbled and educated in the school of hard knocks through the course of a few starter field posts. In places like, you guessed it, Swaziland.

So, with Kristi, I wanted to reset the tone: less hard-nosed, more comradery. I reached into my workbag, pulled out the Bigelow tea and handed it across the desk to her.

'Oh, thanks!' she said, clearly and immediately grateful.

'How are things going for you here?' I asked. 'I mean, life-wise. Your husband is here too, right?'

Kristi turned the project director persona down a notch. 'Well, expats refer to Swaziland as Africa Lite, or Africa for Beginners. It's an easy place to live. I mean, it's not the liveliest place... but there's a great American community here, lots of hiking, dinner parties. My husband got here a couple of months ago and he's having a great time, joined an ultimate Frisbee team with some other guys.'

Here was confirmation of the suspicion I had nursed since touchdown: the Kingdom was a relatively safe place to learn a thing or two about development without posing real harm to yourself or others. A comfortable, temporary way station for established professionals with young kids who wanted to slow down. A place where you could knock off at two o'clock on a Friday without remorse. Where, from your back porch just outside the city, you could revel in an unblemished star-scape every single night of your posting.

'Anyway,' Kristi continued, 'let's talk about your plans for the next couple of weeks. I can tell you what I consider priorities. Your NGO needs to get some visibility. Let's set up some meetings so you can meet some key stakeholders – our Ministry of Health MC Program Manager, some of the other implementing partners. Also, I know you need to hire a local clinical director to lead MC trainings and help establish our quality assurance plan. I can give you some names. We just hired a physician to run our MC clinic in Matsapha – I'll email you a list of the other doctors we shortlisted. You could do some interviews while you're here.'

I nodded agreeably to these suggestions, while thinking about something else entirely. I was asking myself if Kristi could technically be considered a member of what one of my new work friends, a program manager working on an MC project in Lesotho, had jokingly called the Male Circumcision Nerd Circus. Once I had heard the term, I couldn't help thinking about all die-hard circumcision advocates as part of it. My friend had meant it as a good-humored knock at the academic obsession with foreskins, at the impassioned PowerPoint presentations about penises – which sounds juvenile and snarky, I know. It wasn't that we didn't respect our brilliant, principled MC colleagues (and, truly, they were both). It also wasn't that we didn't buy the science. It was more that the whole premise of mass circumcising for HIV-prevention purposes seemed absurd, outlandish and cringeworthy. Just plain weird. Maybe subconsciously we wanted to set ourselves a bit apart; acknowledge, at least to each other, that we were aware of the slight (moral? colonial? corporal? sexual?) squeamishness that attended voluntary circumcising by the millions. Like, who were *we* to tell anyone what he should do with his penis? Well, we were – like Kristi – a couple of female, white, middle-class American Gen-Xers. That's who we were. And devoting the better part of our waking lives to circumcision was just really freaking strange.

I did not get the feeling that Kristi, however, felt conflicted about this. But her situation was different. Kristi wasn't a nurse-midwife. She hadn't been educated to tell clients that circumcising their baby boys was an okay religious or cultural decision, but not a medically justifiable one.

In midwifery school, I recalled just one lecture about circumcision. A pediatric nurse came to speak to us in one of our stale lecture halls. She had handed out index cards with the words, 'What does this card have to do with your PENIS?' printed in fat blue letters on the front. Years later, I found that card buried among my old textbooks and class notes. I was particularly interested in the text on the reverse side, which read:

> This card is equivalent to the amount of tissue missing from an adult's penis after circumcision. It represents a third to a half – approximately fifteen square inches – of the skin covering the normal penis.
>
> The foreskin contains three to four feet of blood vessels, 240 feet of nerves, and between ten thousand to twenty thousand specialized nerve endings.
>
> Circumcision permanently diminishes the sexual feelings of both males and females.
>
> No national health organization in the world recommends circumcision for healthy male infants.

However, that blue card was placed in my baby-catching hands back in 2006, before circumcision was linked not only with HIV prevention but also with protection for several other sexually transmitted infections. At Yale, we were carefully trained to base our clinical decisions on scientific evidence, so I should not have felt icky about backing circumcision once the world had solid evidence to support its epidemiological efficacy. Yet, somehow, the ick factor remained.

No one talked outright about the strangeness of our goodwill Gen-Xer task. Firstly, it was hard to argue with the randomized controlled trials. Secondly, it was equally hard to sit on politically uncomfortable ceremony in the face of millions of people worldwide suffering from a cureless virus and unarmed with a better strategy. Lastly, and it would be remiss not to mention this, the initiative appealed to our egos;

joining the MC Nerd Circus meant that we were part of something pioneering and (pardon the pun) cutting-edge. There was a heady, intoxicating excitement about it all. Here was the chance to be at the forefront of something truly *big*.

And that's what I felt, sitting with Kristi Forrest, Technical Services Director, in her bright blue office in Mbabane, Swaziland. In her hurried manner, there was a sense of mission, of import. The circumcision target for our project in Swaziland, essentially the same target set by Swaziland's Ministry of Health, was about 112,000, or 80 percent of HIV-negative males aged fifteen to twenty-four. Our donors would hold Kristi and her team largely responsible for meeting it.

So – as time progressed – I managed to stuff down the queasy rolling in my gut. Especially during that first trip to Swaziland, when I was taking in so much new information, trying to get a handle on the project, the layout of the country and my role in things. During those first couple of weeks in Swaziland, I took Kristi's list and ploughed through each item like a good little worker bee – dutifully submitting a job description for our MC clinical lead to post in both Swazi and South African papers, then making a detailed spreadsheet of those I considered to be our top candidates, which I emailed off to Erin.

Kristi had stressed that our NGO registration was of vital importance, a requirement for legally doing business in the Kingdom. 'You'll need to find a lawyer who can push the paperwork through,' she had said, decisively closing the subject. I asked my headquarters office if they had any guidance. 'Just ask around,' my own HR manager advised. Ask around to whom exactly? At that point, Kristi was the only other NGO rep I knew there.

But a couple of nights later, Kristi invited a bunch of us expats from the office for drinks at her place, including a

Scottish communications director, Ian, and a program officer from another sub-NGO also in Mbabane for a short start-up stint. I called James, now my regular driver, first to take me into town to pick up a bottle of wine and then to drop me off at Kristi's.

The alcohol run taught me exactly why aid workers referred to Swaziland as Africa Lite. Equipped with a car, cash and a decent command of English, I could see how life in the lower-middle-income Kingdom was utterly straightforward and convenient when compared with much of the rest of the continent.

When I asked James where I should go for a decent bottle of wine and some groceries, he said that expats shopped at one of two locations: the malls or the Plaza. From Mountain Inn, we traveled all of five minutes back into the center of Mbabane, where I was introduced to the old mall, the new mall and the Plaza. The Plaza was a maze of primarily homeware and clothing shops, several banks and a handful of restaurants, one of which traded in wheatgrass smoothies and all-natural nutritional supplements. Across from the Plaza, the old and new malls were smallish shopping centers located next to each other on the same side of the two-lane Dr. Sishayi Road. The old mall had a photo shop, a Chinese electronics shop and restaurant and an assortment of boutique-y type shops selling near-identical collections of shiny getups in an array of synthetic fibers. The new mall housed Pick n Pay, an expansive grocery store that stocked everything from South African reds to organic free-range eggs and the same French strawberry jam I bought at Whole Foods back home. A handy pedestrian walkway that curved over a modest stream connected the old and new malls.

James waited in the parking lot with his hazard lights on as I took about seven minutes to walk the length of the malls before deciding that Pick n Pay was my best option and plunking down the equivalent of eight bucks for a bottle. During those seven shopping minutes, I sized up my fellow shoppers. I had spent enough time in the developing world to appreciate a subtle difference from other countries in the region, although it took a minute or two to put my finger on it. It was something that seemed both unexpected and completely normal: it was the size of the typical Mbabaner. Smiling cheeks were clear and round. Low-cut tops proudly displayed ample cleavage. Toddlers had thighs so perfectly fat, dimpled and Vaseline-shiny that the urge to squeeze them was irresistible.

In this part of the world, I had come to recognize the lean and mean bodies of people whose daily struggles had worn away such softness. I didn't find them in Swaziland's capital. These were the same comfortably, sedentary, KFC-loving bodies I had left behind in the US. I was embarrassed to acknowledge this observation, so laden with stereotypes. Nevertheless, it did beg certain questions, the most obvious being: where was the desolation and destruction wrought by HIV?

I wondered if I were simply wearing American blinders, picking and choosing my observations and missing what was right in front of me. In Malawi, the faces of HIV had been stark and obvious, branded by the 'slimming disease' that left scabby lesions and pained expressions. But that was back in the early days of the new millennium, before widespread access to free antiretroviral treatment. Now, in 2009, in Swaziland, folks had access to the drugs they needed to deal with their diagnoses. Smooth faces held on tight to their secrets.

The evening at Kristi's place was mostly pleasant. Her house was gorgeous, a multi-level number balanced between giant boulders. Kristi was a gracious host – and, it turned out, an excellent cook. I used the occasion to ask the questions I sensed would be unwelcome in the office: 'So, do you guys talk to local staff about the king and all the wives and the whole royal system in light of HIV?'

Kristi's husband laughed. 'It's a wild place, right?'

Kristi was more circumspect. 'I'm careful about what I say,' she explained. 'We can't appear disrespectful.'

This was one of a few moments that signaled to me that I shouldn't get too relaxed with this crowd. The next was when Kristi, several drinks in and musing on the subject of hiring, mentioned an interview technique called the 'silent probe.' As far as I could tell, this technique was exactly what it sounded like – a psychological experiment to see what people said when faced with uncomfortable silence. I hated the sound of it. The third moment was when Ian, the Scottish communications director, also buzzed, referred to the team of Interpersonal Communication Agents – the folks tasked with drumming up circumcision business and usually nicknamed IPCs – as 'skin hunters.' The term gave me the creeps. 'No one wants to call it like it is,' he explained, referring to the incredible donor pressure to produce foreskins. 'It's not easy. Fellas are not exactly queuing up. Someone has to be out there, pounding the pavement, wheedling with them to go for the snip.'

After a few days, Kristi invited me to go along with her and a couple members of her team to a hospital in the eastern lowveld. It was an officious, protocol-bound, hour-long meeting that involved shaking hands with the medical director and the matron and viewing a potential circumcising space off the surgical ward. On the drive back to Mbabane, a small cluster of Royal Swazi Police officers stopped us at a roadblock. A petite female officer stuck her head in the driver's window and asked our purpose. The driver informed her that we worked on the government's circumcision program.

She pursed her lips. I waited to be reproached for violating some arbitrary traffic law. Instead, she replied in English, 'I wish you would circumcise me.'

Her male colleagues, in matching brown uniforms, snickered. I piped up from the back seat: Why would she want to be cut? I feared she'd misunderstood the point of the program – that she was confusing male circumcision for HIV prevention with female genital cutting, which wasn't commonly practiced this far south, and for which I believed no free-thinking adult woman would volunteer.

'Maybe then I would not want sex,' she said. 'I don't want to want it anymore. It is killing us. It's destroying us.'

The laughter stopped. I became aware in that moment how horribly Swaziland, underneath cheerful greetings and Mbabane's superficially middle-class habits, suffered from a true humanitarian crisis.

National statistics told a more complete story. The average Swazi lived on $2,280 per year, and 70 percent of the population lived on less than $100 per month. Unemployment was close to 30 percent. Most of those who had jobs worked in mining, milling, or textile and sugar manufacturing, or were employed by the bloated civil service. That was what was written in official documents, anyway. Locals argued that the biggest export in Swaziland was marijuana, thanks to the fecund Swazi mountains, a highly rural populace, strong demand in neighboring South Africa and a police force that was largely happy to both consume and overlook. My mom emailed me an article she read in the *New York Times*, 'Grandmas Grow Gold in Swaziland.' Just outside of the city limits – and well within it, in places we did not frequent – life was hard, very hard, in ways I could not see or relate to at all.

8

I was in fifth grade the first time I heard the word AIDS. It was 1986. My teacher at Scotland Elementary School, Mrs. J, drew something that looked like a family tree – a graphic I'd later learn to call a sexual network – on our class blackboard to explain a mind-blowing concept: when you had sex with someone, whom she called Mike, you were actually sleeping with every single person Mike had ever slept with. We had already had our first sex education class, boys in one room and girls in another, and this conversation was equally weird.

Mrs. J had a booming playful voice and a smoker's cough, and she tapped the chalk tree branches with a dusty felt eraser. At that stage, age ten, I was sure that the only man I would ever have sex with would be my future husband, whom I would meet in college. This new revelation, this illness, was terrifying but like drunk driving – another careful subject presented by after-school specials on TV – unsafe sex seemed an ominous threat that would never apply to me.

During those childhood years, I spent every summer with my great-aunt Ruth in Provincetown, a seaside resort on the tip of Cape Cod. There, I grew up among men who walked Commercial Street with their hands tucked in other men's back pockets, among people for whom the societal rules that defined my school-year life in a Connecticut suburb held little or no sway.

Provincetown welcomed everyone. Ruth had an artist friend, a trim, elegant woman with perfectly pressed trousers and pastel eye shadow whom I knew, even as a child, to be anatomically male. She had another friend, Jerry, who'd been a Harvard professor until a scandal with a male student led to early retirement. My favorite was her friend Bill, who had sad, watery eyes, drank Rob Roys, and traveled to places like Timbuktu and Istanbul. When Bill's partner of thirty-five years lay dying in their condo in the East End, my mom, then working as a hospice nurse, spent our family vacation at his bedside to relieve a fraction of Bill's suffering at watching the love of his life exiting it.

Probably because of its aura of acceptance and its flair for the creative, Provincetown stole my story-seeking heart at an early age. But I was hardly the first to discover the place. The Pilgrims actually first anchored down not in Plymouth but Provincetown. A few centuries later, progressive generations of eccentrics, intellectuals and geniuses discovered Provincetown: Eugene O'Neill, Tennessee Williams, Jackson Pollock. Once a former fishing village, over the twentieth century it had slowly transformed into a haven for the artistic of temperament and the unconventional of lifestyle. Then, while I was a fifth grader in Mrs. J's classroom, HIV discovered Provincetown and knocked it to its knees.

Seven years later, during the summer of 1994, I – seventeen and a virgin – worked in an army surplus store that stayed open until the bars closed. One night, as I walked home along a mobbed Commercial Street, a grown man dressed in leather, wearing a studded collar with a leash that trailed down to a fingerless leather glove, barked in my face like a dog and then cackled with pleasure when I jumped. Another night, a drunk old man came into the store and asked to see a set of handcuffs in a glass case. 'Oh, honey,' he said, 'you'll learn all about these soon, but we could start your lessons now, if you want?'

The suggestion of sex was everywhere. Provincetown, especially after hours, reeked with the saltwater taffy scent of it. The virus loved it.

That same summer, Ruth's gardener, a handsome strong and silent type I had known my whole life, lost so much weight that only his piercing blue eyes suggested the healthy man he had once been. By the following summer, he was gone. To this, I remember Ruth saying, with a New England stoicism that belied her sadness, 'These days, if anyone gets infected, I have very little sympathy. Is it really so hard to use condoms?'

In Malawi, five years later, when only the wealthy and the well-connected had access to antiretrovirals, the housekeeper I'd inherited from the previous volunteer greeted me with sores the size of bursting grapes on both lips. Eating must have been an agony until the punishments of AIDS finally took him. By the time I moved to Swaziland in another ten years, I had lost count of the number of times I'd thought, 'This has to be the worst way to die.'

9

During that first trip, I did manage to interview and hire a South African doctor as our technical director, a young guy named Morris. A researcher from one of the original randomized controlled MC trial sites, he had just the set of skills we needed for the job: careful, experienced, attentive to detail, a standard-procedures-for-all-things kind of clinician.

So, by the time I left after two and a half weeks to return to the US, at least we had one full-time staff member based in Swaziland. With boots on the ground, Kristi Forrest expected things to move. She was under substantial donor pressure to get past project start-up and into active circumcising. Once I was back in the Baltimore office, she sent frequent emails, often copying in my supervisor Erin: 'Just checking in again. Do we have dates yet for the first clinical training?'

In a word, no we did not. And the reason we did not was that we had a few things to take care of first. We needed to open a bank account, get financial systems in place. We couldn't exactly expect Morris to front the training costs himself – the hiring of the conference hall, the payments for tea and cookies and lunch, the per diem allowances for all the nurse and doctor trainees; we couldn't expect him to go running around Mbabane buying disinfectant solution, buckets, notebooks, wooden penis models. He was living out of the Mountain Inn and didn't even have a car yet (later he would purchase a cheap Dubai import he named Agatha, after an especially compact high-school classmate).

Besides, Morris was busy laying the groundwork for his technical role: establishing quality assurance standards for the surgical services, visiting hospital sites to assess the space and the supplies, working with Kristi and her team to get their Matsapha men's clinic ready for its grand opening. Everything else fell to me, 13,000 miles away at a cubicle office on the US East Coast.

Then Erin, my boss, informed me that Swaziland would be hosting a pilot program to bring in expatriate volunteer circumcision surgeons. As the backstop for Swaziland, I would coordinate that pilot with the World Health Organization. So within a few weeks of my return, I found myself booking my next trip to the Kingdom.

***

October 2009, and back in Mbabane. For the duration of the week, it rained nonstop. I was cooped up in a B&B on Somhlolo Road, working the odd hours dictated by available electricity. I was stressed: reporting in to Kristi, reporting in to headquarters, reporting in to our donors. I would have a call with Geneva in the morning – 'Have we lined up the volunteer doctors for the first circumcision mission?' – then I'd march across town to our lawyers' office on a street that was San Franciscan in its verticality to get the latest news on our still-unsigned registration documents, the same ones required to open a bank account and hire more staff. I paid for our office supplies and a rental car with my travel advance. I also personally schlepped a bunch of penis models over in my luggage, along with a note signed by our CEO, which certified that the plastic phalluses were for educational purposes only.

We were still visiting circumcision clinic sites and thinking through logistics for the volunteer surgeons. 'Do you think American surgeons will eat pap?' I asked Morris, dead serious, on yet another field visit that featured yet another lunch of scoops of boiled maize meal alongside an assortment of fried chicken parts. 'I don't know,' Morris answered, 'you're the American.'

The days flew by in busy blurs, but the long, rainy nights dragged. My B&B's motherly, soft-spoken owner sensed both my anxiety and my stir-craziness. 'If you want to get out of the house for a bit and grab a bite to eat, there's a café named Serendipity just off the side street.'

Perfect, I thought. Using my cheap travel umbrella as a shield against the driving wind, I passed through the gates of her house and turned left on a pitch black Somhlolo Road. With the dim illumination from my cell phone's built-in flashlight, I trekked around puddled potholes, unable to see more than a foot in front of me. I turned left again onto another dark, pitted road, marked with a sign that read *Serendipity, Home of Wellness*. I kept walking until I hit an empty parking lot and then headed for the biggest set of doors.

Inside a dark entryway, a small woman sat at a wooden desk with her head down and her eyes closed. The dining room was lit only by dancing illuminations along the back wall, projections from the flickering candlelight on a few of the tables. It was eerily quiet.

'Excuse me,' I ventured, leaning slightly over the desk. The woman did not stir, not even a flutter of eyelashes.

'Sorry,' I said, a bit louder.

Then she rustled, took her time opening her eyes, looked at

me sideways for a second or two, and lifted the right plane of her cheek from the surface in front of her.

'So sorry to bother you. Are you still serving dinner?' I asked.

'What?'

'Can I get food here now?'

'As you can see, the electricity is out, but I suppose I could check what is left in the kitchen.'

The woman, whom I couldn't properly see, took her time rising from the stool, planted her small hands on the desk and exhaled. When she emerged from a dark hallway, lighting the path with the flashlight glow of her own cell phone's electronic face, she stepped up close to me and looked about twelve inches northward to meet my eyes. We leveled with each other for a fraction of a second. Inside of that nanosecond, she must have decided something about me, a foreigner who had interrupted what was, I am sure, the most delectable of stolen rainy-evening naps. Then she cracked a smile, a cheeky little grin that set her dark eyes to sparkling. 'We have chicken curry,' she said.

'Perfect!' I told her. I devoured a plate of African curry and rice and knocked back three warm Castle beers. My server, feeling her job adequately performed and sensing that we had reached a mutual understanding, turned her braided head away from me and lowered it back onto the desk in front of her. The only patron in the place, I worked away on my laptop until it died.

From that point forward, the restaurant at Serendipity became my comfort zone. Despite the fact that the dark wood-paneled walls and flooring, baroque light fixtures and deep red tablecloths lent a sort of heavy and closed-in feel to the place, I considered it a haven, a sanctuary. The next night, the woman told me her name – Jabu, where she was from, the size of her family, her religious affiliation, the extent of her relentless fatigue, and her dire wish to land a job with an NGO. Any NGO. She told me her name meant happiness in siSwati, which, well, did not exactly fit.

A few nights later, back at the B&B, I lay underneath an electric blanket in a pair of Smartwool socks and jogging tights, messaging Erin on Skype.

'How are things going?' she pinged back from Baltimore.

'Great,' I typed back.

'Anything I can help you with? Wait, hang on, something's up with the dog. Give me a sec.'

I pictured her working from home in jeans and a comfy T-shirt, her hair tied up. I battled a moment of life-projection envy. Yes, it was cool to stay in quirky hotels in unusual locations, funded by my work, but it was also lonely. Once again, I wondered what it would be like to have someone along with me, someone to laugh at the travel screw-ups, someone to tell me to put the laptop away and go exploring. The thought of a stable home life, a dog, the hum of a washer/dryer, and Friday date nights with a hardworking, co-parenting husband brought on a strange ache.

I wrote, 'We're still not legally registered yet. I'm working on it. Got the name of a good lawyer. And things are shaping up for the clinical training in Matsapha.'

I knew why Erin was keeping an eye on Swaziland from afar. The whole MC Nerd Circus was keeping an eye on Swaziland. For this new intervention, quality needed to be impeccable. Any bad press in these early days, and circumcision as an intervention could be jeopardized. 'Sorry, Sam's calling from upstairs… give me another minute,' she replied.

'No prob,' I wrote back, just as Skype alerted me of another message. I clicked on the flashing green light, expecting something from headquarters. When I saw the name, my heart jumped. The Irishman. Of course, it had to be the Irishman.

'Hey, what's up? Looks like you're back in Africa?'

We had not exactly been speaking. This was the first message in about four weeks. Oh, how I wanted to reply, how I wanted to flirt and chitchat. I was bored and alone in a Swazi B&B, wearing glorified long johns. I guessed he was bored and alone in his four-bedroom semi-detached house in Sligo County. I further guessed we were both sipping hot drinks and watching the clock. Was I going to take the bait? I always did. He knew this.

Erin was still attending to her son. The two sets of conversations hung on hold – one paused in comfortable ease, and the other paused in electric anticipation. I opened up the conversation with the Irishman and minimized Erin. No! I stared at his photo on the Skype ID. My fingers twitched. No! No! NO!

I had last seen the Irishman a month before. I had finagled a layover in London – and a quick hop over to Ireland for a long weekend – on my way back to the States after the previous trip. I was two frothy pints in, my legs twisted around a barstool, as we shouted at each other in order to be heard over the raucous voices of a packed pub. A fiddler and flutist were in the midst of a traditional set when the Irishman tipped his auburn head toward mine and let it rest against my damp ponytail and the sturdiness of my skull. That close, he smelled clean and minty, like toothpaste. 'I'm getting a career break,' he said. 'I just found out.'

'You're getting a what?' I shouted back.

It took me a while to get it, but long story short, the priest who oversaw the school where he taught had granted him a year to travel the world. It would be a strictly solo trip, the Irishman explained, one he had been looking forward to for years. Then I understood, and was gutted. At that point, I saw our children as if they were real, flesh and blood – tall, athletic, intelligent. I'd picked out their Celtic names: Cillian and Saoirse.

'Maybe we could meet up somewhere once I've found my travel legs?' he said.

'But you know I have a full-time job now...' was all I could manage to stammer. *Tell me you want to be with me. Offer me a year of adventure and exploration at your side and I will quit that full-time job.* My eyes started to fill. There wasn't enough air in the packed pub.

'I know what you are thinking,' he said, gentle, kind, close to my ear so that I could hear him clearly. 'We've talked about it many times over the years. But a commitment now just doesn't make sense with me off to Asia and you on a regular America-to-Swaziland commute.'

After he fell asleep, I crept downstairs to his bachelor's kitchen, sat at a table cluttered with receipts and train schedules and CD cases, and allowed myself to sob. Stubbornness gave way to unwelcome clarity. I was no longer twenty-five; I was a matronly thirty-three. I felt like a fool, like I'd been a fool for a whopping eight years.

There was a brief time when I thought I would be a career midwife with chapped, over-washed hands and no need for business suits. There was also a time when I thought I'd be the tea-drinking, woolly-jumpered love of an Irishman. Hell, there was a time when I thought I would be both.

I swore that would be our last parting. No more cozy rooms in shabby-chic hotels, no more forays to seaside villages with their quaint rows of squinting windows. I took one more look at his tiny framed Skype head. I cared about him deeply, but we were done. The fantasy was over. I minimized him and reopened the chat with my boss. 'Back?' I asked.

'Here!' she wrote.

'Hey Erin,' I started to type. 'I've been thinking. Can I move to Swaziland for a while? It would be so much easier to work from the region, rather than having to constantly fly back and forth.'

I watched my typed words form on the Skype message bar, and I hit the Send button. I'd mulled it over. Now I needed to take the plunge. No more waffling with either my professional or my personal life. I was getting old. I was getting serious. Let me move to Swaziland, I silently pleaded with Erin. Let me come here and wow you with what I can do. Let me be hyper-focused. Let me demonstrate my inner overachiever. Let me clean up my ridiculous life. Please let me get something right. Send me to this safe, beautiful, bizarre little Kingdom and watch me kick some circumcising ass.

I held my breath.

'Hmm,' she wrote. 'Maybe. Take a look at the pipeline and see if you can make a case for it.'

Huh? It was that easy?

When I got back to the States and floated the idea, it was somewhat surprising to discover that enacting a move to Swaziland necessitated no real powers of persuasion. Our donors – now investing 1.5 million dollars to launch the volunteer circumcision doctor pilot program – liked the idea. If I relocated to the Kingdom, I would be their girl Friday on the ground to ensure that the high-profile program got off on the right track.

I committed to a five-month relocation, after which I planned to return to the States with some solid programming and field experience under my belt, my mind cleared and my self-esteem boosted. Besides, really, what was five months? Twenty measly weeks? I'd endured longer than that at Kibo. Hell, I'd slogged through twenty-four months of mind-numbing boredom as a Peace Corps volunteer by killing time shopping for secondhand clothes and reading every paperback

I could get my hands on. In contrast, Swaziland – Africa Lite – promised to be a stroll in the park.

I came home and announced my plans to move back to Africa. Tellingly, my friends were more surprised by my declaration that I was cutting ties with the Irishman. But I was looking at the very likely potential loneliness and extended singledom of my upcoming months in Swaziland in an intentional, ashram-y way. Because, for God's sake... Swaziland? Playing the dating game in a country where one in four people is infected with HIV did not strike me as the wisest move. But that was fine. Because I was only going to Swaziland for five months, and it was not in search of romance. My objectives were clear: I was supporting the scale-up of a male circumcision for HIV prevention program, thereby effecting a successful switchback on my career path. No more silly international dalliances. I was a proper professional now.

10

When I visited Swaziland, Kristi and I worked from the same office. I went from the feeling I used to get in Baltimore – a nervousness at seeing her name pop into my inbox, to an edgy feeling when the halo of ringlets exited her office in search of one of us. Kristi wanted foreskins. We were there to help her get them.

For a full week in the new year of 2010, Kristi drove Morris and me around quaint Mbabane in her sporty four-wheel drive – a white 1998 Mitsubishi Pajero I bought from her several months later when her growing belly made the two-door vehicle an impractical family car – for back-to-back meet-and-greets with various government officials and UN agency representatives. It was time to step it up. Between meetings, she updated us on the latest personalities and politics at play in Swazi circumcision, while chewing away on some gum. 'Helps with the morning sickness.'

Despite – or perhaps because of – her tendency toward American directness, Kristi Forrest was getting shit done. With shocking speed, Kristi and her team had constructed a state-of-the-art circumcision clinic in Matsapha, a hop, skip, and a jump from the airport, which they called Litsemba Letfu, siSwati for

'Our Hope.' During my NGO's first official program activity, Morris and our team had trained all the Litsemba staff in Swaziland's first clinical circumcision training ever. Then, Litsemba Letfu officially opened and the newly trained team started circumcising. Local celebrities picked up on the trend. Even Mr. Swaziland 2009 was circumcised at the clinic amid much fanfare, as was Prince Masitsela, his Royal Highness King Mswati III's eighty-two-year-old brother. Within the first six months, Swaziland's MC program was averaging an impressive 1,200–1,500 circumcisions per month.

You had to hand it to them: for a non-circumcising country, it wasn't half bad. Especially considering that, before the circumcision procedure, men were offered HIV testing, a loaded choice in Swaziland, where – according to Kristi's Swazi staff – stigma, gossip and fear were the order of the day. The initial positive progress was altogether rather exciting, the sort of coalescing movement people wanted to join. And now that I was in Swaziland in a more permanent way, I felt excited, energized, more invested in this MC business.

Perhaps as a statement about my increasing professional and personal commitment, I decided to get my own place. I was done living at a guesthouse. Kristi had an immediate suggestion: a log cabin on a dramatic hillside in an upmarket neighborhood of Mbabane known as Fonteyn West. James and I went to check it out on a Saturday morning. The area was peppered with tastefully gated compounds not only of impressive size but also of impressive coloring – pinks and peaches and lime greens that reminded me of Key West. Homes were tucked into eroded nooks and crannies and occluded by wrought iron and greenery, like dyed eggs buried in fistfuls of grass. The house for rent was a log cabin sitting at the top of a vertiginous driveway. I jumped at it, as outrageously priced as it was, because, hey, I wasn't paying the rent. And the view – overlooking the green peaks and pines of Mbabane, surrounded by ancient stones – was unreal. The cabin was also a bohemian delight, with outsized furnishings and hand-carved touches, plus satellite TV and the promise of regular internet.

Ayla, my landlady, a willowy Turkish ex-model with a geometric haircut and unique fashion sense (think leopard-print leggings paired with knee-high boots), was doing a brisk rental business on the compound. She had built a cluster of cabins a stone's throw from the front door of her own slightly more deluxe Vermont-esque place, filled them with aid workers and development types, and named the mini-village after herself. She and her partner, an artist responsible for much of the village's design and interior decorating, threw infamous parties. The ex-model, I would quickly learn, liked theme nights and costumes, board games and impala goulash.

Soon after moving in, I realized that I'd just set myself up in the veritable nerve center of the Mbabane expat social scene. On a weekend night, dozens of cars parked along the grass to the right of the driveway as people flocked in. A turntable's thumping heartbeat, explosions of laughter, these continued into early morning. Honestly? It called forth my most introverted self. I felt, much as I had in the Peace Corps, a need to keep my nose clean, to stay above the fray. I was new to the scene. I had a serious job with a serious program. My goal was to be invisible, and barring that, it was to be at the very least respectably ignored.

Ayla and Glen, her artist partner, balked when I chose to stay home. Like my friend Barbara in Tanzania, they said I worked too hard. They said I needed to meet some new people. They said that Jorgen, a divorcee in his late thirties who lived in the cabin next to mine, had been asking about me. 'I'm not much of a partier,' I said.

'Laura, you need to relax,' Glen told me. 'Eventually you realize that people here are going to talk about you no matter what you do. If you don't give them a reason, they'll make one up. You know what they say about Ayla?' Glen asked, dragging on a cigarette. He waited a moment for me to consider the question. 'She's supposedly a lesbian. And me?' He pulled a mischievous sideways grin. 'I'm a drug dealer.'

Glen had a point. What was I going to do, hide out for five months? But even if I kept to myself, Glen and Ayla seemed to like me. Glen told me that I had a nice smile. Ayla invited me to her yoga class. I put up with the mangy, unruly dogs that guarded Ayla's village – five hounds with French names and countless engorged ticks whose muddy paws ruined several work skirts – and kept my nose to the grindstone.

11

Morris and I paid $1,000 a month to rent space in a section of Kristi's office called the Circumcision Partnership Suite. The Scottish communications director, Ian, also had a seat in the suite, as did the two other expats: an American leading the program's research arm, and a British consultant named John, who had once run a Doctors Without Borders hospital in Darfur and now organized circumcision outreach logistics.

The Circumcision Partnership Suite hosted near-daily impromptu lessons on Swazi language and culture. Like the time one of Kristi's finance officers sparked lively debate when she posted this on her Facebook page: *Show me a man who does not cheat, and I will show you a virgin mother.* 'Oh yes,' said the receptionist, 'the measurement of the goodness of a Swazi man isn't whether he cheats, but whether he confesses to it!'

When I drove a Zimbabwean nurse-manager colleague home after work that day, she felt obliged to school me further. 'You should know,' she said, seriously, 'that Swazi men are thought to be the worst cheaters in the region.'

I called upon my Peace Corps skills. Express curiosity rather than judgment. 'Really?' I asked. 'Why is that?'

'Because even if you are divorced and your husband marries

someone else, he can always maintain sexual relations with you as long as you have children together. It's custom because he has paid the bride price, the *lobola*, for you. That is the other thing. The Swazi *lobola* is so expensive that most men can't afford to properly marry, so they just maintain relationships outside of marriage instead.'

It caused me to wonder what else I would learn during the remainder of my five-month stay.

Once a week, we would have standing MC Partnership meetings in the big conference room at the end of the hall. Various representatives from the four participating MC organizations attended. Kristi led the meetings. It was at one of these weekly meetings, sometime in early February, that Kristi started with: 'So, you guys know how I was in Johannesburg last week for the MC communications conference?'

In fact, I did know that. Erin had also flown out from Baltimore to attend. She'd mentioned to me that she'd had a friendly exchange with Kristi after one of the sessions.

'Well,' Kristi continued, 'there was one particular presentation that had everyone talking. This Rapid Response Initiative, an RRI, in Kenya. They circumcised 36,000 guys in three weeks in this all-out, full-blast campaign.'

I still did not see where this was going.

'Anyway,' Kristi went on, 'I guess a bunch of donors and delegates started talking about the RRI in Kenya, wondering why couldn't we do an intensive circumcision campaign like that for an entire country – you know, just direct considerable resources at it, and circumcise the entire five-year national target in under a year.'

That's when it clicked. The US-based MC community wanted to conduct a grand experiment – an accelerated, fast-forwarded circumcision campaign *on an entire country*. And that country would likely be Swaziland.

I went back to my log cabin, buzzy and agitated, and laced up my running shoes so I could properly mull over this prospect. What would such a massive MC effort in the Kingdom mean? An impossible-to-estimate change, undoubtedly. Compression at that scale, whether you are talking time or a can of soda, usually results in some kind of explosion.

But rather than dwell on that, I dwelled on logistics. The most important implication of doing it all in one year was the issue of alleviating a crippling disease burden as quickly as possible, of course, but there would be other consequences, too. Hundreds of nonclinical support staff – site managers, theatre runners, lay counselors, receptionists, data capturers, drivers, cleaners and security guards – would need to be hired. Hotels would be needed to accommodate them. Fleets of *kombis* would need to transport them. Someone would have to feed these thousands of staff and surgical patients. Hospitals would get new equipment, supplies, outfitted prefabricated units and tents. Then I imagined all the attention as the global health world trained its eyes on the Kingdom to watch a grand life-saving experiment unfold.

12

Stephanie Silva was our project's United States Agency for International Development (USAID) Activity Manager, our Swazi-based donor. She linked the funders in D.C. with the NGOs like mine that did the work on the ground. Though she was probably a few years younger than me, Stephanie and I were actually quite similar, demographically speaking, except that she was poised, politically savvy, and had spent the better part of her twenties undergoing a thorough professional education at the hands of the US government while I had followed an impractical anthropology degree by backpacking across Europe, and skirting along the edges of real employment in various global volunteer gigs, before starting my clinical training.

About a month into my relocation, Stephanie sent an email requesting a meeting. In Swaziland, the small field team who managed the HIV/AIDS project funding were based at the US Embassy. She asked that I make a quick trip out there to see her. 'Just want to check in and see how you're doing,' she wrote. 'I also want to touch base with you about a few things that are coming up.' She had proposed three o'clock on a Wednesday.

I knew roughly where the embassy was, if only because it

was within arm's reach of Serendipity, but I'd never before stepped inside the walled complex. Kristi reviewed the landmarks with me; I was to drive just beyond the turn-off to Serendipity and then hang a right at the gravel road across from a church with cock-eyed windows. From there, I was to take my first left onto another pitted gravel road and watch out for the spiked, six-foot, fortress-like wall that ran the perimeter of the multi-block US Embassy complex. The place stood out like a sore thumb among the green brushy scrub and spindly pines, the skittering scavenger dogs and a handful of modest cement-block homes.

I parked the car on the side of the road, so that it teetered with the left-side tires mauling manicured grass, and the right-side tires resting on red dust. I bundled up my gear and headed for the Fort Knox main door of the security gatehouse. It was, predictably, dead-bolted, a fact I discovered by yanking it with all my weight a few times.

Someone spoke from inside a glass security window next to the heavy door. 'Madam, you must sign in. What is your name? Where is your ID? Do you have an appointment?' asked a uniformed guard.

After stating my name several times, handing over a business card, and telling the security team that I had a three o'clock with Stephanie, a female officer divested me of the entire contents of my workbag. (After this, I kept everything but a notebook and pen locked inside the car.) When I finally got through the whole security rigmarole – an airport-like process involving a metal detector, a conveyer belt and X-ray machine – an escort walked me from the gatehouse up a perfectly paved side road through perfectly landscaped flowerbeds to another building with several white, gleaming Land Rovers parked in front. A slender, biracial receptionist welcomed me, offered me something to drink (I declined), and led me to Stephanie's office. As I followed her through a fully outfitted kitchen, past a boardroom and down a hallway, I thought about something I'd been told – that every stick of furnishings was imported from the States, right down to the plush carpet we were walking on.

I was jittery. Not because I had anything in particular to feel nervous about, but because Stephanie was my donor. Which was weird because she was exactly the sort of person that I'd studied alongside in New England: intelligent, hardworking, someone who processed information quickly and made judgments just as swiftly. But the power dynamics that controlled this particular set of circumstances prevented easy friendship. In Swaziland, I was a sub to Kristi's prime, and both Kristi and I were the grateful benefactors of Stephanie's financial decision-making. And when the shit rolled downhill, as it invariably did, it started in some office building in D.C., rolled to Stephanie, progressed to Kristi, and landed somewhere in the vicinity of someone like me before being passed off to someone I supervised. 'You just wait,' Kristi told me early on, not unkindly. 'You'll fuck up, too. You'll think you're doing everything they want, but then, out of the blue, you'll get your wrist slapped.'

Stephanie stood up as I entered her office. She encouraged me to take a seat in front of her desk, reaching behind me to close the door. Then she sat down. Composed, she sipped water from a Nalgene bottle. It was hard to believe she could be the wrist-slapping type. She was polite and inquisitive, although also a woman who could take charge when needed. Her face and arms were olive, and beneath thick brows, she had big dark eyes. A single gold chain around her neck, nothing fussy. A framed photo on her desk displayed a dozen smiling college women in sports uniforms – rugby, maybe? In another, she stood in front of an ocean backdrop in between a kind-faced, fleece-wearing couple I guessed to be her parents. She appeared tired now, compared to her photo selves, a woman who responded to email seven days a week. She steered the conversation directly to business.

'So, you've heard discussions about an RRI for Swaziland?' Stephanie asked. Later, she told me that the name 'Rapid Response Initiative' would likely change, as leadership within Swaziland's Ministry of Health felt that people would be turned off by the word 'rapid.' Rapid might be okay for Kenya, but it was too aggressive for Swaziland, they said. Swazis preferred to be eased into things; they needed time to adjust to new ideas. Stephanie and the donors back in D.C. thought that 'accelerated' might go down more easily. They had begun to refer to the Swazi version of Kenya's RRI as the ASI: Accelerated Saturation Initiative.

The US-funded circumcision program in Swaziland had barely started, and – up to that point – we had thought the targets quite ambitious. But in contrast to the program Stephanie was describing now, our current program suddenly seemed easy, relaxed and underwhelming.

'If this plan passes through the Swazi Cabinet,' Stephanie said, 'we'll look to you to assist with human resources. It means that the volunteer circumcision doctor program needs to scale up quickly. To perform the number of procedures we're talking about here, we're going to need many more doctors than Swaziland has. We'll also need to figure out how to source hundreds of nurses and support staff.'

We did not talk about money or know-how, but we both knew that what we were referencing would require plenty of both. 'We should have official confirmation about the acceleration by next month.'

'Great!' I said. Not at all great, was what I thought. Hundreds of nurses? I had been in Swaziland full-time for a month. My organization consisted of two people: Morris and me. Our 'office' was two crowded desks in a rowdy, packed conference room, and my filing system was a series of folders lined up on the rough-hewn desk in the corner of my cabin in Fonteyn West. I had no clue how to mobilize hundreds of doctors, nurses and support staff in a micro-country suffering from a critical shortage of human resources for health.

After the meeting, I eased into the driver's seat of my rental. As I reversed onto the gravel road and circled the perimeter of the embassy's thick wall, I reached into the glove compartment for a pack of Dunhill Lights.

There is a Peace Corps saying that goes, 'Join Peace Corps South America and become a revolutionary. Join Peace Corps Asia and become a philosopher. Join Peace Corps Africa and become an addict.' I was not a smoker in the US because of course I knew better. As a clinician, when I counseled my patients about smoking cessation, I always started with, 'Quitting smoking is the single best decision you can make for your health.'

Here, things were different. That first inhale took the edge off. I suspected that it was the only time when I fully breathed; the only time my lungs' tiny alveoli opened their branch-like arms wide enough to steal healing oxygen from the increasingly toxic world around me.

13

I don't exactly remember the first time I met Clara Thomas. She had slowly made her way into the network of 'circumcisers' (the term other Swazi-based NGO workers used to describe us) by way of a policy project also funded by the US government. Because her NGO was working with the Swazi government to draft and finalize its HIV-prevention policies and strategies, she, like the rest of us, found herself in Swaziland in late 2009/early 2010 at the time of the Accelerated Saturation Initiative discussions – the right place at the right time to make public health history. Until the ASI conversations, Clara wasn't a permanent feature on the expat scene. She came and went every few months for a couple of weeks at a time. Hers was academic, high-level work – unlike the messy, day-to-day circumcision service delivery stuff Kristi and I were mired in. But I liked her instantly. Clara was a petite woman in her forties with a gentle face and a shock of short, mostly gray hair, a tomboyish Midwesterner with a goofy sense of humor. Her CV included stints as a firefighter, which was hard to believe given the fact that the protective equipment must have weighed more than she did. She had also worked as an emergency room technician. Then – after years of night classes and weekend practicums – she became a clinician, going on to serve half a dozen long-term development and aid posts in places that the US State Department told people not to visit.

Eventually, we started bumping into each other often. Because Clara also used the restaurant at Serendipity as her Mbabane getaway of choice, we would see each other there in the evenings and on weekends. She would have a plate of half-eaten food on one side and a laptop on the other, typing and chewing, lost in a virtual reality. She'd perk up when she spotted me, peer out above reading glasses that had slid all the way down the bridge of her nose, and say something corny like, 'What's a nice girl like you doing in a place like this?'

Once, leaning from her table to mine, she asked, 'So, what's your take on the whole Swazi thing?'

'Sorry…' I said, snapping out of work into sudden awareness of my surroundings, 'which Swazi thing?'

'I'm interested in your opinion,' Clara said. 'What do you think is going on here? Like, why is the Swazi epidemic still getting worse while countries like Uganda and Botswana have turned their HIV incidences around?'

God knows why Clara Thomas thought I'd have an answer to that. 'Not a clue,' I said. 'I've only been here a few months.'

'I'm not buying it,' she said. 'I can see the wheels turning in your head. I know you've spent some time in this part of the world. Stephanie told me that you're a midwife. I'm a Nurse Practitioner. So, we get what it's like to take care of real people, not just manage programs. Did you care for women with HIV in clinical practice?'

'When I was working in Tanzania, yeah, a few. You?'

'Lots. In the States. Back in the early days, when it was really bad. Actually, it's amazing how similar the situation was then to some things I'm hearing here now. I can relate to that feeling that, at a certain point, you just didn't know what to do anymore. Like you're just running frantically in place, exhausted from the effort of getting nowhere. You start to feel fatalistic and expect that those who are at-risk will be infected by thirty years old no matter what you do.'

Later I would learn that when Clara was posted to a Chinese rural health clinic, she took to sleeping under her office desk next to the space heater because it was warmer than her frigid apartment. She still cut her own hair with kitchen scissors. 'So, on one hand,' she said, 'I get how the government has run out of steam on this.'

'Yeah.'

'On the other,' she continued, 'for God's sake, enough with the three-hour meetings where following proper protocol is more important than making decisions and everyone's walking on eggshells because we're so desperately afraid of offending the chairman!'

I laughed. 'Well, that's some refreshing honesty.'

'Believe me, I get myself in trouble sometimes. But from where I sit, it looks like we're all on the same side here, trying to do the same thing. Maybe it sounds Pollyannaish, but I'm here because I really want to help. We may work for different organizations, but I don't have much patience for the politics.' She was still peering at me over the top of those plastic-rimmed lenses, small hands gesturing. 'If we can't work together, be honest with each other, and have some fun while we're at it, what are we doing here?'

Just then, I felt a tap on my shoulder and spun around. It was Cindy. Cindy was married to John, the British consultant in Kristi's team who oversaw procurement. During campaigns, he would also organize client transportation, and the set-up and takedown of short-term circumcision sites. Cindy and I had met a few times. She and John lived just down the road from Ayla's place in a Hansel and Gretel sort of house bordered on all sides by forests. That night, Cindy was wearing a pair of black leggings with a yoga mat under her arm. I stood to give her a hug and made quick introductions.

'How is it that we haven't met yet?' Cindy asked Clara. 'You work with my husband, John, right?'

'Different company, but similar projects. Come, have a seat. Get a drink. We're having a deep, philosophical conversation about HIV in Swaziland.'

'Oh God,' Cindy fake-groaned. 'I'm not sure I want to be part of that conversation. I'm trying to get back into yoga to get a break from it.' Before running into us, she'd probably been headed home after an evening class – the Serendipity complex had a separate building that served as a gym.

'Cindy works on the psychosocial end of HIV,' I explained to Clara. 'She runs girls' groups in some of the rural schools and community centers.'

'So you and John are both working with NGOs here? No wonder you don't want to talk shop! Do you think you guys will stay here for a while?' Clara asked.

I was keenly invested in Cindy's answer to that question. With both her and John, I saw the promise of real friendship, a rare find for people on short-term contracts, those who viewed Swaziland as a pit stop in a green pasture en route to a greener one. I wanted good, solid people to stay by my side through the ASI. I really liked them – smart, ambitious, humanitarian, with just a subtle whiff of fuck-you defiance. In their previous work with Doctors Without Borders, John and Cindy did disaster. They did emergencies. I got the feeling that, if pressed, John would say that all this prevention and policy stuff was boring.

'I doubt it,' Cindy answered. 'There's something dark about this place... ' she said. 'It's bizarre, for a country that's so beautiful.'

Was she referring to the dead body that had washed up

– without a tongue – beside a river in Pine Valley, on the outskirts of the city? We had all been shocked to read about it in the paper, equally fascinated and horrified by the neutral *Times of Swaziland* rendering of a *muti*-motivated murder. One of Kristi's program assistants told us it happened from time to time. The missing body parts – which sometimes included genitals – were used for ritualistic purposes.

'What do you mean?' I asked her.

'I don't know.' Shaking her head, Cindy carefully back-pedaled. 'The way I feel is probably heavily influenced by what I do. You read the statistics about abuse here. Nobody talks about it. But I gotta tell you... I go out to my girls' groups and hear some really crazy shit.'

By then I knew that what Swazis called *tibi tendlu,* and what we might refer to as dirty laundry, was all too common in the Kingdom. A well-known 2007 study found that one out of three Swazi girls between the ages of thirteen and twenty-four had been sexually abused. In a previous conversation, Cindy had told me that these survivors were four times more likely than their peers to become infected with HIV, and twice as likely to be suicidal. Most of the girls Cindy worked with were orphans, and many were infected. Often, she'd said, caretakers did not disclose the girls' HIV status. The old *gogos* gave them pills and told the girls that the drugs were to treat nonexistent colds or asthma. Cindy did not interfere. Instead, she focused on theatre, dance and art therapy. One teenager drew people eating other people in bright Crayola colors. When Cindy asked her what the drawings meant, the girl said that she was recreating the images she saw in her dreams.

Cindy was a therapist. Unlike us, she still dealt with individuals. Heard and saw the case-by-case stories. 'You guys just have such a narrow focus with your circumcision thing,' she said. 'This stuff is complicated. It's deep. You could circumcise every single Swazi guy, and it wouldn't change the situation here.'

Driving home from Serendipity that night, my brain buzzed. I replayed the conversation with Cindy and Clara as I passed through the nighttime stillness of the center of town. Toward Coronation Park, I always got the willies – the skinny trees and dense shrubbery struck me as good cover for bad behavior. My headlights flashed off jagged rocks as my newly acquired Pajero twisted up Mountain Road, the crazy formations with their menacing grandeur and their eons of trapped energy. Even in mid-summer, they wept, droplets squeezed from somewhere within their mineral creases, the stone leaking ceremony and blood and *muti*, the ancient laws that we foreigners would never quite grasp.

14

From the time I arrived at our so-called office at seven-thirty in the morning, it was a scramble. Morris, our technical advisor – Dr. Morris, as he was known here – was a consummate researcher. He was used to the hermetically sealed environment of a university-led randomized controlled trial. He liked protocols, organization. His discomfort with the make-do, on-the-spot workarounds that characterized our 'start-up phase' was obvious. He asked about our travel reimbursement policy, our phone policy and our overtime policy. I searched my NGO's database, trying to find sample files I could adapt, because we had no such policies. He was also beginning to complain about working like squatters in our prime's office. He was tired of waiting in line to use the printer, of having the whole office overhear phone calls. Also, at that stage, I was still forward funding everything, maxing out my daily ATM withdrawal allowance to cover program costs because we still didn't have a bank account.

Eventually, a Baltimore-based program finance manager agreed to come to the Kingdom to help us with 'compliance' issues. My supervisor Erin had applied some heavy pressure for this to happen, because despite the fact that he was fairly senior in the finance department of a global health organization, the guy hated to travel. For the duration of his weeklong visit, he stuck with KFC – local food being too risky. When I saw him at the airport, with his unscuffed docksiders and a briefcase, I felt intense relief. It was as if my dad had just showed up, kitted out with TurboTax or car repair tools or résumé advice, to help me sort out the basics of adulthood. I think Morris felt intense relief too – as, I suspect, did Kristi Forrest – to know that our distant headquarters office was staffed by such competent, procedurally minded individuals.

It had been close to a year since my first visit to the Kingdom, but the Registrar of Companies still hadn't signed our official NGO registration paperwork. My finance manager wanted to understand what the holdup was. I leveled with him. 'The Swazi lawyer we've hired, the one all the American NGOs use and pretty much the only game in town for this kind of thing, only makes a theater of rustling stacks of loose paperwork and clearing his throat every time I go into his office. Nothing is happening.'

I did not tell my finance manager that the lawyer often did not take my calls, his secretary forever saying he was in court. That when I tried to nag in person, he took one look at me – tall, white and female – and kept me waiting for ages. My finance manager nodded slowly. 'I'll talk to our CFO,' he said. 'We'll figure this out.' Oh, thank Jesus, I thought.

Together, we met with the top (read: only) three accounting firms in the Kingdom and selected what we considered the best one to handle our financing needs. (Hallelujah, no local bank account needed!) I handed over about two thousand dollars' worth of receipts, while our finance manager hammered out contractual details, reviewed submission forms and discussed US government regulations with the firm's heavy-set Zimbabwean director.

I tried as hard as I could to catalog all of the paperwork in my brain. Damn it, I was going to learn. This, right here, was my own Master of Public Health degree. I would prove my worth on this trial-by-fire testing ground. The finance manager and I also went through the project budget, expenditures and pipeline in painstaking detail. We were underspent.

'You have enough in here, I think,' he said, 'to hire somebody to help locally with program administration.'

Awesome. I drew up a scope of work, placed an ad in the two Swazi papers, interviewed a bunch of bright young Swazis, and hired the most cheerful, most genuine-seeming of the bunch – Thandi, a twenty-five-year-old with a business degree and a five-month-old baby. Two days later, she pulled up a chair next to Morris and me in the increasingly cramped Partnership Suite.

By the time our finance manager left, I felt exhausted but better. We had marginally improved systems, though things were still tense in our shared project office. My relationship with Kristi was collegial, but the professional power differential made things weird. I was also struggling to form real connections with the Swazi women in the office. They tacitly agreed to educate me, but they didn't seem all that interested in befriending me. No one invited me to their house for dinner, no one offered to show me around. I thought about my Tanzanian friend Rachel and wondered why this place was so different. Or was it that here in Swaziland, I was different?

That said, generally speaking, I had the same feeling in Swaziland that I did at Kibo Hospital: I could make it through the week as long as I was guaranteed a full-bodied mental break on the weekend. For that escape, I usually headed straight for Serendipity.

Returning to Serendipity one Sunday in February, six months after the rainy night I'd first stumbled in, I was tense.

Now that I'd been in the Kingdom for a while, all the little eccentricities were starting to grate, like a new lover whose endearing quirks have graduated from adorable to annoying. Jabu, the restaurant server, strolled out onto the sunny veranda to ask if I knew what I wanted. On a whim, I asked her, 'Hey, Jabu, do you guys offer massages on Sundays?'

By then I had ventured beyond Serendipity's dark restaurant to investigate the other businesses that the 'Home of Wellness' complex housed. In true Swazi fashion, Serendipity was a one-stop shop for anyone seeking a treadmill, an aerobics class, steak and chips, a facial, a manicure, a haircut, a milkshake, nutritional supplements, exclusive wines by the bottle, Christian reading material, Reiki healing, biofeedback, or massage. Swaziland was a blank canvas and the temptation to paint everything all at once spawned a multipurposeness that was almost comical in its extremity.

'Yes, of course. Seven days a week,' Jabu said. The line of her square jaw was set, her tone confident. She tapped the palm of her small hand against the top of her skull where I assumed the tight weave tormented with a ferocious itch.

'Great! Can I book one?'

'What time?'

'Now?'

'Uhh…' Jabu thought for a moment, still tapping the top of her head. 'No problem. I need to just check one small thing.'

She turned, her compact person fitted into a starched white button-up and black trousers, and headed back into the restaurant. She sauntered directly over to the receptionist's desk in the building's entryway – which serviced the restaurant as well as the therapy rooms down a side hallway – then picked up the phone and emitted rapid-fire siSwati into it. Then she hung up and approached my table. 'Please wait for just one minute,' she said. 'The therapist is coming now-now.'

A few minutes later, a cappuccino arrived. I sucked in the foam and dunked a biscuit. The liquid disappeared, and a deferential waiter removed my cup and saucer. I sweated into the thin fibers of my black T-shirt. My knee-length denim skirt cut into the tops of my thighs. The wispy hairs that did not quite stretch into the loops of my messy bun fell into my eyes.

The muscles between my shoulder blades were so tight that vertebrae cracked every time I moved my head from side to side. I tested it, dipped my right ear toward my right shoulder. A crackle-crack ripped down the cervical spine.

Exactly at that moment, a gentle, English-sounding male voice said my name like a question. When I lifted my head, I was face-to-face with glowing white: white tunic, white flowing pants, wide white smile. I was blinded.

'Are you Laura?' the voice asked again.

I was also, apparently, mute.

'Sorry, did you book a massage?'

I managed to nod.

'Please, come with me,' he said.

I tried to compose myself as I followed him up a small set of stairs and out of the restaurant, past Jabu's receptionist station, and down the hallway that housed the therapy rooms and the toilets. He was tall and slender, the back of his bare head and his hands a rich brown. In sandals, he moved like a yogi, graceful and muscular at the same time. I pictured him at 5 a.m. in a Spartan bedroom somewhere, legs wrapped in the lotus position and eyes closed in prayer. I bet he fueled himself for days on nothing but cup after cup of spiced tea.

I couldn't tell exactly *what* this guy was, ethnicity-wise. Egyptian? Latin American? But with that English accent. Prep school somewhere? In any number of American East Coast cities, this guy would have been catnip for an entire market share of liberal, wine-sipping, Lululemon-wearing thirty-somethings who craved a titillating taste of the exotic. (In other words, me.) Then I hit an intellectual speed bump. With that voice, and that smile, and those looks, what was he doing *here*?

By then we had arrived at a door proclaiming 'Adam's Treatment Room' on a hanging tile, and I was stepping inside. His room was a familiar enough setup, like any number of massage studios I had passed through in my life. The pseudo-spiritual doodads – wind chimes and jeweled statues of Indian gods and wafting incense – could have come straight from the 10,000 Villages shop across the street from my old Baltimore apartment. We stood inside the threshold in silence. We looked at each other – our eyes on an even plane. Then he suddenly lit up with an idea. 'Would you like to start with a foot massage with essential oils?'

After the week I'd had, that sounded divine. 'Sure.'

I watched this Adam of Adam's Treatment Room open the lower cabinet of a heavy wooden wall unit to retrieve a whirlpool footbath. 'Okay, why don't you just take a seat there,' he pointed to a plastic deck chair. 'I'll be right back.' He smiled. I smiled in return. Then he stayed exactly where he was, with the footbath under his white sleeve, as if he had completely forgotten his mission. 'Right,' he said softly to himself and exited toward the bathroom next door.

I let my heavy bag slide off my shoulder. Then I lowered myself onto the hard surface of the plastic chair and kicked off my flip-flops. It occurred to me that the denim skirt had not been a wise fashion choice – surely, he would be able to see right up it from an ankle-level vantage point. Then I caught myself. Because, well, I was there for a massage; I'd be undressing soon enough.

I cannot say that I was fully comfortable with that prospect when Adam returned and set the water bath carefully by my feet. He walked to the wall unit again to retrieve several small glass bottles of essential oils before switching on a CD of the usual plinky-plinky relaxation music, the combination of wind instruments and nonintrusive chanting that spas worldwide favor. Drip, drip from a medicine dropper into the warm, bubbling water at my feet. A quick glance to check the ring finger of his left hand: bare.

'How do you know how much oil to use? And how do you decide on which ones are needed for which clients?' I asked. I wanted him to tell me of the insomniac in need of lavender and the worrywart who craved the balancing effects of sandalwood. I wanted him to sing me a lullaby about spiritual diagnostics. I wanted him to be a healer.

'I experiment,' he said. 'I'm just starting to incorporate this reflexology into my sessions.' The voice was something else: southern in its speed and its rhythm, but punctuated with educated precision. It was impossible to peg him. And with his gentleness and almost feminine desire to please, I couldn't confidently say that he appeared straight.

'It smells wonderful,' I said.

He brightened. 'Actually, I haven't been doing this for very long. I mean, I am certified. It's just that I only began to work as a massage therapist in Swaziland about a month ago.'

'Really?' I pretended to be surprised.

He cupped one foot with both hands, and slowly worked a knuckle firmly down a cordlike tendon.

'Yes, I lived overseas, in the States, for the last ten years. Florida. I was there working on the cruise ships,' he said. 'So, what brought you to Swaziland?'

'I work for an NGO,' I said. 'HIV prevention.' I was not about to mention the penis part.

He held my gaze for a soft moment. 'As a Swazi, thank you for what you're doing for my country.' By then, he'd progressed from massaging one foot to the other. After he'd finished with the second one, he wiped his hands on a fat, blue towel and said, 'Please remove as much clothing as feels comfortable and lay face down here,' he said, touching a hand lightly to a covered massage table. 'I will be back in a few minutes.'

As he disappeared on the other side of a closed door, I faced an impossible choice: to remove or not to remove... everything? He would be used to this, right? I told myself to act natural, which was a joke. I'm a blushing introvert; I don't really do natural. Nevertheless, it was surprisingly easy to get out of my head once the massage began. Adam's fingers began working out months of tension. I got lost in it. Until his phone rang.

'Sorry, darling, can you please help me here? I completely forgot to switch off my phone.'

There were only two of us in the room so the darling in question had to be me. I lifted my face from a tissue-covered breathing-hole in the massage table and turned slightly over my shoulder to bring him into view. He held up his oily hands in a not-guilty, shrugging gesture. 'The phone is in my pocket? Could you just remove it for me? I have to stop wearing these white outfits. I just get them covered in oil.'

There was no way to lift my body from the table, lean over to his drawstring pants and pull out the phone without exposing my bare torso. I bit the bullet, shimmed over to the side of the table. He edged closer to facilitate my reach. The phone continued ringing. When my fingers skimmed the edge of the pocket, I could feel the warmth of his skin, the tautness of muscle and the quick sharpness of hip. Fishing for the top ledge of his phone, though, I suddenly felt something else. Not felt with my touch, but felt with my gut. It wasn't a thrill. It wasn't even sexual, really. It was like déjà vu, except that it was more of a conviction than a memory. A voice inside my own skull, clear as a bell and with shocking certainty, announced, 'You will be lovers.' The words were said as if, in fact, we already were. Like my mind was announcing the most obvious thing in the world.

Then, as though there had been a sound delay on a phone line, a crackle and a gap, I reacted. Wait, what? What was that? Was it just the voice of lust – a prosaic, limbic-brain urge? I mean, come on, a massage therapist? Really? What a cliché.

I stretched another few inches, and he lowered his head so that I could put the phone to his ear. He said, 'Yes, darling?' into the speaker. (Oh! We were all darlings to him!) He clucked in agreement into the phone. Finally he said, 'Ciao', and then to me, 'Thank you. I apologize for that. It wasn't very professional, was it? Could you just put it right back there, in the pocket?' he asked, motioning downward with his chin.

'No problem,' I said. I grazed his skin once more and resettled my face back into my breathing-hole. He reorganized the towel at my waist, careful to preserve modesty now that we'd restored the therapist–client rules.

He circled a shoulder blade. 'You carry your stress up here. Have you considered starting a simple meditation practice?'

He was rerouting my circulation. Speaking was out of the question. Adam lingered then, for just a moment, over three milky moons just below my right shoulder. They were marks left from moles removed twenty-five years earlier, scars that in eight years the Irishman had never once noticed. Adam brushed them lightly with the tip of a finger. 'I can see where your wings were once attached,' he said softly. It should have sounded incredibly cheesy, but it did not. It pierced my heart.

After I'd dressed, Adam knocked politely on the door and stepped back into the room. I figured that this was the part where I paid and thanked him, he said, 'It's a pleasure,' and

I left. Not so. It turned out that Adam was extremely chatty. He required zero prompting, just launched right into whatever topic struck his fancy, which, in that moment, was his religious upbringing.

'We were Catholic, but my *gogo* was more open-minded. Even though she was a rural Swazi woman with eleven kids and spent her life in the *bundus*, she was wise. She used to pull me close to her and look in my face. She'd say, 'My child. Look at all those freckles on your skin. Like a map. I can see all the places you will travel in your life.' She knew I would leave Swaziland. It made her sad, but it also made her proud.'

I leaned against the edge of the massage table, feeling warm and heavy. This was something I loved, something I had done a thousand different times in a thousand different rooms: to listen, rapt and wide-eyed, to life stories that were wholly alien to anything I had ever known.

Adam continued, 'We had a special relationship, me and Granny. When she got sick, I used to come up from Joburg to visit her. I had started working in a casino down there, and I would get off work and drive straight through to Swaziland. She was so sick that you could actually smell her insides rotting if you sat close enough. We knew she did not have much time left, and the doctors had her on a special diet. But she would slip me money and ask for two things. Polony and beer. I thought – who cares? This woman is dying. Let me do something that will make her happy.'

'What's polony?' I asked.

Adam looked at me, puzzled, as if he had forgotten I was there. 'Oh, right, how would you know that? It is some kind of processed meat, a South African thing. Very artificial, full of chemicals and preservatives.'

'Oh.'

'I'm actually a vegetarian. Started a few years ago, slowly at

100

first, just cut out the red meat. I'd been reading a lot about it, once I started exploring spirituality. Then I completely changed my lifestyle. I used to go clubbing a lot, too, in my twenties... but I lost the taste for that too.'

I nodded with encouragement and pictured him fifteen, maybe twenty years younger, on a throbbing dance floor, shoulder-length dreadlocks swirling around his face, the trance of the music crawling in through his pores.

'Later, once I moved to Fort Lauderdale, I discovered Barnes and Noble and spent hours reading books about meditation and how to live a more responsible, more aware life. That was before you could find everything online,' he said, which then prompted me to visualize him sitting on the floor, naïve, lost in his own dreamy world with a book spread across his lap, while heads turned all around him. 'After a while, I just couldn't stomach the casinos anymore either.'

'Wow,' I replied, unsure. We smiled through an awkward moment. 'Hey,' I asked, 'did you go to Waterford? I bet you know a friend of mine, a guy from Malawi. You probably graduated around the same time.'

I'd assumed, based purely on his accent and the articulate way that he spoke, that he had been educated at the elite Waterford United World College in Mbabane along with the children of Nelson Mandela and Desmond Tutu, where I further assumed he must have met my Malawian ex from my Peace Corps days, a Waterford alum who'd gone on to Harvard.

Adam answered without bitterness. 'I wouldn't have known him,' he said. 'I went to an all-boys Catholic school in Manzini.'

'Oh,' I said again, embarrassed.

When I finally picked up my bag and made a move toward the door, I handed him the sweaty cash that had been balled up in my fist for the duration of our extended chat. He bowed his head in a 'namaste' kind of gesture, pulled back for a moment and then embraced me suddenly.

'What is it about you?' he asked, 'You aren't like other Americans. There is something so…'

When words failed him, I interrupted. 'Fragile?' I asked. It was a scab I liked to pick, fully aware that I had no game face, that the whole world was privy to my inner life.

He laughed. 'No, not at all. Why would you say that?'

'I don't know,' I said, eyes down, enthralled by that voice. I gripped the doorknob to go. 'Should I keep it open, or would you like me to close it?' I asked.

'Open,' he said.

15

Increasingly, I spent my evenings working from the Serendipity restaurant in the hopes of running into my sexy massage therapist. Apparently, other important things happened there too. I heard about these things from Clara Thomas – who now, for reasons I didn't understand, seemed to have a direct line to the Nerd Circus. Clara was at Serendipity for a lunch meeting in February, rubbing elbows with a table of global circumcision experts planning the historic Swazi Accelerated Saturation Initiative.

The way Clara described it to me afterward, the vibe at Serendipity was cordial. Stephanie Silva, our USAID donor, well-spoken and professional, represented the American dollars that would finance the groundbreaking intervention. Funding for the ASI would come through the President's Emergency Plan for AIDS Relief, or PEPFAR, George W. Bush's brainchild and arguably his most laudable legacy. To the tune of 70 billion dollars, PEPFAR's contribution to HIV/AIDS care and treatment worldwide over the preceding decade had been enormous – supplying antiretroviral drugs for millions of people, training hundreds of thousands of healthcare workers, and now hoping at least partially to fund circumcision services for the approximately twenty million adolescent boys and men who needed them. But, as Stephanie would remind us several times, channeling millions of dollars to Swaziland for the ASI – an untested undertaking – would mean diverting those funds from equally burning needs elsewhere.

This was why heavy hitters attended such discussions – a representative from USAID in D.C., one from the American Department of Defense and a third from the Center for Disease Control and Prevention (CDC), three of the big American agencies that divvied out PEPFAR dollars. This, I realized as Clara set the scene, was my imagined Nerd Circus personified, the epidemiologists and doctors and MBAs who served as the government-funded magicians of financial decision-making. How exactly these decisions were made was then, as now, a mystery to me. It was not my job, or my business. My job was to hit the ground running when the accounts were settled, when (on your mark, get set...) the starting pistol fired.

According to Clara, there was really only one major agenda item for that lunch gathering: everyone needed to be sure that both the US and Swazi governments were equally committed to the value of a national accelerated circumcision campaign and would put all available muscle and resources into implementation. I cannot say for sure who represented the Swazi side in that careful conversation, but I can guess. The Minister of Health, the outspoken Director of Medical Services and the Chairman of Swaziland's Male Circumcision Task Force were likely candidates.

I imagined that Jabu, my server friend, took their lunch orders, utterly underwhelmed by the group's air of shiny importance. I imagined that they ordered their midday meals – salads and lattes for the Americans, slabs of beef and sides of potatoes for the Swazis – and that they would have settled down to business only after Jabu brought the last of the warmed white platters and circled the table with liter-sized plastic bottles of Bulembu spring water.

As napkins were laid across laps, sips were taken from water-filled glasses and forks moved from plate to mouth, the representative from the CDC would have assumed the spotlight and walked everyone, once again, through the research. The basic message to the Swazi delegation was that the faster circumcision targets were reached, the greater the impact.

In Swaziland, in theory, 150,000 circumcisions in ten years would prevent 64,000 HIV infections. With the same number of circumcisions in one year, the number of infections prevented jumped to 88,000. Speed mattered. To the hypothetical 88,000 men, women and children at risk of HIV infection, it mattered a lot. The difference could be valued at 650 million dollars of savings in antiretroviral therapy and associated care, treatment and support costs. In short, the CDC rep apparently said, the ASI would be an opportunity to do something huge, important and concrete, on the scale of a mass-vaccination campaign. Clara said that he let the numbers speak. The Swazis got the point.

As everyone picked at the last of their lunches, the Swazi policymakers stated emphatically that they wanted the ASI. Maybe this, they thought, would be the epidemic game-changer. One of them spoke of the commitment from His Majesty King Mswati III, the Swazi spiritual and political leader, and promised that the Ministry of Health would back it. They knew what was at stake. For years, they had watched as people poisoned themselves with weevil tablets, unable to bear the thought of a life with HIV. They spent their weekends at funerals. A network of orphanages dotted their beautiful countryside. What was not at all normal was now a way of life.

PEPFAR did not ask my opinion in March 2010, but if

they had, I would have unhesitatingly supported the ASI in Swaziland. Eighty-eight thousand HIV infections averted? Are you kidding? I wanted a front row seat for that! I imagined embarking on a series of ASIs throughout southern Africa, bolstered by the hard-earned experience I had gained in Swaziland. Whereas at first I had only seen the mind-blowing logistics involved, now I found egotistical solace in the idea of playing a key role in one of the most ambitious public health campaigns ever conceived. I needed the ASI to be approved. Moreover, I needed it to be an unmitigated success. I imagined sitting next to Kristi and Clara on conference panels where we would talk about a humanitarian crisis, where we would know beyond question or doubt that we'd truly made a difference.

In early March, the Ministry of Health presented the project, now widely known as the ASI, to Swaziland's Cabinet. We came up with some clever reworkings of the letters – A Simple Incision, Another Snipped Individual – to buy a few laughs and offset the anxiety while we waited for approval. I guess it was hardly a coup when the ASI was endorsed. A 27-million-dollar contribution to an HIV-prevention scheme – who would turn that down?

However, it was hard not to wonder why the offer was extended to the Kingdom in the first place. Why not somewhere else? Three major factors probably tipped the scales in Swaziland's favor. Firstly, and most obviously, was Swaziland's unmatched 31 percent HIV prevalence. And, at 8 percent, its very low circumcision prevalence. So, in terms of getting the biggest bang for HIV-prevention bucks, Swaziland could not be beat. Secondly, the small, hilly country was contained within a confined geographic area populated by a single ethic group. It was a ready-made, self-defined testing ground. Thirdly, as a technically middle-income country surrounded on three sides by South Africa, the country that then boasted the healthiest economy on the continent, Swaziland was a relatively easy place for NGOs to do business. Infrastructure was decent. In addition, the road system was good, owing – according to popular rumor – to the traveling needs of the king's private fleet of BMWs.

At the same time, though, Swaziland was an oddball choice for a national accelerated circumcision campaign. Swazis did not have an active tradition of circumcision as a religious or cultural practice. Traditional circumcision, as an initiation rite at puberty, was once practiced in the nation but it ended sometime in the 1800s when King Mswati II decided that the potential morbidity and mortality caused by the procedure, as well as the post-op immobility, was getting in the way of the military needs of a nation warring with the Zulus. With the passage of so many generations between then and now, Swazis considered themselves an uncircumcising people. This is a key point, so I am going to repeat it: *in Swaziland, having a foreskin was utterly normal*. Being uncircumcised carried no negative cultural, social, or sexual associations.

Think for a moment about what we would be trying to do with the ASI. Think about texting while driving. Think about cigarettes (I only had to look in the mirror for that one). Knowledge alone does not motivate the vast majority of us to change our behavior. It does not overcome the powerful force of our primitive brain. We Americans are no different: one study found that New Yorkers didn't alter their ordering preferences one iota after fast-food chains started publicly posting the astronomical calorie counts of their meal deals. However, in Swaziland there was an extra layer of complication. Asking an older, partnered man to undergo circumcision was like asking a married guy to start using condoms. The clear but unspoken subtext to his partner was this: I am at risk so either I am sleeping around or I think you are.

By then, three-ring circumcising tents were appearing all over sub-Saharan Africa, and it was increasingly clear that the greatest program successes happened in places like Iringa, Tanzania, where being uncircumcised was common, unlike much of the rest of the country. So, for men from Iringa, aware of this difference, the procedure resolved a source of embarrassment. It gave them, in an especially impressive bit of public health lingo, 'access to sexual resources' when they traveled outside the region. This was quite a different prospect from the circumcision cold call in Swaziland, where our program tried to convince perfectly healthy men to have surgery on their perfectly functioning dicks, which already had plenty of access to sexual resources.

But such discussions were so far above my pay grade that I was only vaguely aware of them. Back at headquarters, Erin gathered intelligence wherever she could, and we tried to piece it together over Skype. The story was constantly changing. When would the ASI actually start? Pressure mounted. All of us, regardless of NGO affiliation, were told that we needed to demonstrate extreme competence in our current 'unaccelerated' program in the run-up to the ASI if we wanted a piece of the action.

A few weeks after Clara told me about the high-level lunch at Serendipity, Stephanie called a meeting to discuss preliminary planning. The US government wanted our on-the-ground design input as they prepared to write the request for proposals for the ASI. So, seated in a circle in a boardroom inside of the US Embassy's high security compound, we raised our hands like well-behaved schoolchildren and spoke in abstractions. It was clear to me, sitting quietly in the back, that this was the time to be seen and heard. The night before, Erin had Skyped, 'You know, certain VIPs are already staking their careers on the success of the ASI.' In a secure, spotless room with central air in the US Embassy in Swaziland, I watched several people – all Americans – jockey for position, prepared to do exactly the same thing.

16

He had sidled up his Pick n Pay shopping cart alongside a young Swazi woman and the two were chatting away in siSwati like long-lost siblings. So, at first, he didn't see me. This gave me a few seconds to gather my thoughts, and to panic about being a sweaty, post-jog mess.

It was how things always seemed to go down in the Kingdom. Eventually, I would learn to brush my teeth and hair before jumping in the Pajero, exiting Ayla's village and driving down the winding pot-holed road into town to grab that emergency carton of milk or roll of toilet paper. Because, guaranteed, I'd see someone I was either trying to impress or trying to avoid. The worse I looked, the more likely the run-in. Ayla's boyfriend Glen had told me once, 'What you've got to understand is that this entire country operates like a single village.' I never felt that dictum to be truer than when I ventured to Pick n Pay.

I had not seen Adam in the three weeks since the massage. During the first two, I obsessed over the crazy epiphany I'd had about the two of us while I was extracting his phone from his pocket. By week three, I'd pretty much dismissed the whole thing as narcissistic delusion. And now? Standing there next to a bunch of ripe-looking produce at Pick n Pay? Well, let's put it this way: when he looked down into his cart and the light hit that deep downward groove in his cheek, it killed me.

Christ, I thought to myself, must I really do this *again?* Must I fall for another local looker? I mean, honestly, had I not thoroughly exhausted that motif? I reminded myself why Swazis were supposed to be off-limits. I recalled the commitment I had made to myself about limiting my involvement with Swazi penises to my day job. I would have ducked down another aisle – not because I didn't want to see him, I had been dying to see him, but because I was suddenly red-faced and in possession of a quarter of my usual IQ. Except by then I had been spotted and had little choice but to blurt out something lame.

'Hey!' I said. 'It's so good to see you. I wanted to tell you that I've actually started meditating.'

I was very much aware that my chest was outlined in concentric rings of perspiration on a T-shirt that had holes in the armpits. I could feel the dozens of prickly burrs stuck to my jogging socks. Under such conditions, the meditation thing was all I could come up with, having leapt to the memory of a remark he had made while working out the knots in my shoulders.

It wasn't a lie, either – I truly had tried it. Well, just once, on the hard tile floor of my log cabin's bedroom with a pillow wedged under my butt bones. My eyes refused to stay closed, and every time they popped open, they landed on an oil painting of a reclining naked woman that hung above my bed. Instead of focusing on my breath, I had focused on that woman, wondering if the model was Ayla, my property owner, and if Glen had painted her.

'I have to say, I'm finding it pretty painful,' I said over my grocery basket, cradling its contents – a loaf of brown bread and a six-pack of Castle stout. The Swazi woman who had been speaking with Adam pulled a Blackberry out of a patent leather purse and started typing.

'What if I come over and give you a quick lesson?' Adam suggested.

After I had said 'Perfect!' in a voice that was far too enthusiastic, I hustled as quickly as possible out of Pick n Pay, paid the collector for parking and zoomed out of the parking lot.

Amazingly, the next night he actually did come over. When he arrived at my place, he was wearing white yoga pants and a white T-shirt with an image of a silver heart printed over the location of his actual heart. It took a certain sort of man to wear a shirt like that, I thought; I just wasn't sure which sort of man it was.

He stepped inside. 'Hello again!' He beamed. He seemed a bit jittery as he scanned my living room and kitchen combo. 'This place is amazing! How much do you pay for it?'

'It's about seven thousand emalangeni a month?' I told him. At the current exchange rate, about $1,000. 'Come on in. Sit wherever.'

He did sit, on a low-slung Adirondack chair, one of Glen's creations. 'Are you joking? Seven thousand? These guys know they can charge that much because your NGOs pay for it. It drives up the rates for everyone else.'

It felt like a reprimand. 'Really? How much should we be paying?'

'For a place like this,' he looked around, 'no more than five thousand. I mean, it's nice and everything, but...' He stopped, took careful stock of what must have been a stricken look on my face. 'I'm sorry. That was out of line, wasn't it?'

I smiled weakly. It was every aid workers' biggest insecurity: that we are all a bunch of privileged white assholes – limousine liberals; professional do-gooders prancing around Africa basking in the sort of luxury we cannot afford back home.

'I'm sorry,' he continued, 'it's just that we're looking to move. Right now, we are staying in Manzini, and it is not really working out. I am trying to see what is available in this area. I love it up here. It's so peaceful, so quiet. I'd love to be surrounded by nature.'

We? Who exactly was this 'we'? A braver woman than I would have asked.

He glanced in the direction of my fridge, and then I watched his eyes travel to a cluster of rotting bananas and avocados in a bowl. What was going on here? Was he talking like this – a mile a minute – out of nerves? Was he stoned? Still, there was something… a wandering, unselfconscious innocence in the way he spoke. I gave in to the warm music of it. Who needed meditation, or medication, with him around?

'Can I get you a cup of tea?' I asked when he also, as if sensing a subtle change in me, relaxed into a stretch of silence.

'That would be lovely.' He seemed torn about whether to say some more, then decided to go for it. 'I really apologize, but do you have anything to eat? I've been running around all day, and haven't had a chance to grab anything.' Then he lifted his T-shirt for a moment to rub his growling belly, a childlike gesture that offered a lingering eyeful of a serious six-pack. But just as I got up to look, he had an idea. 'No, wait! How about this! I'll make us something. Let me see what you have in the fridge and I'll pull something together from what's there.'

'Good luck.' I conducted a quick mental inventory: half a loaf of bread, about four beers, a block of molding mozzarella, a nearly empty pint of milk and some wilting spinach leaves. I imagined his house stocked with local fresh produce and organic greens. I imagined that he had a juicer and a sprouting machine.

He bounced off the chair and headed straight for the sink where he carefully washed his hands with a squirt of dishwashing liquid. Then he rinsed them and closed the tap with his elbow, like a surgeon. While he emptied the entire contents of my refrigerator onto the kitchen counter, and opened the cabinets one by one to examine and consider, he talked about his travels on the cruise ships. 'I love Peruvian food,' he said. 'Have you ever tried it? The best meal I've ever had in my life was in Aguas Calientes at the base of Machu Picchu.'

From the comfort of a handmade couch where I sat cross-legged in a pair of cut-offs, I listened to his soothing voice and watched through my glass-paned door as the sky turned first pink and then orange and a fat sun sank between the ridges of the Fonteyn hills and crickets and frogs tested their nighttime songs.

He pulled out a half-empty packet of linguine and lit the burner under a pot of water. I nodded, fascinated and unsure of what to make of this man who was friction and awkwardness one minute and complete ease the next. He sautéed spinach in olive oil, and then added some milk and shredded cheese. The living room filled with a warm vapor. When the pasta was tender, he drained it through a sieve, and carefully lifted half of the noodles onto each of two dinner plates. Finally, he lowered both plates onto the coffee table, and said, 'Please be careful. It's hot. And I really do apologize. It might not be very good.'

'Well, you can't exactly be held accountable for that. You had next to nothing to work with.'

He looked down at his plate, straight-faced, and then smiled. 'That's true. It was desperate in there. How do you survive? I mean, I grew up without much food in the house, but that wasn't by choice.'

'I eat out a lot,' I said, shoving a forkful of dangling linguini into my mouth. 'I just don't have the energy to care once I get home. It's just me, so it's hard to feel motivated.' I swallowed. 'Oh my God, this is so good!'

'Really?'

'Yes! Amazing.' This was said through a mouthful of pasta, eyes trained on the Sean Connery grooves running down his cheeks. I watched Adam eat, twirling one piece of pasta at a time, spearing a bit of spinach before artfully bringing the tidy bite to his tongue. He ate like a European. Refined, using his knife and fork in tandem, the way the Irishman did.

'Laura, you really must look after yourself,' Adam said. 'Get more rest. I know you have a stressful job. I can see the strain that it takes on you. It shows on your face. That indentation, there, between your eyebrows.'

We were both sitting on a scratchy woven reed mat. He reached across the pine coffee table and touched my forehead lightly. It shocked me that I didn't feel anxious. I actually felt okay. Better than okay, I felt cared for. I felt good enough, as if I didn't have to perform.

'You're right,' I said. 'But... I don't know. Work is the thing that keeps me going. Work is what holds me up. It's what's real. It's a purpose.'

'What about the rest of your life?' He put down his fork and knife to concentrate on me.

'Oh well... I'm just getting out of something. Eh, I don't even know if you could call it a relationship.' I figured I didn't need to go into details.

'You know, it's funny, I am actually dealing with something myself. It has been over for a long time, even before we arrived in Swaziland last year. There is no love left but she is having trouble accepting that. And, well, she's a foreigner here. I tend to find myself in situations like this. I've had bad luck in relationships. My aunties would say it's like a curse or something.'

'Oh?' How much could I pry here?

'Anyway, I don't want to involve you in our problems. But,' he said, and waited for several beats before continuing, 'I do feel like I can really talk to you, and I'm grateful for that. I'm finding it hard to connect with people here, which is strange. I grew up in Swaziland, but I left for too long.' He smiled, and scratched his shaved head – a style that appeared to be a concession to premature balding – with one long finger. 'Sorry. Anyway, what were you saying about your situation?'

I shrugged. 'It was a long-distance thing. I've known for a long time that it wasn't going to work out, but it's hard, I guess, when you really care about someone. Anyway, it needed to happen. But now I'm getting older, and I'm slowly becoming one of those lonely, workaholic, global single ladies.'

'One of those what?' he asked.

I explained the phenomenon to him. 'I'm sure you've seen them. You know, the women who start out as aid workers or volunteers and then realize that they are more at home away from home? They dress in printed kaftans and beaded tribal jewelry and they haven't washed their own dishes or done their own laundry in years?' He looked at me like he hadn't the foggiest idea what I was talking about. I realized these were my own judgments and fears.

'Maybe it's just that I can see how it would be so easy to become one of them. To get so caught up in the work. It all feels so important. Then the years pass and you realize all your friends back home are having kids' pool parties and sleepovers and trips to Disneyland and you're alone in some godforsaken place, still smoking cigarettes and getting wasted like a teenager.'

It was a surprisingly honest confession. I regretted it

immediately. But I felt safe with Adam. I felt seen. Here was a man who had yet to ask me what kind of music I liked or what films I watched, who probably didn't feel guilty when he went a week without catching up on the *New York Times*. Whatever sandpaper rubric he used to siphon and pigeonhole, it was not the same one that I had scraped against since childhood. It was intoxicating. I admitted to myself that I had a true crush on someone for the first time in years.

'I wouldn't worry too much about that. We find the right people at the right times,' he said. 'The people who'll teach us the lessons we most need to learn. It sounds like you'd gotten to the point with each other where you weren't growing anymore. That is the time to go. The trick is to leave with as much respect as you can.' He suddenly caught himself. 'Hey, what time is it?'

I picked up my phone. 'Close to nine.'

'I'd better go.'

He brought our empty plates to the kitchen, and then gathered his car keys. Neither of us mentioned meditation. He walked out onto my little porch, shivered and then stepped back inside. He snuck a look toward Ayla and Glen's house. 'It's cold out there.'

'Well, you're sort of lacking in natural insulation,' I observed, nodding toward his bare head.

He didn't answer before he pulled me close. Just like he had in his massage room. He smelled like incense and mist and tobacco, like how I imagined a village in the Himalayas to smell. 'There's just something about you,' he said again. 'Something so... open.'

What did that mean, I wondered, as he stepped out, all white under a vast cover of stars.

17

I started regularly attending MC Task Force meetings when I relocated to the Kingdom. They lasted for hours. In March, in the midst of another protracted and squirmy Task Force meeting at a cramped conference room in one of the Ministry of Health buildings, I passed a note to the Swazi World Health Organization rep. On it, I'd scribbled, *How many total doctors in Swaziland?* He wrote back in his careful gentleman-doctor handwriting: +/- *120. More on the register, but... brain drain.*

Swaziland, like many low- and middle-income countries, suffered from a serious shortage of skilled healthcare providers. The math was straightforward: a staggering 10,000 people for every lone doctor. Compare this against the 400 people per physician ratio in the US. When overwhelmed Swazi-based doctors got opportunities to work in higher-income countries, they grabbed them, creating the so-called 'brain drain' that exacerbated the healthcare crisis. Incentive schemes and salary bumps often failed. With such a staggering difference in compensation between developed and developing countries, investments African governments made in educating their health workers consistently benefited higher-income countries instead.

So the handful of Swazi, or foreign, clinicians who worked in the Kingdom were too busy caring for sick people to be overly concerned with circumcision. More to the point, policies around MC were clear: circumcision could not divert attention from urgent curative and emergent healthcare needs. However, this generated another catch-22 since, in Swaziland, doctors were the only cadre authorized to do the actual cutting in a circumcision procedure. This was different from, say, Kenya, where trained nurses could perform this role.

It boiled down to one unavoidable reality: Swaziland would need outside surgical assistance to perform close to 150,000 circumcisions in less than a year. Hence the volunteer doctor program I was leading. This was touchy territory. The Swazi government recognized that it did not have the human resources it needed to carry out a project it had endorsed, yet it didn't want to see the majority of ASI money channeled to non-Swazis.

It was an odd situation. In a field that fetishizes 'sustainability,' a concept best conveyed by the old 'teach a man to fish…' aphorism, what the ASI proposed was anachronistic. By intention, it would not improve systems or strengthen existing in-country healthcare infrastructure. It would get a one-off job done quickly, safely, effectively and affordably. And, after the ASI – that is after 80 percent of Swazi adolescents and men had been circumcised and a culture of circumcision had been established – the ongoing task for the government would be much more manageable. It would consist only of the 'mop-up' (circumcising the remaining 20 percent) and circumcising those adolescents who aged into the MC target group every year.

So, everyone – Swazis and Americans alike – implicitly understood that we were going to have to drum up a bunch of outside doctors for this ASI circumcising sprint. Sourcing those extra circumcisers, and figuring out how to set them up in Swaziland while making the most of available Swazi human resources – who would do that?

Well, it was becoming clear that the responsibility would sit with, in large part, me.

18

It was now March 2010. Our first batch of volunteer doctors, four American urologists, would arrive in a month. Kristi's team put together a three-week 'Back to School' MC campaign during the school holidays, late April to early May, to coincide with the doctors' visit. School-aged kids were always the easiest sell – they were available, and in general, their parents controlled their healthcare decisions.

We were hopeful that Back to School would make for an impressive showing, both for the high-profile visiting doctors and for our donors, in the lead-up to the ASI. It was supposed to function as a sort of mini pilot test for the systems that would ultimately support the huge ASI. But I was encountering a serious problem. None of the four volunteer doctors was yet registered with the Swaziland Medical and Dental Council. No registration, no circumcisions.

We had started the process weeks beforehand, putting together the notarized original documents that needed to be FedExed to Swaziland – a prospect that made me nervous, given the alarming number of frequent-flier miles that my own documents had racked up on their way to the Kingdom. I took to buying the administrative assistant of the Swaziland Medical and Dental Council take-out KFC, hoping that would increase my odds of getting the surgeons successfully registered. I also drove her all over Mbabane. But it was useless. She would not lubricate the process. There was only one decision-maker at the Swaziland Medical and Dental Council, and she was not him.

Head of the Medical and Dental Association, Chair of the MC Task Force and Deputy Director of Health for the Ministry of Health, Dr. Bheki Mamba was a busy man. He was frequently out of the country, which was annoying given that he personally needed to sign off on every registration application. Kristi had explained all of this to me well in advance. 'If there's one person you need to charm in Swaziland,' she had said, 'it's Dr. Mamba.'

I didn't want our volunteers to know any of this. I wanted them to think that this program was a well-oiled machine. I'd been a volunteer enough times in my life to know what was required. First, these people needed a guidebook. So, over the course of several Castle Milk Stouts on a Friday night (more wild times in the field), I liberally borrowed from Peace Corps Swaziland's documentation to draft a twenty-page orientation packet. It told volunteers not to expect functional internet or functional toilets. It included graphics of electric plugs and currency conversions and suggested a packing list and a primer in siSwati, found online, full of words and phrases that I didn't know myself. The first page was the official introductory letter from the Swazi MC Task Force, which said, 'Your participation in the program is considered humanitarian assistance in disaster relief, not medical tourism. It will not be a few circumcisions in the morning and a game of golf in the afternoon.' These volunteers were expected to circumcise as many foreskins as possible during their ten-day visit.

Just two weeks before the volunteer doctors expected to

arrive, Dr. Mamba's administrative assistant summoned me back to the Medical and Dental Council office, where I learned that the entire country's registration documents were stacked, dusty floor to dusty ceiling, in unlabeled, un-alphabetized cardboard boxes. She was in a bad mood and I had arrived without fried chicken. Apparently, she was still missing several critical forms. Not one of the doctors yet had so much as a plane ticket.

My eyes welled up as I got back into my car. A vile string of profanities issued forth as I reached for the catch of the glove compartment for my pack of Dunhill Lights. It was rush hour in downtown Mbabane and I sat fuming at the red light by the Engen garage, blowing smoke out the window. A familiar, mentally addled homeless man approached the idling car. He wore fingerless gloves and two different unlaced sneakers. His hair was a riotous mass of matted, sun-bleached dreadlocks. I fixed my gaze in the middle distance and heard a gentle hoot-hoot from a car horn directly to my right. Fucking minibus drivers, I thought, always hitting on you at traffic lights.

'Laura!' a voice called.

Oh my God, I knew that voice. I swiveled my head in its direction – and there was Adam, my meditation coach, chef and massage therapist, sitting high in the right-side driver's seat of a blue Chevy truck. Our faces were about a foot and a half apart. 'Stop by Serendipity and say hello sometime!' he said before the light changed, and he pulled out into the intersection.

I held my breath, unspoken words clogged in my throat, as the Chevy became a tiny blue pinprick on the horizon and then careened down the mighty Malagwane.

***

In early April, just before our volunteers were set to arrive, I flew to France to run the Paris marathon. I had planned the trip before I knew anything about the ASI or Back to School, and after serious internal debate, I decided not to change my plans. At first, it was a great decision. Following a four-hour run that wasn't nearly as grueling as I'd expected thanks to months of high-altitude training in the Swazi mountains, in Paris I spent entire evenings without a single mention of penises. I felt the weight of stress lifting, found a renewed readiness to take on the challenge that lay ahead.

On paper, the timing should have been perfect. Our volunteers were to board an airplane on the West Coast of the United States bound for South Africa just after I boarded my return flight from Paris. I should have beaten them back to the Kingdom. Except that I never got as far as Charles de Gaulle airport because a giant cloud of Icelandic volcanic ash choked the skies of Europe and an entire continent was grounded until further notice.

From my little pension near the Moulin Rouge, I tried to manage things from afar. I whooped with joy when our new program assistant, Thandi, wrote that all four volunteers were successfully registered with the Medical and Dental Council days before their scheduled arrival. I was less enthusiastic, however, when she said that officials had one of them held in customs at the Matsapha airport.

West African by birth, now a urology resident in California with a US passport, the young doctor was taken to a holding room in the small airport – somewhere between the women's restroom and the shop that sells the cheap plastic blonde-haired, blue-eyed dolls – for questioning. She sent an email from her dying Blackberry to let everyone, and I mean everyone, know what was going on. This meant that, nauseatingly, our funders in D.C. and Geneva, the elite of the Nerd Circus, were getting the blow-by-blow of her detainment. Eventually, the WHO rep bailed out the exhausted volunteer.

Relief! They had all arrived. They were all registered. And, by God, they were ready to circumcise.

19

Dr. Mamba, the MC Task Force Chairman and head of the Medical and Dental Council, was at his best when he issued the urologist volunteers a warm welcome at the Mountain Inn. That is what I heard, anyway. I was still captive in my Paris hotel room at the time. When I met them the next night, in any case, they were in fine form.

Bleary-eyed from overnight air travel, I'd stopped at my cabin in Fonteyn West just long enough to take a shower and put on some proper professional clothes, which I decided meant a knee-length skirt, boots and a sweater. I'd suggested that we convene at the old mall in a dark corner restaurant called Finesse. Next to Serendipity, it was the most foreigner-friendly eating establishment in the capital.

I'd asked James to pick up the team of doctors and ferry them from their scenic rooms at Mountain Inn the mile or so into the center of town. Driving through three stoplights, past the traditional market and the ladies selling secondhand clothes in successive heaps – an area called *gobondzela utsatse* or 'bend and pick' – eventually James parked his van in front of Truworth's display of skinny mannequins in skinny jeans, close to the brook that divided the new and old malls. A walkway bordered the edge of the parking lot. It was a socioeconomic litmus test; on one side, the path led to the florescent lights of KFC, and on the other to a wrought-iron spiral staircase, a bounty of potted plants, fairy lights and a sign that announced Finesse Restaurant in curlicue letters.

I could identify each of the doctors sitting at the softly lit table easily after studying their passport photos for weeks. George Salsby was the calmly in-control head of the team. Then there was Grace Abara, our formerly detained urology resident, and two other senior and experienced urologists – Rick Davis and Burt Wallace. Burt Wallace was the first of the volunteers to introduce himself. A stately African American man with an authoritative smile and a warm handshake, he stood up when I walked into the cozy, firelit restaurant.

'Well, no one told us you were so tall!' he said. 'I'm Burt, and here's what we really need to know,' he began, his expression stony and serious. I steeled myself for what I was sure would be some kind of impossible-to-please-surgeon complaint. 'How fast did you finish that race?'

I exhaled and pulled over a chair. Dr. Salsby poured me a glass of wine from a half-empty bottle. 'So,' I said, as we settled into the meal, 'you guys were at your sites yesterday and today. Tell me everything. What did you think?'

They were brimming with questions, suggestions and ideas.

'The diathermy machines run hot – you can't put them in direct contact with the clients' skin,' said Grace.

'Yeah, and services are slow to start in the morning; the first procedure doesn't happen until ten or ten-thirty. The clients have to be transported into the clinics, so there are delays there, and then they get held up in counseling for an hour,' Dr. Salsby, added.

I carefully noted everything on a pad of paper.

Rick Davis jumped in, 'Oh, yeah… And everybody wants to

know what happens with the foreskins. Why is that? What do people think we're going to do with them?'

I explained to them that, after a lunatic character on a Swazi soap opera suggested it, plenty of Swazis believed, or said that they believed, that circumcised foreskins were ground into a common cooking flavoring called Benny Spice and used as *muti*. 'It's a particularly stubborn myth. And no amount of education about proper medical waste management seems to dispel it.'

Then conversation took a pleasant, casual turn. We talked about families: who had how many kids, how old they were, and how accomplished. That's when Burt busted out his digital camera, scrolled to a photo and then handed it to me. 'Do you know who that is?' I looked at the picture. It was Burt standing with his arm around a slender woman. She looked familiar. 'Nancy Pelosi?' I ventured.

'Yup!' he said, liking this game. 'Just one more.' He slid his glasses into a better viewing position and set once again to scrolling. 'How about this one?'

I looked. 'Hmm… I don't know who that is, sorry,' I said.

'Really?'

Burt had every reason to be surprised, because, as he went on to inform me, the jolly-looking man in the second photo was a friend of his, the head of PEPFAR. I felt two things: one, ashamed of my ignorance, and, two, an intense desire not to screw up.

Rick had a final question before we said our goodbyes for the evening. 'So, what are our chances of meeting the king while we're here?'

'Hmmm…' I began carefully. This was probably the most important thing the volunteers needed to know: they could not, under any circumstances, publicly bad-mouth the king. 'You guys need to understand that, to Swazis, the king is not just a man. He is holy. He has, like, superpowers.' It seemed like the easiest, most concise way to explain it. 'And I think the chances of us meeting him are pretty much nil. Sorry. But while we're on the subject, there's something else we should probably chat about. You might want to tread carefully around the whole polygamy issue, too.'

In Swaziland, ancient patriarchal traditions related to land rights and caretaking had given way to Christianity and modernity, but that didn't mean that monogamy was strictly enforced, legally or socially. I had heard enough MC Partnership Suite office gossip to know that while 'being a player' seemed to earn a guy bragging rights with his buddies, that sort of behavior was not taken lightly by romantic partners. I was told that it was common for both men and women to respond with retaliation affairs, and what Swazis called *iso ngeso,* or 'an eye for an eye,' became a vicious cycle of damage – emotional, psychological and immunological. Americans, including me, coming in to 'fight' HIV had some strong opinions about all this. I recalled my great-aunt Ruth's words: is it really so hard to use a condom?

'As outsiders,' I advised, 'it's best not to go there.'

***

I was at the office the next day when I got a panicked call from Lungile, a nurse who was working with Burt at our government hospital site. 'Laura, can you please get us some MoliPants? It is an emergency. The boys are refusing to come until we have them.'

It was the first time I had ever heard of MoliPants. However, after she explained what they were, I acted as swiftly as if she'd just reported a stock-out of sutures or antibiotics.

MoliPants were, in a word, underwear. Made from white mesh, each pair rolled up to the size of a cotton ball. They were disposable, ninety-two cents a pop on the local market, and came in tissue boxes of twenty-five in sizes medium and large. They did a fine job of keeping everything in place, but they weren't necessary. Ordinarily, the post-surgical penis was wrapped in gauze, and taped head-up against the stomach. A boy's own clean cotton underwear was recommended during this post-op phase. Recovery room nurses described this very specifically. But boys liked MoliPants, liked them enough to refuse to board buses bound for the public government hospital that didn't have them. Disposable undies were more than a nice touch; they told the client he was valued. And all the Back to School boys wanted to feel valued. At private clinics.

The lack of MoliPants at Burt's hospital uncovered something interesting. It turned out that Swazi teenagers were educated consumers who could and would call the shots. We would now have to ensure that every public site had everything, down to the last detail, that the private clinics did. Never mind that the circumcision itself was free for all clients. Never mind that the boys were transported to and from their surgery and the follow-up visits free of charge. Never mind that all of the sites met quality assurance standards defined by the World Health Organization and the Ministry of Health or that providers were identically trained and, in fact, rotated between sites.

On one level, it irked. These guys were getting high quality, expensive preventative care *for free* and they were complaining about disposable underwear? I mean, really, people – this was a measure taken to preserve their health and the health of their loved ones. But, on another level, who could blame them? The MoliPants used in the Swazi circumcision program were remarkably similar to the disposable undies secured against the groins of postpartum women in American hospitals. In my past life, I would never have called them a luxury. I called Kristi to help organize an emergency shipment of multiple boxes of MoliPants to Burt and Lungile. She had them delivered the very same day.

For me, the MoliPants moment was just another day on the ground in Swaziland. I didn't think to mention it in reports back to my supervisor. But somehow, in the small world of the MC community, it made its way to Erin in Baltimore. 'Dude, I just heard about the MoliPants drama,' Erin wrote over Skype.

'Yeah. Didn't see that coming. But don't worry, we sorted it out. Kristi got right on it. We made sure all the sites got them.'

'Well, that's why we're calling this volunteer mission a pilot, right? We are working out the kinks before the ASI. These are important lessons. Gotta say, though, it's looking like Swaziland is… unique.'

'What do you mean?'

'I mean, this isn't the first school holiday MC campaign we've supported, but it's the first time clients have demanded certain supplies. Our clients in Tanzania are willing to wait all day and are just grateful to get the service.'

I felt my heart rate quicken slightly with a rush of rivalry. Like, well, how very nice for Tanzania.

'Definitely nothing straightforward about circumcision in Swaziland, Erin, that's for sure.'

'Oh, and I also wanted to talk to you about something else. I took a look at the early ASI ad sketches you sent, and I have some concerns,' Erin wrote.

To date, Swaziland had not had a national circumcision campaign. No billboards advertising the benefits. No national radio spots touting satisfied customers. The government wanted to ensure that the 'supply,' hundreds of doctors and nurses and well-equipped facilities, was in place first. So the introduction of ASI advertising and promotion would be carefully planned and timed. It now looked as if Clara's organization would replace Kristi's as the prime organization for circumcision programming once new ASI funding came through, with Clara at the helm, working with a marketing firm in Johannesburg. The firm had been quietly meeting with focus groups in Swaziland, designing graphic images that would appeal to young Swazi men. The early sketches favored stylized animated faces of attractive Swazis with various captions. Although 87 percent of Swazi men were reportedly willing to undergo circumcision, between the wanting and the doing lived a limbo of fear, inconvenience and hesitation. A smart, effective communication campaign would make all the difference.

'Why didn't they use real people in the ads?' Erin asked.

'The marketing team felt that the avatars were more universal,' I answered. 'It's easier to imagine yourself in the place of a sketched face rather than in a real, specific one.'

'But what's with this one of a traditional Swazi guy surrounded by three women?' (The caption read, ostensibly spoken by the gaggle of pretty girls, *We will wait for you!*) 'Isn't that encouraging multiple concurrent partnerships?'

The quickened pulse rush returned. Erin wasn't here. Erin didn't get the nuances. Erin wasn't dealing with this stuff day in and day out. I was. I didn't have time for the negativity. Demand creation wasn't our responsibility. I had other things to worry about, like the group of American volunteer circumcising surgeons I was responsible for. I reminded her of this.

She seemed to get the message, and dropped the subject. 'How are they holding up out there?'

I told her I called them every day to see how things were going. I shared a story Rick had told me the day before. Once he realized most of the boys understood English perfectly, he chatted with them. They were young and afraid so Dr. Davis tried to put them at ease. 'I come from the United States,' he told them. 'Do you know where that is?' Most of them did. They knew the movies, knew the music. 'I have a practice in California,' he would go on to say, as the polite, shy children would steal sideways glances at him and say nothing. Except for one, who, in response to that last piece of information, asked, 'Are you here to practice on me?'

The boys tried to be brave, Rick said. They were scared, but many also wanted the procedure. I was surprised to hear this. Was a culture shift happening? Were they starting to feel circumcision peer pressure at school? Apparently seven-, eight- and nine-year-olds turned up at our sites and lied about their ages, hoping to convince the clinical team that they met the minimum age requirement of twelve.

After the first couple of days, I realized that the volunteers did not need to engage in prolonged phone chats with me to feel 'supported'. After all, these were highly competent, professional adults. Besides, I had other things to distract me. Adam and I had been emailing each other. He had gotten my details from Jabu at Serendipity. I wrote to him about silly things – funny bits of my circumcising days, random office gossip and missing Dunkin' Donuts sesame bagels. He wrote about moving from Manzini to Mbabane, about his friend visiting from the UK, about realizing it was time to shave his head again.

One night, the tone changed. He sent an email at 4 a.m. in which he asked, *What have you done to me? I cannot sleep. I wish I were in your arms. I miss your smile. You are so beautiful in so many ways.*

I read those words the morning of another MC Task Force meeting. Happy hormones lit up a thousand receptors as I watched Dr. Mamba, the Task Force Chairman and others puppet their way through my surreal working life. I snapped back to reality long enough to report to Dr. Mamba that the volunteers were doing well and that they were happily circumcising away.

'The care and feeding of Americans abroad,' the ever-optimistic Clara joked after we emerged from the meeting. 'I don't envy you! Hey, want to grab lunch? I'm always starving after I've had to sit through one of those meetings.'

'Me too,' I agreed.

'So, where to?'

'The 'Dip?' I proposed.

'The what?' Clara asked.

'The 'Dip. You know, Serendipity?'

'Is that what you old-timers call it?'

'Since when does being here full-time for three months longer than you qualify me as an old-timer?'

'Don't you think that three months here equates to years anywhere else?'

'Clara, didn't you tell me that you worked in post-genocide Kosovo?'

'Yeah, but at least there you knew exactly where you stood.' She looked back toward the Ministry of Health office complex to make sure no one was within earshot, then she lowered her voice to a whisper, 'Here, it's all this passive-aggressive behind-the-back bullshit. We need to get this thing moving *now*. We need to make decisions about structure, about systems. We're still debating the same stuff – circumcision technique, mobile sites versus fixed – that we were talking about when I got here months ago.' She sighed. 'Whatever. Okay, I can drive.' We tumbled into her rental car and vented about Dr. Mamba's duck-and-dodge decision-making. She indicated into Serendipity's gravel parking lot, and we spent a few minutes gathering our laptops and bags. It was understood that this would be a working lunch.

'Hey, Clara, I've just got to pee quickly. Grab us a table.'

'Sure.'

I heard Clara ask Jabu for a table on the patio outside the restaurant. Then I slipped down the hallway toward Adam's treatment room. I pressed my ear to the door. If there was plinky-plinky music playing, I planned to tiptoe back to the restaurant. I heard nothing. I knocked softly.

'Come in.' A pair of socked feet hit the floor and pattered toward me.

The door opened, and suddenly Adam was standing there, assailing me with the wide smile and the chocolate-skinned yoga arms.

'I'm finally stopping by to say hello,' I said.

'You look lovely,' he responded. It was not the kind of statement you knew what to do with from someone who'd told you in your last conversation that he wasn't free.

'Thanks. I am, umm, working. Here for a meeting. How are you?'

'I'm okay, I guess.' He looked at the floor, in a puppyish, please-ask-me-why-I'm-not-really-okay way.

I bit. 'What's going on?'

'All this stuff I told you about when I came to your place that time... remember? At home? I'm just feeling really down.'

'Do you want to talk about it? Maybe I could come back?'

'Not today. There's too much going on.'

Too much going on? From what I could surmise, he had just been taking a nap in the middle of the afternoon on his massage table.

'Why don't you book a massage?' Adam suggested. 'And then we can just talk. You don't have to pay, but that way no one here gets suspicious. The walls have ears, you know?' He pointed with his chin to Jabu sitting on her stool at the receptionist desk, where she was flipping through a copy of

You magazine. Without question, she was listening to every word we were saying.

I agreed and then went out on the deck to a table where Clara was waiting with a mug of coffee.

'Did you fall in?' she asked.

'I'm not feeling great.'

'Really?' She gave me a concerned look. Organized her features into her clinician face. 'You know, you actually do look quite flushed.'

***

On the ninth and last day of the volunteers' visit, we organized a modest celebration in their honor. At first, there was a festive spirit in the small conference room at The George Hotel in Manzini. The volunteers dressed in formal wear. Teams came all the way from Pigg's Peak and Mankayane, showing up an hour late. By then, the finger snacks were gone, and Stephanie, Kristi, and I were on our Blackberries, restless and impatient.

Eventually, we had enough participants to get started. The soft-spoken director of the public hospital in Manzini spoke first. 'We were so blessed by these volunteers,' he said. 'They fit into the teams so well.' Each of the volunteers nodded toward the Senior Medical Officer, a dignified gesture of fellowship.

'Thanks to our American friends, we reached an all-time circumcising record at our clinic last week, over seventy procedures in a single day!' a stocky young Zimbabwean doctor who ran the medical operations at the men's clinic in Matsapha told us. Although the coordination of the volunteer doctor program fell to my team, we'd worked closely with Kristi and her colleagues on placements. This young doctor served – quietly, respectfully and intelligently – as the moral compass of the MC program. He reminded me of Rachel, in the sense that both instinctively understood the complex job of cultural interpretation. In a debonair suit and tie, he gave the requisite words of welcome and thanks. Then, he started to speak about one of his patients. Teaching through story, just like Rachel.

'Some of you know,' he said, 'of a case we are currently managing, a rural boy who so desperately wanted to be circumcised that he had attempted to perform the procedure on himself. He positioned his penis on a toilet seat, and then brought down the lid with force, hoping to sever his foreskin.'

Several of us audibly drew in our breath and shifted around in our seats.

'The boy was rushed to the hospital with serious injuries,' the doctor continued. 'But it tells us that we need to appreciate that a shift is happening here in Swaziland. With the Back to School campaigns, young boys now want to be circumcised. We must offer safe, high-quality services. We must be ready for what lies ahead.'

What lies ahead… the words sent butterflies to my stomach. *What lies ahead?* I repeated the question in my mind. And my mind provided an answer, with confidence: 88,000 HIV infections averted.

That end, I had always believed to be worthy. The means, however… Here, I was shocked to realize something: this circumcision business wasn't weird to me anymore. It wasn't absurd, or outlandish, or loaded, or cringeworthy. I was no longer conflicted. The intervention had become gutsy, intrepid. It had become right. I had joined the Nerd Circus.

20

After I'd said my goodbyes to our first fantastic group of American volunteer surgeons, I emailed Adam. 'Any chance you are available for a massage around seven tonight?'

'Of course,' he had replied. 'I also need to see you.'

When I arrived at Serendipity that Saturday evening in early May, Adam was in his treatment room, hunched over his plastic chair. He wore a black turtleneck, pressed black pants and black slip-on dress shoes. He looked small and guarded, like a stranded turtle. I knew so little about him, although I knew our lives and circumstances to be so very different. Yet, like Swaziland itself, something about him appealed directly to my heart.

I hoisted myself up onto his massage table and scooted back so that my legs swung from the edge. I looked at him. Then I looked at the floor, suddenly unsure of what I wanted to say. I suspect he knew this.

'It's gotten so much cooler these last few days,' he began. 'Have you noticed? The weather has definitely turned.' His face was pinched. I noticed for the first time that his nose had once been broken; it cast a diagonal shadow across dark hollows underneath his eyes.

'Are you all right?' I asked. 'You look tired.'

He sighed deeply. 'There's so much I want to tell you, but I don't know how.'

'Remember, I'm not as fragile as I look.' Then I realized that my jokey, assertive tone was wrong. I softened. 'What is it? I can handle it.'

His brown eyes watered. My chest tightened.

'I don't know how this happened,' he went on. 'How I've allowed myself to develop these feelings. It was a mistake – I knew it was over with her before we left the States. But now she's stuck here.' He inhaled deeply before continuing. 'You remember that first time you came to Serendipity?' he asked. 'Jabu called me and told me that her best customer needed a massage, and that I'd better drive fast. Then when I arrived, I asked where my client was, and she pointed to you, sitting on the veranda, working on your laptop. I looked over and saw you, your face – you were so focused on something you were reading. It was so strange. I looked at you, and I felt like I couldn't breathe. I knew it wasn't physical attraction,' he said, which stung a bit. 'But I couldn't understand what it was, what it meant.'

He gave me a searching look that made me feel exposed. 'Laura, you need to know that I'm in a relationship and I'm not the kind of person who cheats.'

Perhaps all cheaters believe this of themselves. How many people actually set out to deliberately deceive? Besides, what's the party line on infidelity in a place where it's the social norm? But Adam was different, wasn't he? More wounded child than asshole player? I did not sense the arrogance of a man who cashed in on his good looks to score, who wielded loving smiles, warm hugs and spiritual talk with a seducer's selfish agenda. It was confusing, far too confusing to try to figure out in that loaded moment.

I wanted to kiss his face. I wanted to hold him and tell him that everything would turn out all right. I took the two long steps over to his chair and put a hand on his cheek. Then I knelt so that we were face to face, and pressed my thin, dry lips to a wet spot next to one of his closed eyes. I intended to leave it at that. After all, he was attached. Then he turned his face and the kiss on his temple became a soft kiss on his mouth.

Eventually, the outdoor lights snapped off, and several sets of headlights sent beams through the blinds on the window. 'We need to go home now, darling,' he whispered. He looked me squarely in the eyes. 'Please don't let this wreck your head.'

I arrived back at my little cabin that night equally elated and uneasy. A cartoon angel sat on one shoulder, and a devil on the other. The devil said, 'For all these months of striving and stress, your prize is a passionate encounter with your enigmatic crush – well done!' The angel scolded, 'You cannot be with this guy. You may be single, but he isn't.'

Adam did not yet know that I was a Jedi master in the art of head-wrecking. Dark hours passed in a combination of jittery excitement and mental hand-wringing. I finally got up to check my email. There in my inbox I found another prize. From the Johannesburg airport, Burt Wallace had sent a message to his buddy, the head of PEPFAR. In it, he praised the Swazi volunteer program and Kristi and me personally. The first true test of my new professional life was made, in that moment, a resounding success.

21

That spring of 2010, Male Circumcision for HIV Prevention programs were gaining traction across the eastern and southern African region. Although a determined band of vocal objectors tried to poke holes in the data and questioned the secret agendas of the researchers, funding for MC programs (and the competing NGO interested in leading them) increased.

Erin and her team took a different approach in every country, experimenting with implementation models to learn what worked. Kenya and Tanzania had the most successful programs. Our teams would perform 10,336 circumcisions in just six weeks across five sites in Iringa, Tanzania. But even there, in the days leading up to the most successful campaign, no one knew what would happen. Client demand was not guaranteed anywhere. Anxious staff screwed together surgical lamps, unpacked boxes of circumcision kits and prayed that guys would show up. No one expected the thunderous stampede to the clinics that followed. That first day of the history-making campaign, surgical teams worked until 10.30 p.m. to clear the waiting room. Every day thereafter followed suit.

So, while Erin and her team celebrated Tanzania's successes, other countries – like Swaziland – were proving tougher nuts to crack. In Malawi, for example, policy leaders questioned the correlation between circumcision and HIV status since their numbers ran counter to trends elsewhere. They also feared a conflation between voluntary medical male circumcision and circumcision as a statement of religious affiliation. In Lesotho, programmers butted up against a cultural tradition of non-medical circumcision (often only partial) as a part of adolescent initiation ceremonies.

Circumcision touched the nerve of specific sociocultural dynamics in every country, every region, which played out in unique ways according to the context and the personalities of those in power. This was a time of observation, of information gathering, of risk. Was there any way to predict where the intervention would be embraced and where it would not? Some would go on to argue yes, and others would say no. Careful study and repeated trials take years, decades, and a whole lot of money. We had funding cycles that turned over with the frequency of every new administration, with incredible pressure to produce results in a relatively short period. The behavior of populations didn't follow the predictable mechanics of physiology. For MC programs, trial and error, along with frequent course corrections, would become the preferred implementation approach. With donor-funded programs and sky-high targets, it was really the only option.

'What's going on with the nurse issue? Any progress?' Erin messaged me on Skype. 'Let me know when you're ready to connect with Sarah.'

Sarah was the British program manager who had organized the successful Kenyan circumcision campaign upon which the ASI would be built. Sarah and Erin had met at the HIV Conference in downtown Johannesburg in January, when Sarah and her team presented the mind-boggling results of their thousand-circumcisions-a-day Rapid Results Initiative.

Now, in May, we needed Sarah's help. As much as things were different in the Kingdom, we still had a thing or two to learn from the Kenyans, and not much time to learn it. PEPFAR wanted more volunteers on the ground – like, yesterday. Not just doctors. We all had the crushing, belated realization that there were not enough available nurses in Swaziland either. The latest I'd heard from Clara – who seemed to now have our local donor Stephanie's ear, and who was proposing potential scale-up scenarios for the historic campaign – was that the ASI would require 20 to 50 doctors and 200 to 400 nurses, every day, for twelve months, an untested plan of almost inconceivable ambition.

One of our D.C. donors organized a small delegation of Kenyan officials to visit Swaziland for an official country-to-country how-to on an accelerated MC scale-up. I got Sarah's email address from Erin for an unofficial one.

Unsurprisingly, when gathered with the Kenyan officials, Stephanie, Clara, Morris, Dr. Mamba and Swaziland's National MC Coordinator on Serendipity's sunny veranda, it became clear that Kenyan guidance would be of limited practical use. The Kenyans suggested nurse-led clinical teams, by policy a no-go in Swaziland where circumcision could only be performed by doctors. They suggested conducting services in tents in hard-to-reach areas. This was non-negotiable for Dr. Mamba, who, after a visit to a circumcising 'camp' in South Africa, found surgical tents unhygienic. The Kenyans seemed confused. What exactly was the vision for the Swazi scale-up, then? Where were we going to get the necessary staff, and where we were going to house the services?

Dr. Mamba informed the group about the pilot volunteer doctor program. What about nurses, they asked? 'Even if doctors are cutting, wouldn't nurses be needed for the counseling, the pre-op screening, the surgical assistance and the post-op recovery care?'

That is still under discussion, Dr. Mamba answered.

'Well,' one of the Kenyan officials carefully said, 'you know that we now have hundreds of MC-trained nurses, more skilled even than necessary for the Swaziland program. Actually, if you are able to train more... Kenya has approximately six thousand unemployed registered nurses. You know, for us, there is a great deal of competition for very few nursing posts. We could talk about how to mobilize and train unemployed, available nurses for your campaign. Proper channels would have to be followed, of course.'

Oh my God, I thought... Six thousand nurses!

After the meeting, Stephanie pulled Morris and me aside. 'I just want you both to be aware,' she told us, 'that the ASI will likely be covered by the *New York Times*. We should be prepared for that kind of publicity to generate large numbers of volunteers.'

I politely informed her that a minor avalanche of volunteers had already started. With word of the program spreading, suddenly dozens of doctors were signing on through our NGO's website. They were gung-ho. They wanted dates. They wanted to clear their surgical calendars. We responded with 'Thanks for your interest, we'll get back to you', because – Stephanie's optimistic predictions aside – we still didn't have a clue when the ASI was actually starting. None of us had a signed work contract or knew where or why the money was tied up.

That night, I wrote to Erin to pass on the news about a potential goldmine of Kenyan nurses. 'That's awesome!' she wrote. 'But let's not get our hopes up yet. We've got to have a Plan A, B, C and D here.'

I asked Sarah, the British NGO program manager who worked on the Kenyan rapid circumcision program, to recommend six strong Kenyan nurses for our second volunteer mission set to start in just three short weeks.

'Off the record, Sarah,' I asked at the end of our conversation, 'do you think this ASI could work?'

She was quiet. I wondered if the line had cut out. Then she said, 'Yes, I think it could work. But only if there is sufficient client demand. That is the critical unknown.'

I felt like I was bouncing up and down nervously at the starting line of an ultramarathon I hadn't trained for. Clara, on the other hand, had become sort of otherworldly, almost possessed, as though she was vibrating with a supercharged energy. Somehow, she had become a self-appointed leader for this coalescing spirit of ASI excitement and planning. The reason for this – why Kristi's organization would not prime the new ASI funding award, and an organization who had never led an actual circumcision service delivery program would – was never entirely clear to me. Nonetheless, based on conversations happening in PEPFAR Mbabane as well as PEPFAR Washington D.C., Clara got the distinct impression that she should be preparing to take charge once Swaziland was out of pilot mode and into the full swing of ASI. She told me, 'I'm picturing roving tent villages all over Swaziland, like beehives of activity, where all the ASI staff will set up shop, going chiefdom to chiefdom, like a vaccination campaign or a census.'

Although we did not say it aloud, we both expected this to be the most momentous year of our lives.

Clara was preparing, asking questions, networking. I was her go-to for information about the current Swazi circumcision program, the one Kristi led, and I was okay with that. We needed each other. When Clara heard things, snippets of conversations during meetings or passing comments afterward, she'd often reach out to me for verification, or explanation, to debrief, or just to gossip – like working women everywhere. So I wasn't surprised when she sent me this text one afternoon: 'Problems with post-surgical penis appearance? Let's chat.'

Because, although the MoliPants drama had died down, another circumcision drama was breaking. Reports were coming in. Boys were complaining. Things do not look okay down there, they were saying.

'Drink at the 'Dip at six?' I responded.

We each had a glass of red and committed to a leisurely few hours of sipping and analyzing. The Swazi police, particularly toward the end of the month, and particularly Thursday through Sunday, got a little overzealous with the speed traps and the breathalyzers. They had joined forces with the *Times of Swaziland* in a photographic name-and-shame campaign against drunk drivers. The prospect of that kind of publicity scared the crap out of me, and I settled in for a nice, long, mostly sober, evening.

'So what's all the hoopla about?' Clara asked, peering over the top of her glasses with her usual mix of seriousness and goofiness.

'Well, you know Swaziland switched surgical techniques, right? It's likely related to that.'

This was the fallout of a directive coming down from D.C. PEPFAR wanted Swaziland to shift circumcision techniques in preparation for the ASI – from the sleeve method, which although cosmetically superior was more difficult to perform, to the faster and somewhat cruder forceps-guided method. Experts argued that the forceps-guided circumcision would be simpler to teach to non-surgeons. It was also speedier. Each minute mattered when cranking through forty-plus circumcisions a day – when circumcising a whole nation, a whole subcontinent.

Finally, the Swazi MC Task Force agreed to switch techniques. This had an unexpected consequence. The nether regions of Swazi guys circumcised in the last month looked markedly different from their previously circumcised friends. Too much swelling. Blackish discolorations at the suture sites. Fifteen boys came back to the hospital to complain. They feared something had gone horribly wrong with their surgeries.

Morris was nonplussed. He had personally performed thousands of forceps-guided circumcisions. It did not look pretty two days out, he told us. That was normal. The difference between a forceps-guided cut and a sleeve cut was like the difference between a vaginal birth and a caesarean. A caesarean-born baby looks neat and tidy; a baby born vaginally has been through the wringer. 'But give it a few weeks,' Morris said, 'and you can't tell the difference.'

This was a PR problem, not a surgical one. Since 2007, nearly ten thousand Swazis had had sleeve circumcisions. Their friends, we now knew for sure, had seen them, working up the nerve to go under the knife themselves.

I imagined how it went. This year's Back to School clients arrived home, walking very slowly, bandaged and sore.

'How do you feel?' the circumcision veteran asks his shuffling friend.

'*Eish! Bhuti*, is this normal?' the newbie responds, dropping his MoliPants for a look-see.

The veteran is shocked. That is not what his looked like, and he straight up says so. '*Nkosiyami!*' (Translation: OMG!) 'There is something wrong with you! You'd better go back.'

Even nurses were worried. They hadn't seen post-surgical wounds that looked like this either.

'You guys didn't send around a memo about the change?' Clara asked.

'Well, everyone in the Ministry knows, and anyone who was trained in the past few months knows,' I said, feeling defensive. 'But I guess it's possible that if the follow-up visits happened outside of Back to School, some providers may not know yet. Anyway, the clinical team is conducting site visits now to address any communication gaps.'

'Well, we need to be paying close attention here. Messaging is everything. Rumors, bad press, misinformation, that could spell the end of the ASI.'

Did she think I didn't know that? But before I could respond, I heard a voice on the platform behind our table. Adam. It sounded like he was walking a client to the door, closing out a conversation. How many times had I come to Serendipity hoping for a run-in that never happened? And now here he was, and I was trapped in a conversation with a coworker about swollen penises. His voice trailed out the front door. A moment of possibility passed. Clara sipped her wine, unaware of a change in the landscape as I absorbed a sudden blow of loneliness and loss.

I'd told no one about Adam. For several long weeks, since our encounter in his massage room, Adam had come over late in the evening. He parked his midnight blue Chevy pick-up behind the cabin on the far side of Ayla's village and walked the unlit route to my door like a caracal, the nocturnal yellow-eyed creature that lurked in the Swazi mountains.

I was on edge, alert to the ever-present possibility of his surprise arrival. I mistook rain pounding on my tin roof for the sound of car wheels crunching up the gravel on the steep, oil-slicked driveway. I stretched out on my watermelon-printed duvet – in the dark, since, after a spectacular explosion that sent sparks flying and blew out the TV, I had learned to unplug everything when the storms hit. Fat ice cubes fell from the sky, deafening as artillery fire against the roof. Wind whipped against the windows and lightning flashed in perfect electric Zs and I longed for him. I bargained with myself, thinking I could increase the chances of a visit if I put on pajamas, as if the more I behaved as though he wasn't coming, the more likely he would.

We engaged in this surreptitious nonsense because Adam still had not ended his relationship. I knew just a few things about the situation. They had been together for about three years, after meeting in casino work in the US. She was from Eastern Europe. They lived together in a house less than a mile away from my cabin with six rescue dogs that weren't house-trained.

'We sleep in different rooms,' he told me. 'Have for months.'

'Why don't *you* just leave?' I asked him. 'Even if she refuses to go, no one is holding a gun to your head.' I hated myself for becoming the sort of woman who meddles in another's relationship. I hated that I had to ask this.

He explained that he had left, many times. Each time, he had returned. Quick to learn the power politics of southern African families, his girlfriend went to Adam's mother, to his aunts, and pleaded for their intervention. They told him he should never have brought her to Africa if he did not intend to take care of her. 'It's my culture,' Adam said, sounding hopeless.

I found the statement absurd. What about happiness? Free will? Individual agency? He was nearly forty years old.

'Please be patient,' he said. 'I promise I will sort this out.'

Adam rationalized the whole thing. He seemed to think that that as long as we didn't have sex in the strictest sense of the word, he wasn't cheating. I thought that was bullshit. He tried to explain, 'It's not that I don't want to make love to you. It's just that when it happens for us, I want it to be right. I want it to be perfect. I don't want any guilt or ugliness attached to it. I see something beautiful for us and I don't want it spoiled.'

It seemed an arbitrary line to draw, this set of rules that kept a fragile moral high ground intact. Still, I loved those precious few hours, those nights at my cabin. He cooked the most incredible feasts out of scraps in my fridge. We laughed. We talked and talked and talked. Sometimes we kissed. Sometimes we didn't.

One night I noticed two tiny scars along his breastbone. Like when he had discovered the marks on my shoulders, I ran my finger across them tenderly. 'How did you get these scars?' I asked. His answer was cryptic. 'That's my eleven,' he said, and covered the spot reflexively with one hand. 'It was done to me when I was very young, during a dark time.'

'What do you mean?' I asked, immediately suspecting a history of abuse.

'It was a sort of Swazi religious thing,' he said. I didn't push.

But this was how it went, right? The slow and careful revealing of the self to another. We were getting to know each other in our own way, even if it was not how most couples did. We didn't go on dates. We didn't call each other on the phone and talk for hours. We didn't talk on the phone at all, actually, because his girlfriend policed his call register. Instead, I waited, an exquisite torment, for the sound of his Chevy's wheels.

Yes, in my moral universe, what I was doing was wrong. But I had to hear his voice, had to be around him. Maybe this was part of my ongoing education, the relativism, the loosening of black-and-white value judgments. I was skimming the surface at work with well-spoken, business-suited, tea-drinking, middle-class Swazis. Meanwhile, after hours, I was coming to know another Swaziland altogether.

23

One evening, Adam surprised me by suggesting that rather than working his culinary alchemy at home, we should go out to eat. A rush of hope and excitement – his relationship had finally ended and we were celebrating! I shut down my laptop and changed from a work skirt into jeans. Maybe we'd bump into someone from the office and I could make casual introductions. Maybe I was leaving the secret shame behind.

Adam selected Finesse – the dark, wood-paneled restaurant tucked away in the back of the mall where I had hosted our first group of circumcision volunteer doctors. Its key selling point was that, in a town marked by very little choice, Finesse wasn't Serendipity. We sat down at a candlelit table near the front of the restaurant. He chatted away comfortably. I nibbled on sliced bread. He ordered a plate of French fries. (Next to a joint of rolled Swazi Gold, greasy English-style chips were Adam's vice of choice.) I opted for butternut soup. Then his cell phone rang. He looked at the incoming number, rose from the table, and strode to the patio outside. 'Hello, Princess,' he said as he walked. Gall rose like a fireball in my chest.

After about ten minutes, he came back to the table, shaking his head and laughing.

'What?' I asked, stewing.

'I forgot that I'm not supposed to use the English word for princess when speaking to royalty.'

Adam never was clear on the nature or origin of the friendship between his father and the current king's father, the beloved King Sobhuza who ruled the nation for eighty-two years, but they had been close for decades, since Adam's father was a young man and the king an established, middle-aged monarch. Then it dawned on me that Adam had just been speaking not to his girlfriend but to an actual princess – as in, the daughter of a Swazi king. Sometimes the differences between us, between our realities, were almost farcically stark.

'She's an old lady now, but she used to come to our house to hang out with my mom when I was young. They would get drunk together.'

He explained. Adam's father had died in a car accident on the old Manzini-Mbabane road on 8 November 1977, when Adam was just six years old. For most of his life, it had been difficult for Adam to distinguish truth from protective myth, but he knew that his white dad once had a family in his native South Africa, an Afrikaner wife and son. He also knew that his father, his namesake, had a weakness, a preference if you will, for black women – a predilection outlawed in Apartheid South Africa under legislation known as the Immorality Act.

The pressures of racist South Africa eventually drove Van Rensburg senior, Adam's father, away from the largely Afrikaans town of Carolina, just over the border and into the more tolerant Kingdom. At age forty-two, Adam's father found a fifteen-year-old girl in a blue and white school uniform waiting outside the Swazi Inn for a lift up the Malagwane. Lisaya, the girl who would become Adam's mother, did not know that this man was a confidant of, and advisor to, her king. She just knew that it was time to get away from the family farm in the southern town of Hlatikulu, from cobras the width of a grown man's arm, and from priests and schoolteachers who did unspeakable things to pretty girls. Van Rensburg told her he would pay her school fees. Speaking in siSwati, he offered to become her sponsor. That's all it was, in the beginning, before they fell in love, before they set up a house together, before they had two healthy, brown-skinned boys with wild Seventies afros. Before they regularly entertained royalty in their living room.

Lisaya's choices were difficult for her family to accept. Once, Adam told me, her eldest brother tried to spear her. Adam was about three but still remembered it. They were visiting his *gogo*, Lisaya's mother. After seven years of cohabitation, Adam's twenty-something mother had finally brought her nearly fifty-year-old, white, common-law husband to the farm. *Gogo* was secretly rather pleased that her pretty daughter had done so well for herself, but Uncle Peter, *Gogo*'s volatile first child, didn't share her opinion. He looked at his sister with fury, asking, 'Who is this old *mlungu* who has made you his whore?'

Mercifully, Pete had been drinking, which affected his aim. Still, the incident left a mark. Within weeks, Adam's father paid *lobola* for Lisaya, a handsome bride price, and then he married her in a traditional Swazi ceremony. His father's message to Lisaya's family was clear: he was not like other white men. He loved and respected their daughter.

On his death certificate Lisaya's husband, Jacob Adam Van Rensburg, was said to be a fifty-two-year-old divorcee whose occupation had been 'Officer in Charge for the Royal Residence,' a job title that mystified even his young wife. An electrical engineer by training, Adam's dad eventually served as head of maintenance for all of the royal palaces, as well as the manager of the Swazi government's fleet of vehicles. But that was thirty years earlier.

'Holy shit,' I said softly.

I was, through this impossible tale, conned, charmed and fascinated into accepting, for yet another day, the unchanged circumstances of our imperfect situation. Here's why: remember the bit about wanting a sweeping, storybook, swashbuckling life? Well, now that life was sitting right in front of me in a pair of jeans and a faded Levi's T-shirt. Here it was, squeezing chili sauce over a pile of French fries. I hung on every word, my eyes wide and my heart aching for more, more, more...

24

Everyone knew Adam's girlfriend, or wife as they called her since there is no significant distinction between partner and spouse in siSwati. I saw her once. I was sitting at a table, working on my laptop and sipping a cappuccino. I knew her immediately. She had a curtain of middle-parted honey-colored hair and a delicate face. She wore torn jeans and heavy army boots. Any day now, I thought to myself, this sleaziness would end.

All my initial bravado and justification was gone. I disliked what all this said about me, and even more, I disliked what it said about Adam. I wondered if I was a *makhwapheni*, which meant, quite literally, 'The one you keep in your armpit.' Glen, of Ayla and Glen, taught me the term when he had said, 'Laura, I'm beginning to think the reason you never come over is because you have a *makhwapheni* hiding somewhere.'

'A what?' I asked.

'A *makhwapheni*... You know, a little secret romance. We never see you around anymore.'

For a split second, I thought the cat was out of the bag. That maybe he had heard the blue Chevy on the driveway or had seen Adam huddled in his hoodie, walking up to my front porch, fending off the five dogs with French names. Then Glen clapped me on the back and told me he was only teasing.

Adam continued to be less conflicted over the situation. When he didn't have any appointments scheduled at Serendipity, he joined my site-scouting and organizing trips. I was constantly on the road. Immediately after the American volunteers left, I was already preparing for the next batch: three Ethiopian surgeons and six Kenyan nurses set to arrive in three short weeks.

At nine o'clock on a Tuesday morning, I knocked on the door of his treatment room at the 'Dip. He was reclining on the massage table, engrossed in a book entitled *A Course in Miracles*. 'You up for a road trip today?' I asked.

It was cloudy and cool as we drove up to Pigg's Peak, a town born at the turn of the twentieth century when British prospectors spilling over from South Africa found gold north of the Komati River. The drive from Mbabane, toward the Oshoek border and then north, past the Hawane and Maguga dams, featured green, mist-covered hills inhabited only by the fat Nguni cattle that fed off them. We passed the occasional 'live chickens for sale' sign, an abandoned establishment named the Stop Fussing and Fighting Carwash, and clusters of entrepreneurs selling identical cords of damp firewood in neat piles. We sat in comfortable silence, making our way up toward Maguga, as the road twisted and opened into a mountainous pass, a gorgeous waterscape below. Adam pointed to the left of the highway. I looked down to see the rolling hills and a brook that gurgled around soft stones.

'This was my dad's land,' Adam said.

I looked again. Children splashed and shrieked in the water, getting the short pants of their school uniforms wet. Bright clothing lay drying on the higher rocks. Women stood barefoot, scraping sudsy garments against each other and chatting. I took in what he had said: this perfect spot had belonged to his father.

Past tense. Now it appeared to belong to no one, or to everyone. I had been in Swaziland long enough to know that nation land was not the property of any one person. It was shared, granted by the king to the country's chiefs, and by the chiefs to the people. For the price of a cow or two, every man could *khonta* a portion of this nation land to pass on to the next generation. It was the birth right of the Swazi male.

'What happened?' I asked. 'Did your dad have to give it back?' I thought that maybe it had something to do with the transition of kings, that perhaps land granted by one was not honored by the next.

'Now it belongs to one of the king's wives. King Sobhuza called in a favor with Dad. One of the royal sons – a wayward prince, you could say – was in trouble and he needed a place to lay low. The king knew Dad would keep his mouth shut. Dad didn't live long enough to get the land back,' he said. They had that kind of relationship – the jolly, blue-eyed, thin-lipped Dutchman and the tribal king, a direct descendent from the sacred Ngunis. They trusted one another.

Adam's family was staying in the army barracks in Matsapha then, in a home assigned by the king to facilitate easy access. As a child, Adam remembers waking up in the middle of the night to the sound of the king's Cadillac pulling into the drive. King Sobhuza II would chat with Van Rensburg until just before sunrise, when Adam would hear the two men wish each other well and then the sound of a car engine as the king disappeared.

Listening to this, I was somewhat stunned. I glanced out my window to see hundreds of soapstone carvings lining the roadside, countless stone hippos bathing in miniature stone pools and stone ashtrays shaped like hands.

'You want to stop?' Adam asked. My appointment with the

Senior Medical Officer at Pigg's Peak Hospital was not until after the one o'clock lunch hour. 'Why not?' I decided.

Adam swerved and parked, and we stepped down and out of the Pajero. It was chilly, a bit on the windy side, and there wasn't a single carver in sight. 'They're around here somewhere,' he said. 'Probably off having a smoke. They'll be back.'

Sure enough, within minutes the carvers returned. And, sure enough, they were stoned. Their eyes were bloodshot, their movements expansive and slow. '*Eytha, bhuti!*' they said to Adam, shaking hands and trading small talk. Then they gave me a cursory scan. From the color of my skin, they read tourist and shifted to English. 'Look at this one. Here, sister, did you see this?'

Adam sensed my annoyance and distracted them with conversation. He took a particular interest in one of the artists, an older man with huge arms and tangled dreads. When we got back into the car, I asked Adam what they had been talking about. He flashed a mischievous grin.

'Oh, come on, just tell me,' I said.

'Remember how, the other day, we were talking about how sex can be spiritual?' he began.

How could I forget? I'd been caught off guard when he'd asked me if I knew what sacred sex was. 'Is it something you might be interested in trying, when we're ready?' he'd asked shyly. How he still confused me, this southern African male who was every bit the sensitive, articulate, non-competitive type I associated with a privileged generation raised by feminist mothers on talk therapy and public television.

'Yeah, I remember,' I answered, growing wary.

I had listened that night as he explained that part of the practice of spiritual sex involved learning to honor each other physically, and battled the urge to scoff. I had little patience for the navel-gazing, life-is-a-journey-of-self-discovery hoo-ha that passed the time among Serendipity therapists. Then there was the fact that we were not actually even having sex yet. But, hey, if this handsome man wanted to honor my body, far be it from me to argue! As we left the stone carvers and drove north along the misty road, Adam explained that he had requested the stoned stoneworker to carve symbolic genital replicas for us.

'You did *what*?' I spun around in the passenger seat to face him.

'Oh, darling, don't be angry. He loved the idea.'

'I'm sure he did.' I imagined the stone carvers standing in the chilly breeze, passing a joint between them, hysterical over Adam's pornographic request.

I could see that my irritation and sarcasm wounded him. Time to change the subject. 'So, about what you said earlier – didn't you think it was strange that the king and his men came to your house in the middle of the night?'

'It had always been like that. It was normal enough to me. The king doesn't travel around in the day visiting people like an ordinary person – he discusses anything important in the middle of the night,' he replied after a moment. 'I guess I knew the man in the Cadillac was important, but I didn't understand who he was, what being a king meant. I was just a child.

'But then it all fell apart. After my dad died, men came to our house and asked my mom about dad's assets. She told them that she knew nothing. Even as young as I was, I recognized them. They were the same men who came in the dark with King Sobhuza to see my dad.'

After his father's death, the men came again and asked Lisaya for her husband's papers. She had not known what they were talking about. She was twenty-six years old and up until that moment, her husband had taken care of everything, made sure Lisaya never worried about the daily economy of their household. Money flowed. Adam remembered his father's penchant for American cars, always four or five Chevrolets or Fords parked out front. After the men came, the cars disappeared. Within days, pretty much everything else was gone too. Whatever remained went up in flames when an inexplicable fire consumed the place. Disaster swooped in and swallowed them whole.

As the early eighties rolled in, it was as if the experience of the whole nation mirrored Adam's personal tragedy. Traditional structures were crumbling. King Sobhuza II – the benevolent father-monarch who had ruled the nation for over sixty years, who'd granted favored status to Adam's white father, who'd fathered over seventy kids of his own – also died. His adolescent successor was at the prestigious Sherborne School in the UK, and an in-between government, led by the Queen Regent, took the unsteady helm. This threw the country into a tailspin of confusion and speculation. Then nature punished Swaziland: a cyclone left fertile land flooded and useless. Lisaya looked for work. The boys went off to a Catholic boarding school where Adam was often hungry and his brother Jaco started getting into trouble. Also around this time, HIV made its stealthy entrance through the open borders of the landlocked kingdom.

Staring out the window, I imagined the unusually pretty child that Adam must have been, the only kid in the neighborhood with store-bought pajamas. I imagined him peering down a dim hallway to watch his hulking father speak hushed siSwati to the aging Ngwenyama, the Lion, and his most trusted men. Then suddenly that father, and almost everything else, vaporized. The last time Adam saw his dad, he was at the morgue at Mbabane Government Hospital. Six-year-old Adam watched as Van Rensburg lay on a stainless-steel table while an orderly, an old man in a pressed white uniform, washed blood from the body.

'Who were those men, the ones who came to your house asking questions?' I wanted to know.

'They were members of the *liqoqo*,' Adam explained, 'the king's inner circle of advisers.'

'But how could your mom not have known anything?'

'Those days, wives belonged in the kitchen and the bedroom. Business was Dad's thing.' I wondered how this sort of arrangement could have produced a man like Adam, so gentle and considerate and such a wonder with a paring knife.

He sensed my reaction. 'No, no, no. Dad was a great person. Everyone who knew him said so. He was always laughing. Very personable. Loved to entertain. Both my parents did. He taught Mom how to cook. I remember that he used to lift me up and pinch my nose between his pointer and middle finger.' He imitated the movement, wiggling his hand back and forth, smiling at the memory. 'He was big. He had these big hands. The Swazis called him *Mubi*. It means 'Ugly'.'

'Yikes. That's pretty direct.'

'No,' he laughed, 'not like that.'

We were driving up the mountain now; to our left was a precipitous decline, the highway fading below. Adam looked at me, taking his eyes momentarily from the road, to explain. I channeled my mother and slammed my foot against an invisible brake pedal on the floor of the passenger side. 'Sorry.' Adam adjusted in his seat, and exaggerated his focus. His hands, large and square and finely formed, his dad's hands, in the textbook ten and two o'clock positions.

'It's a Swazi thing. They say "ugly" when they really mean "beautiful." Swazis have a way of teasing, using opposites to speak truths. I don't know. It is hard to explain. I guess you don't realize these things are odd until you try to make sense of them for someone who isn't from here. Anyway, I don't think those men appreciated the king's favoritism toward Dad. At one point, maybe five or so years before he died, the *liqoqo* kicked Dad out of the country. They told him to go back to South Africa to sort out his documents and then didn't allow him into Swaziland when he tried to come back in.'

A squad had awaited Van Rensburg at Oshoek where they flatly refused him entry. Van Rensburg found a phone and called the Ngwenyama. Then he got back into his Chevy, waved goodbye to the henchmen, and drove back toward South Africa. Meanwhile, the king joined a royal cavalcade traveling from Lobamba to Bhunya for an official engagement. Attendants were surprised when the procession stopped suddenly at Mankayane. Van Rensburg had just arrived there himself, having snuck right through the unattended alternate border at Sicunusa. The king got out of his car and said very loudly, 'See this land here? I am giving it to Van Rensburg! From this day forward, Van Rensburg will be regarded as a Swazi citizen. He will not require documentation to enter his own country.'

How many people who witnessed that scene really took the white man as a Swazi? How did they feel about this man who had assumed one of a very limited number of well-paid government positions, and grasped that land without so much as a single cow paid in compensation? How many among them would have thought him just another foreign crocodile?

25

Swaziland tolerated foreigners like Adam's father but held them at arm's length – with good reason. Swaziland had managed to preserve its powerful monarchy, remain an intact people and culture, while white colonizers drove other regional groups back to barren homelands or corralled them into townships. One could reasonably surmise that the strategies Swazis employed to ensure the preservation of their status – including the careful management of outsiders – were extremely effective.

As word about a possible influx of Kenyan nurses hit the streets, I witnessed such strategies in action myself. Swazi nurses responded to this news swiftly and unhappily. They argued that the government had insufficiently consulted them about the circumcision program. Had they been properly involved, they said, they would have worked with program planners to design local staffing solutions. We got the point: project-related funding should stay in the Kingdom. Keep the Kenyans out of it.

Eight thousand disgruntled nurses is a substantial and real problem. The backbone of the entire Swazi healthcare system and the day-in, day-out soldiers on the frontlines of an epidemic, nurses ran the network of rural clinics that serviced 80 percent of Swaziland's population. Theirs was challenging, frustrating work. The government often paid salaries late. Drug stock-outs were common. When given the opportunity, nurses supplemented their incomes with NGO-paid workshops, clinical trainings like ours, where they would pick up per diem and transport allowances in addition to some new knowledge and skills. In this way, the aid industry regularly paid for school uniforms, airtime, *kombi* fare and dinner. The proposition of a yearlong ASI would have glittered like fat piles of gold coins, like the stash famous Afrikaner Paul Kruger was said to have buried somewhere in the Mbabane mountains on his retreat from Pretoria to Maputo.

The situation called for immediate damage control. I booked an appointment with the Registrar of the Swaziland Nursing Council. She heard me out with no small degree of empathy, fully absorbing the complexities of the situation, and then said, 'I have something that might help you.' She reached into a drawer and pulled out a stapled printout: a computer-generated list of eighty nurses and their phone numbers. All were foreign-born, living in Swaziland, unemployed, registered with the Council, and immediately available to work for the ASI.

'Foreign but *resident* nurses,' the registrar explained, 'are not prioritized for employment here. We have a limited number of government postings, and, as in all countries, the public sector prefers that equally qualified Swazi nurses fill them. However, many nurses from unstable countries like Zimbabwe or the DRC register with us annually. Some are lucky and find work in the private sector. But lots of them stay with relatives and wait and hope for a job.'

Okay, eighty nurses were not four hundred, but they also were not none.

'Start there,' the registrar said, 'while I talk to our nurse leaders. We'll need to manage this carefully, but I'm confident this can be resolved.'

I felt better, comforted, and now armed with the names of eighty technically local nurses. My supervisor Erin cheered over a long-distance line. Clara said, 'Great news.' I planned to update our donor Stephanie Silva at the next weekly MC Task Force meeting.

But things got off to a tense start when Stephanie opened the meeting with this question: 'The Swazi Cabinet approved the ASI back in February. In March, they requested that this Task Force prepare a detailed implementation plan. Colleagues, it is now the end of May. How do we explain to the Cabinet, and to our funders, why we don't yet have an implementation plan?'

Papers shuffled. Throats cleared. Dr. Mamba, our chairman, agreed that we were behind schedule. 'Is it reasonable,' he asked the room, 'that we could prepare a plan for review by this Task Force in two weeks?' Everyone nodded. Then silence. Lord knows he wasn't going to write the thing, so who would? I looked around. Clara, seated next to the National MC Program Coordinator, raised her hand and suggested that the two of them take the lead. Dr. Mamba and Stephanie were satisfied.

'Laura,' Dr. Mamba said, 'what is the update on the situation with the nurses?'

I shared the list.

'Eighty nurses is not enough,' Dr. Mamba concluded. 'I suggest that we continue to move forward with the Kenyan collaboration.' He reminded the group that he was referencing the 'leasing' of trained, experienced MC nurses from Kenya. 'The human resource component will make or break the ASI. We cannot afford to take any risks. We must be over-prepared.' The sentiment could have come directly from the mouths of our D.C. donors. I guessed it probably did.

'Does that sound reasonable to you, *Make* Charity?' Dr. Mamba asked, as he looked to a dignified woman seated toward the front of the table. Charity – one of Swaziland's most senior nurses, and a member of the Swazi MC Task Force – was a large woman who claimed her space with ample layers of ruffles and flounce. She wore bright yellows and hot pinks, and complex, beautiful braided hair styles. Other members of the Task Force always addressed her as '*Make*', siSwati for mother, out of respect.

'Indeed it does,' Charity responded conclusively. 'We must ensure we have sufficient nursing capacity. That must not be overlooked.'

Two weeks later, the same group gathered in the same room. Clara narrated a PowerPoint. 'At full scale,' she said, 'fifty teams will perform twenty thousand circumcisions every month. This will require five hundred staff and volunteers every day.'

A number flashed on the projector screen: 152,000. This was the number of circumcisions to be completed in under a year, each one performed on an HIV-negative Swazi male between fifteen to forty-nine years old. This target constituted the modeled degree of 'saturation' required to exert a population-level HIV-prevention impact, vaccine-style.

While we absorbed this, a timeline appeared. Phase I, it read, would start in September 2010 with sixteen teams, Phase II in October with thirty-two teams, and Phase III in December with forty-eight teams, timed nicely with World AIDS Day. It was nearly June already. My heart and head pounded simultaneously.

After the meeting, I went straight to Kristi's office. I read her the numbers and the timeline. We knew there was no way that the US-financed mechanism for the ASI would be issued and executed quickly enough. The current circumcision program – the one Kristi led – would need to start the work and forward fund it. We also knew we did not have the luxury of pushing back against the timeline. She called in her core team. John, the logistics consultant and ex-Doctors Without Borders director, started furiously scrawling on a whiteboard. Dozens of calculations: staff, circumcision kits, minivans, surgical equipment. September was only a few months away. Supply orders would need to be placed *now* if the stuff was going to arrive in the Kingdom on time.

'Where will the circumcisions be done?' John asked.

'We still don't have a final decision,' I answered. Clara had posed the question, again, at the Task Force Meeting. Maybe at the existing 223 healthcare facilities scattered around the Kingdom, almost all of which were wired for electricity? Or at the 810 schools throughout Swaziland? Or the fifty-five *tinkhundla*, or community centers? Attendees had looked at the numbers seriously and made assenting noises but no one voted for one option over another, which was standard. The Swazi MC Task Force was not big on conclusive decisions.

Therefore, this was all, essentially, guesswork. John, Kristi and I talked about the proposed timeline, which included two major 'surges,' each lasting two months and maxing out at forty-eight surgical teams.

'Surges?' John asked. 'Really? Does anyone else find it bizarre that we're talking about a circumcision campaign as if it's the war in Iraq?'

***

I saw Adam when I could. Ducking back to his massage room after working lunches at the 'Dip, my heels clicked against the black floor tiles. An Ann Taylor dress comical against the backdrop of spiritual knick-knacks. He often took my hand and lifted it to his sternum, a gesture I knew to mean, 'You warm my heart.'

I didn't talk to Adam much about work. He was my respite from it. One Tuesday night, he came to my cabin and we talked until 3.30 in the morning. Once more, he rested a pointer finger tenderly on the space between my eyebrows where stress and concentration wore a permanent groove. Tiny lights, like fireflies, flashed across my closed eyelids.

'Tell me more about your life,' I said. 'Get me out of my head.'

I sponged up each detail, was moved to discover that his cultural heritage was a source of both pride and shame in near equal measure. In Swaziland, a child of a black mother and a white father, Adam had grown up an outsider. Darker-skinned Swazi kids teased him, called him double-brain, as if the black and white mind were so distinct that they were forever in conflict.

Once outside of the country, Adam was a chameleon. With his tan skin, height and strong features, he was mistaken for nearly everything but African. In the southern US, people thought him Hispanic. In Turkey, they assumed he was Arabic. In South America, he was a gringo. As a blackjack dealer with a nametag that read 'Adam Van Rensburg, Swaziland,' a Floridian card player had asked, 'Swaziland? Is that a theme park?' For years, Adam got the disorienting feeling that the country of his birth was fantastical and that he didn't really belong anywhere.

As usual, the pathway of conversation twisted and turned across time and experience in a decidedly nonlinear way. Eventually, Adam landed on the topic of his teenage daughter. He had mentioned her to me before, but I hadn't pressed it. I knew he had met the girl's mother – a biracial woman named

Dotty, eleven years his senior – at his first job as a card dealer at the casino in Nhlangano. Dotty, a floor manager, saw that the seventeen-year-old Adam had potential. In Swaziland's tightly knit 'colored' community, she'd never known someone like him. Here was a double-brain who wouldn't cheat on her, wouldn't hit her, and who'd be soft with her three young kids. Adam was still learning how to handle the moneyed lifestyle. There were entire nights that he could not remember. She told him not to worry, she was taking precautions.

That Adam – polite, mild-mannered and spiritually minded – would become a father before twenty sent shockwaves through the family. Adam's friends were equally stunned. 'That old auntie?' they asked, incredulous.

If the pregnancy was part of a plot to ensure that Adam would stay with Dotty in Swaziland, it failed. When he left, things got ugly. Dotty didn't want the monthly wages he sent, she wanted the sweet teenager who'd painted murals on her walls and regularly bought her new shoes from Johannesburg.

'It was terrible,' Adam said. 'She refused to tell my daughter that I was her father. She told her that I was an uncle.'

'Hmmm…' I said, signaling understanding, but with sleep taking over.

'But Dotty wasn't well. She was drinking heavily. And she was starting to get ill.'

'What was wrong with her?' I asked.

'The same thing that makes everyone sick in this country.'

Suddenly, I was completely awake, hyper-alert. How easy it had been up until that moment to work in the HIV business and keep it all safely stowed away in a drawer; neutral, theoretical, outside of the bubble of my own intimate life. Ruth's gardener, my Malawian housekeeper, others I worked with and befriended – could be compartmentalized. Not one of them took me down into the snake pit of Mrs. J's fifth-grade blackboard.

It was a couple of days before it sank in. My wake-up call, the sudden proximity of the virus to my own bedroom was the everyday reality of every single sexually active person living in the Kingdom of Swaziland. Like Provincetown in the late eighties.

Still, in that moment, I felt entitled to my fear. 'Your ex-girlfriend has HIV?'

I knew it was rude. I knew it was insensitive. Of all people, I should have been so much more chill about this – I mean, didn't we now talk about HIV as though it was a treatable, chronic disease, like diabetes or hypertension? Besides, what right did I have to freak out, here? What did I really know about the status of the sexual partners of my previous boyfriends? How could I honestly say that he was any more reckless than I had been?

'When was the last time you got tested?' I asked.

'Six months ago,' he said. 'They tested us regularly on the ships. But I'm happy to test again, if it would make you feel more comfortable.'

'I think it would.' I promised I'd do the same.

We weren't sleeping together yet, but in a country with a massive HIV epidemic driven by heterosexual intercourse, it made the safe-sex talk something more than just responsible adult protocol. I felt the shock and disorientation of my professional and personal lives crashing into each other.

'Don't get upset, darling. We are just talking. Besides, it's not like Swazis are the only ones sleeping around.' He stopped for a moment, on the brink of asking something, but unsure that he wanted to know the answer. He steeled himself. 'For instance... who else have you been with in Swaziland?' he asked.

I bristled. What was he suggesting?

He studied my face. 'I know how Americans behave when they come over here. They're lonely, young and hooking up.'

'Whoa… hold on a second. Don't lump me in with people I don't even know. Don't confuse me with the twenty-five-year-olds at Glen and Ayla's parties, drunk, horny and throwing themselves at you. For the record, I have never been one of those girls.' With all the fervor of indignation, I started to believe my own propaganda. I wanted Adam to think I was good. I wanted him to believe that I was worthy of the wings he had bestowed upon me.

'It doesn't matter,' he decided. 'We're not there yet, anyway.'

Oh, how well I knew that.

'You know, it's also difficult for me. I think we will know when it's time. I've been praying for a sign.'

A sign? Seriously? How about you get your own place? How about you leave your girlfriend? That's the kind of sign that would work for me. I didn't share his trust in the cosmos. I believed in personal will. Yes, our differences were cultural, but they were bigger than that.

If only his smile wasn't so disarming. If only he didn't supply me with the one bright spot in an otherwise ungratifying slog of an uphill anti-HIV battle. Maybe then, I would have the guts to end the melodrama and walk.

26

Six Kenyan nurses and three Ethiopian doctors landed in Matsapha on 21 May 2010 for the second of our volunteer 'pilot' programs, raring and ready to go. Gordon, barely five feet tall and head of the Kenyan team, greeted me with a grin, exposing an empty space where front teeth once stood. He reached out his hand, gave mine a firm shake, and said, 'I am confident that with minimal assistance we will be able to serve the Swazi people.'

While we were keeping the Kenyans' involvement pretty quiet given the political sensitivity, PEPFAR felt we needed to lay the groundwork for the nurse exchange now, sure that we'd eventually smooth things over and establish a pipeline of available nurses for the ASI. The Swazi government had signed off on a correspondence requesting thirty-five more nurses for the next big campaign, Back to School II, in August. These six Kenyan nurses constituted a cautious first step in what was expected to be a southern African thoroughfare of international circumcision support.

It did not get off to a great start. A week after their arrival, I got a call around midday. 'Laura? This is Gordon. We are at the hospital, but no clients for circumcision again today.'

Shit, I thought, school was starting up again so the kids weren't coming. We were now relying on older adolescents and men who never turned up in the kind of numbers schoolkids did, but we usually had a modest turnout at our standing circumcision sites even during non-campaign periods. Except now, for some reason, it seemed they weren't showing up at all.

I traveled out to the program's hospitals to try to figure out what was happening. Where were the clients? Just days before, I'd received an e-blast from headquarters touting the still ongoing and overwhelmingly successful circumcision campaign in Iringa, Tanzania. A priceless photo showed the back of my friend and colleague Remi in a surgical gown and cap, opening a clinic door to a waiting horde of eager boys and men. Swaziland and Tanzania: same organizations, same messages, same circumcision services... and a dramatic difference in men's interest.

'Have you seen the IPC agents? Do we know if there is a problem in the communities?' I asked our volunteers. There should have been around a hundred of these agents, the so-called 'skin hunters' contracted to approach potential clients and recruit them for circumcision. The volunteers looked at me like they didn't know what I was talking about.

It was frustrating, after all the time and effort and money spent planning. In the weeks before their trip, the Ethiopian surgeons had rescheduled patients in their home hospitals. Kenyan MC teams had parted with their top nurses. The volunteers had collected, certified and sent over one hundred registration documents for the Medical and Dental Council; they'd run around getting police clearances and school verifications and licensing proof in cities many miles from where they lived and worked. We'd written letters to excuse days off from work. We'd purchased malpractice coverage and travel health insurance, bought air tickets, organized airport pick-ups and drop-offs. We'd conducted proficiency assessments. We'd purchased cell phones and loaded them up with airtime. Arranged emergency management plans for each site since Swaziland's ambulances didn't run at night and were often without fuel during the day. For what? So they could take their $77-a-day per diem and go shopping?

True, this volunteer mission was sandwiched between the two high-demand Back to School campaigns. It was a concession to donor pressure to show how quickly we could mobilize and deploy international human resources. As such, we knew that we wouldn't have record-breaking numbers of clients. But this was embarrassing. Medical professionals joined volunteer missions to contribute their time and expertise to true emergencies. Red Cross volunteers flew into earthquake- or tsunami-ravaged destruction. Doctors Without Borders staff provided care in the midst of civil wars. This? Well, this was not that kind of volunteering.

When I arrived back at the Partnership Suite, I knocked on Kristi's office door, prepared for an acrimonious discussion.

'Kristi?' I started, wishing I didn't sound so meek. 'I wanted to touch base with you. I'm sure you've seen the statistics from the volunteer sites… they're getting less than ten clients a day per hospital. Do you know what's up?'

She called Ian, the Scottish communications director, into her office to join the discussion. 'The IPC agents are working as hard as they can to bring in clients,' he assured me.

I didn't want to imply that they weren't doing their part, or that we weren't working hand in hand. None of us had been thrilled about a second volunteer mission so fast on the heels of the first. But, still, the sudden dramatic dip in demand just didn't make sense.

'Well, it's sort of strange, right?' I asked them. 'I mean, the

Back to School numbers were exponentially higher than this, and so are the daily numbers at the Matsapha clinic.'

'Converting potential clients is a tricky thing,' Ian said. 'You've got to remember that we are talking about surgery here.'

Kristi nodded. 'I mean,' she jumped in, 'have you ever had surgery? Preventative surgery?'

'Right,' Ian said, 'not an easy decision. Imagine that you're making that decision when you'd never even been to a dentist in your life. Never had an injection. Never seen a scalpel before... and it's your willy they're about to use it on.'

I got it. I was on board with all of that. It wasn't news to me that circumcision was a hard sell. Still, we were supposed to figure that out, right? I mean, other countries were doing it.

'Most people don't realize,' the comms director continued, 'that it's typical to run at a 30 to 50 percent no-show rate. People sign up for the procedure but write a false name and phone number just to get the IPC agent off their backs.'

Kristi added, 'Client demand isn't like a faucet that you can turn on or off, or up or down. Believe me, we are doing our best to get clients. The IPC teams didn't have enough time to regroup and restrategize after the Back to School campaign with the first volunteers. Ideally, we would have built in a delay, let things get quiet for a while, then start the push for another volunteer mission.'

'Sorry,' I said, 'it just wasn't possible.'

'I understand,' Kristi said. 'I know how hard it is to push back when the donors are insisting.'

'I'm just concerned about what happens if the volunteers go back to their home countries and say that the Swaziland circumcision program is a waste of time, expertise and money.'

'We're all concerned about the optics here,' the

communications director said in a rare acknowledgment of the pressure he was now under.

Their necks were also on the chopping block. Either we would revel in glory together, or we would go up in flames together. It was clear that coordination needed to be tighter, lead times needed to be longer. I could see the worry on Kristi's pregnant face, the bags under her eyes. A rent was forming in the carefully created ecosystem of the Partnership Suite.

Meanwhile, our volunteers bored even of shopping once they realized that the selection and prices were better back home. They tried to help rustle up business. They gave community talks on the benefits of circumcision and offered impromptu continuing education lessons for hospital staff. In three weeks, the volunteers averaged nine circumcisions per team per day. This was nowhere near PEPFAR's cost-efficient recommendation of forty circs daily.

The day before the second batch of volunteers left, we set up a reception in the boardroom of one of the mission hospitals. It was the same hospital where one of our American volunteer surgeons had been busy circumcising just a month before. I sat toward the back of the room, behind several rows of Swazi nurses in standard-issue red sweaters and white skirts. A decimated tray of quartered sandwiches – chicken mayo, cheese and tomato – lay on a table to our right.

Again, the gentle and serious medical director stood up to say a few words. He ran through the requisite thanks then invited one of the volunteers to speak.

Gordon, the gap-toothed Kenyan nurse volunteer, stood from his seat in the front row. He wore a suit and tie. His hands gripped a torn piece of lined notebook paper. One of the Ethiopian surgeons, an outgoing, young and very beautiful woman, winked at him from the chair next to mine. The ease between the two had developed so quickly that I got to imagining a different reach for the ASI. I imagined relationships born over disposable circumcision kits, connections made over blue O-hole drapes with timid penises shyly peeping through, masked faces smiling over skin sparkling wet with Betadine. I imagined love blossoming between Ethiopian and Indian volunteers, between Kenyans and Swazis, between Zambians and South Africans and Americans. As Gordon began his speech, I thought of the changed direction of lives – the very conception of lives – we might someday attribute to this circumcision madness.

'We are so grateful,' Gordon said, 'for expanded worldviews, for the opportunity to experience a new place and form new friendships. We, the team from Kenya, understand how serious the situation is here in Swaziland. It is the same for us at home. We must support each other. We will continue do everything in our power to prevent the further spread of HIV in our communities, and we are here to help you to do the same. We send a prayer to the Kingdom of Swaziland. You will stay with us always.'

The red-sweatered nurses ululated and clapped. Gordon smiled his gappy smile and tipped his head toward the floor. My heart burst with pride.

Clara Skyped me that night. 'How were the numbers this week?'

It was such a buzzkill. Why was it always just about the numbers?

'Not awesome,' I responded.

'There are two things we're going to have to figure out if the ASI is going to work. First, we're going to have to convince every Swazi guy that there's something valuable and immediate in it for him. Second, we're going to have to be prepared to take the heat if anything goes wrong – there seems to be a general unwillingness here for people to stick their necks out.'

I was impressed. I'd had the same frustrating epiphanies about sticking with the status quo, about avoiding confrontation at all costs, but only through my secret relationship with Adam. 'You may be right...' I wrote noncommittally.

27

'She's gone. Left the country,' Adam said through the phone line. 'It's over. I'm hoping we can go to Bushfire together this weekend.'

Something about the finality of his tone made me bite my tongue. Of course, I absolutely wanted to know every agonizing detail, a comprehensive playback of who said what. But I was busy being mature. That, and I didn't think he'd tell me. Besides, I figured the particulars weren't nearly as relevant as the outcome. This was a critical lesson in my ongoing Swazi education: do not expect to reason out the logic behind events, just be grateful when things surprise you by actually working out.

'I would love that,' I said.

I had been praying that this moment would arrive since the first time we fell asleep together in the double bed in my log cabin in Fonteyn, our foreheads almost touching and our bent knees pressed against each other under the duvet, the large, square palm of his left hand settled warm and heavy on my right cheek. When Adam said, 'Sleep, angel,' a beautiful wave of contentedness had washed over me.

For months, I had figured myself a fool. Not anymore.

The Bushfire music festival was an annual event at the family-run House on Fire venue in Malkerns. The festival was so named because it took place at the end of May, the start of winter, a season marked by licking flames that consumed entire mountainsides of dry brush. Every year, the event brought tens of thousands of people streaming into the Kingdom.

Bushfire 2010 was so cold that Adam wore a long woolen army coat and a beret to keep his bare head warm. We drank plastic cups full of Castle beer from a keg and wrapped our chilled arms around each other. Among the thousands of revelers hailing from all parts of southern Africa, the mixed couple that we now were was wholly unremarkable. Soon, both of us were tipsy. A non-drinker throughout his thirties, Adam had little tolerance and I was a workaholic marathoner with next to none myself.

For the weekend, acres of Swazi sugarcane fields became a vast complex of vendor and food stalls. A main stage and the jumbotrons next to it pumped first with Afro beats, then bluegrass, then old school rock. Bodies were everywhere. People lounged on the ground with picnic baskets and bundled up babies. Adam and I let the crowd push us toward the margins, where even the tall grasses seemed to sway to the music.

Eventually, we decided to check out the acts inside the actual House on Fire itself – a multi-tiered indoor amphitheater. High-heeled wooden angels hung from the ceiling and inspirational quotes were embedded into the rock walls. Bedecked with trippy aphorisms and mirrored mosaics, House on Fire was part temple, part gallery, part Amsterdam coffeeshop. Once inside, I sat down at a booth near the bar and watched the words and figures on the dressed-up walls merge and move. A quote from Rumi: *There is some kiss we want with our whole lives, the touch of spirit on the body.*

Adam was looking at me in that way he did, soft and admiring. His brown eyes, when I tried to focus on them, unmoored me. Everything in my field of vision blurred. He said, 'You look lovely.' This was what he said when he wanted to say something more. This time, bold with booze, he continued. 'I still don't understand what it is about you. You are the only woman I've ever met who I can imagine spending the rest of my life with.'

I laughed, a response he found puzzling. No one had ever talked to me like this – without guile, without intellectual sparring, without careful avoidance and the terror of risking love.

In that moment I knew I had fallen for him, hard. It was the accent I mistakenly placed much further north on a world map. The smattering of freckles across brown skin. The way he made me feel so accepted and so seen. I wanted this perfect moment to last the rest of my life, with the walls moving and the music pumping and my head spinning. All of it became, in a moment, surreal: a sweet man in an army coat and a beret, a House on Fire, a nation crippled by AIDS, a cane field in a kingdom full of thousands of happy people, a teenage couple making out at the next table. Doctors. Nurses. Donors. Foreskins. Light. Dark. All mixed up.

Adam leaned across the table to kiss me. He smelled like tobacco. As his warmth moved toward me, I closed my eyes. 'You think too much,' he said before I felt the softness of his lips.

We wandered back out to the cane field. In the middle of the swaying crowd, I spotted two familiar blonde heads. John, the circumcision logistician and his wife Cindy, clustered with a group of expats. I gave each of them a hug and I introduced Adam.

Ayla, my Turkish landlady, was standing next to Cindy

throughout this exchange, wearing a wig that made her look like Medusa. 'It's a *sangoma* wig! Can you tell?' Ayla asked, as she fingered the ropy locks. She'd come with Toby, a twenty-three-year-old American photographer also living in the fishbowl of Ayla's Village. He was sporting a pair of neon yellow, skintight pants and cowboy boots.

'Nice pants, Toby,' I said.

'Twenty emalangeni at the Mbabane market!' he pronounced proudly. Clearly, at $3, an absolute bargain.

Then both Toby and Ayla, visibly curious, looked at Adam, his arm linked in mine. Adam hugged and greeted them both before politely excusing himself to use a port-a-potty. 'It's the beer,' he explained. I watched him walk away from me, a long line of grey – careful, delicate – and wondered, is this real? Is this really my life?

As for Adam, on his way to the toilets, amid throngs of festivalgoers, he felt something else: an object hitting his beret, a condom – thrown down from a parapet by reps from one of the Kingdom's many HIV-prevention programs. They literally rained down from the sky like silvery snowflakes throughout the night. Everyone knew what happened at Bushfire after hours (and, yes, there were more than a few off-color jokes about the festival name). Adam tucked the crinkly foil packet into his pocket. Here was the sign he had been waiting for. Finally, a free man, the wait was over.

I knew none of this when we tumbled in through the door of my cabin, light-headed and chilled in the early hours of the morning. As we crawled under the covers, eager for warmth but shedding layers anyway, I sensed something different. An intention, the emergency brake released, energy no longer reined in. It was not just that we had fallen in love; it was that we were so at ease with each other by then. No fumbling, no awkwardness. Softly, into my ear, Adam said, 'I want to experience everything in this life with you.'

28

As delicious as my personal life had become in certain ways, my work life hadn't followed suit. Now it was June, and our next big circumcision push, Back to School II, was two months away, during the school break that began in August. A spotlight beamed from the East Coast of the United States toward the tiny Kingdom. D.C. told us that this Back to School campaign – the largest ever in Swaziland – was the *real* trial run for the ASI that would shortly follow it. The number of bodies under discussion for Back to School II was overwhelming. I'm not sure which was more daunting, the quantity of prospective clients or the quantity of prospective caregivers. I thought about neither group as individuals. I thought about them as a mass, achieving life only in their complete and collective entirety. The now-famous photo of the surgical-scrubbed Remi opening the door of a Tanzanian clinic to a sea of males – that image was so powerful because of the sheer number of them.

Adam and I had no lazy honeymoon period after we publicly became a couple, no languorous days spent under the covers. By the end of the day there was nothing left of me but impotent fumes. I crashed at nine every night and slept like the

185

dead. I did not keep in touch with my people at home. I had no clue about babies born, about graduations, about the everyday tragedies and victories of the people I loved. My childhood best friend was diagnosed with ovarian cancer; I offered little support. When my Skype beeped with an incoming message, I pretended I was in a meeting. I had hundreds of nurses and dozens of doctors to find. Everything else vanished.

As the five months I was originally supposed to spend in Swaziland neared an end, it was pretty clear that I wasn't going anywhere. So I scheduled a quick US trip to check in with headquarters and my parents.

However, time at home was not time away from circumcision. From the cushy reclined seat of an Amtrak train to New York City, I wrote to the Indian Urological Society, formally requesting as many doctors as they could spare. I shamelessly spelled out the daily per diem – expecting that, in some cases, a volunteer circumcising job in Swaziland might be more lucrative than their current government-funded jobs. From a lumpy couch in Provincetown overlooking tangled blueberry bushes and a wildlife estuary, I spoke with the Department of Defense in California and discussed the feasibility of releasing military urologists from their rotations for month-long stints in an African kingdom. From the I-95 in New Jersey, I took a call from Solomon, our major USAID donor in D.C., who was panicked about the Kenya-Swaziland nurse partnership. Why were things not moving faster? We needed names. We needed commitments. Sitting on my childhood canopy bed in Connecticut, I Skyped with Clara, now the unofficial ASI Project Director.

'How is it to be home?' she asked.

It's okay, I told her. And life in Swazi?

'About the same as you left it,' she said.

Then we got into it. She wanted to know where each of our

volunteer doctors was coming from. She wanted confirmed numbers, month by month.

'I can't give you that yet, Clara,' I said.

'When will you be able to?' she pressed.

'Soon,' I promised. 'But in order to confirm volunteers, I need dates. I need definite numbers of teams by month. You give me the specifics, and we'll make it happen.'

We were stuck. She wanted the number of volunteers to determine the plan. I wanted the plan to guide our staffing search.

'Isn't this fun?' she asked, tongue-in-cheek, at the end of our conversation.

'Oh yeah, it's a real laugh-a-minute.' I took a very large gulp from the wine glass in my hand.

And, then, from my stripped apartment in Baltimore, just before my scheduled return to Swaziland, my email exploded with disappointing news about the Kenyan nurse exchange. The Swaziland Nursing Association had made their displeasure public, and we had officially lost permission to 'borrow' the thirty-five nurses Swaziland had carefully requested from the Kenyan government for the next Back to School, set to start in a matter of weeks. I clutched the list of foreign nurses from the Registrar of the Nursing Council and vowed to track down every single unemployed one of them. Then I counted the remaining days we had to train them.

***

To say that Charity – Swaziland's senior nurse member of the Swazi MC Task Force – was an imposing woman did not do her justice. She was regal, but not intimidating; she called me 'my dear' and frequently asked that we stop for roadside mangos or potted plants on our long drives back from site visits. It took me a while to figure out that the folksiness was part genuine warmth and part political strategy. Charity was a master of backdoor diplomacy, something I didn't fully appreciate until the day of the showdown with the Swaziland Nursing Association.

The tone of the meeting was, as expected, formal. Attendees filled ceramic mugs with tea and squeezed around a too-small conference table at Mountain Inn. After the requisite opening prayer, and Charity's introduction, I laid out the dimensions of the MC human resource problem. This required zero mental energy. Had I suffered a traumatic brain injury in a near-death crash on the Malagwane, I would have remembered the statistics. I projected the number of doctors and nurses that we would need throughout the ASI and posed the obvious question: 'This is how many we need… now let's talk about how many we have.' The floor was open, the subtext clear: how were we going to get enough staff to circumcise 152,000 guys?

The president of the Swaziland Nursing Association spoke. I blamed him for a secret appeal to Charity and the chain reaction of confusion that had reached the American embassies of two southern African countries and derailed my brief vacation in the States. All systems were set to fast-track the nurse request from Swaziland to Kenya when Charity had suddenly and inexplicably slammed on the brakes.

The Nursing Association president chose his words carefully. His organization, he said, was in complete support of the Back to School campaigns and the ASI, and he congratulated the team for their hard work to date. 'Creative solutions to the nursing gap are certainly necessary,' he said, 'but we feel very confident that those solutions can be found within Swaziland's borders. For example, in August,' he went on, 'between ninety and a hundred nurses will graduate from Swazi training institutions. What if they all went to work

for the ASI after graduation and then were prioritized for
employment after the completion of the project?'

But, I thought, nationwide, healthcare facilities complained
bitterly of being dramatically understaffed. Weren't these new
nurses needed to fill existing vacancies?

The president continued. 'And we have another idea.
Hospital matrons and facility in-charges have already
established annual leave schedules. Why doesn't the Ministry of
Health use these lists to staff the ASI, month by month? There
are over one hundred Swazi nurses on leave at any given time.'

Clever, Mr. President: an option that allowed Swazi nurses
to be double-paid – first by your government, and then by
mine – for the same period. Then I stopped. Hang on a second
here... we needed nurses. And if Swaziland had them, on
leave and ready to work? Well, maybe that was an idea worth
entertaining.

At this point, the country director from another American
NGO jumped in. Active in HIV/AIDS care and treatment,
she was concerned about the ever-shrinking nursing pool in
Swaziland. 'The ASI will dramatically increase the number of
men who are tested for HIV. Approximately 23,000 HIV-
infected people could be newly identified. To manage the care,
treatment and support of this additional client burden, even
more nurses will be needed. Do we really think Swaziland can
provide this many skilled healthcare providers?'

'The issue of recruitment,' the Nursing Association president
reminded the room, 'is a global issue with ethical
considerations. When you recruit from another country, you
deprive them of a valuable resource. We do not want to cripple
another country's healthcare system. Besides,' he added, 'these
conversations should not be conducted at our level.' This was
a clear dig at us foreign NGO workers. 'The nursing officer
should be the one to negotiate with her counterpart in another

country. These should be government-to-government arrangements.'

Charity stepped in. She attached herself to the problem not of ethics but to that of culture. Before my very eyes, Charity – once a champion of recruiting international circumcision nurses to reverse the trend of new HIV infections – did a 180. 'Can Kenyan nurses speak our language?' she asked. 'We want nurses who can communicate with Swazi clients.'

Stephanie, our local PEPFAR Activity Manager, piped up from the back of the room. 'Let us bear in mind,' she said, 'that the gesture made by the Kenyan government to share educated nurses *who are not currently working* with Swaziland was actually one of goodwill.'

Stephanie and I both knew that if Swaziland, or my organization, couldn't produce enough nurses, the ASI was done.

'Let us explore all other avenues first,' said the Nursing Association president. 'I think we can prove to you that Swazi nurses are capable of managing this task.'

Well, if the Swaziland Nursing Association needed to see the size of the nurse gap in black and white, no problem. We'd give it to them. My team volunteered to lead a Swazi nurse 'quantification exercise.' We would regroup once the data was in.

Then, something unexpected happened. After we ran an ad in the newspaper intended to smoke out all the unemployed, eligible nurses we could find, nurses came streaming into our office in droves. Each nurse arrived with a résumé in one hand and a sad story in the other. Each one, it seemed, was supporting numerous family members. Each one was the primary breadwinner in his or her family. I asked our new Ugandan program assistant, Roberta, to handle them.

'Keep careful track of names and contact details,' I instructed her. 'Don't promise anyone anything. Right now, we just need numbers.'

Roberta, all ninety pounds of her, wore green glitter eye shadow and five-inch heels. She did not bat an artificial eyelash at the nonstop tales of woe. From the Partnership Suite, I listened to her interview nurses in a small conference room, aloof and alert to nothing but the facts. At one point, I heard an interviewee start crying. Roberta did nothing – no reaction whatsoever.

'Maybe you could have offered her a tissue?' I suggested afterward.

Roberta looked at me with confusion. 'But, Laura,' she said, 'we cannot give them false hope.'

I remembered Kristi's 'silent probe.' Roberta was the master of it. Why was she being so cold to these nurses, whose only crime really was being desperate for work?

I went home and told Adam about it, asked him if he had any suggestions for how to give Roberta some gentle feedback about being, oh, a bit friendlier?

'Angel,' Adam said, 'she isn't Swazi.'

Then it clicked. In this part of the world, emotional alliance followed bloodline. It followed tribe. Outside of that, you owed nothing.

With my stay in Swaziland indefinitely extended, I needed a more permanent living situation. I had outgrown the fishbowl of Ayla's Village. So upon my return I moved to a house named Little Rock in Pine Valley, an area known for glorious mountain views, experimental architecture and a handful of well-known eccentric inhabitants.

The place was beautiful and overgrown, tucked away down a windy dirt road and deep in a curving crevice of the valley that abutted the Black Umbeluzi River. The electric iron gate was marked with the number 676, an identification intended not for a door-to-door postal service (there was none) but for the Buffalo Soldiers security company. Inside the gate, a cornucopia of fruit trees, cascading bougainvillea and wildflowers exploded. Peering out atop them: a bell tower.

The current tenant, a young American aid worker, talked quickly while showing me around the place. 'I've loved living here. But it's time for me to go,' she said. 'I've been waiting for two years to get internet. It's never going to happen.'

I poked my head into the curtained spare room, which she had converted into a makeshift office, and wandered through the kitchen. It had a fridge, minimal cabinet space – square wooden boxes affixed to the concrete wall – and a two-burner countertop gas stove. She noted my reaction to the modest outfittings. 'A bit like glamping, isn't it?'

'Huh?' I asked, unfamiliar with the term.

'Oh, you know, glamorous camping.'

An apt term, given that the house was truly a halfway point between indoors and out. A huge rock outcropping marked the way between the kitchen and the back door, another poked out from underneath a rickety green ladder that led to an upstairs loft sleeping space. 'That's gotta be a bit challenging after drinking,' I guessed.

'Tell me about it. Not too much fun in the middle of the night in a pair of slippery socks, either.'

Something about the place, the ladder in particular, reminded me of the cramped maritime apartments, each in its own primary color, with unique celestial names – Jupiter, Neptune, Borealis – that sat atop Captain Jack's Wharf in Provincetown where I'd spent so many happy hours as a sunburned kid. The wharf's wooden planks were the same shade of green, and the slapdash construction bore the same do-it-yourself hippie charm.

She pulled back another curtain. 'And the bathroom.' I gasped. It was nothing short of majestic, palatial even, with three steps leading down to a two-tiered throne room. The crowning glory was a blue-tiled shower that could have accommodated an entire kindergarten class.

I followed her into the sitting room, up another set of steps and past a few more rocks popping out from beige walls. A sliding glass door opened onto a spacious veranda, and, beyond, the most spectacular view of a lush valley bisected by a mountain stream and a humming, white-tipped waterfall. Two green mountainsides filled the periphery on each side, scaling up to daunting heights and sprinkled with more odd-shaped rocks and skinny pine trees. It was the stuff of *Lord of the Rings*. She smiled. 'That's what did it for me, too.'

The compound consisted of three separate units: Big Rock, Little Rock and Rock Pad. The owners, who lived in Big Rock, had done what many Swaziland property owners do: anyone with ample land and a few bucks to spare threw up a cottage or two. With Swaziland's booming development business, it was pretty much a guaranteed moneymaker. But the economic benefits were offset by an increasing sense of claustrophobia. In a country where privacy was nearly impossible to come by, it surprised me that anyone lucky enough to secure a bit of breathing room so willingly sacrificed it. However, faced with expensive private school fees and the cost of food, fuel and utilities on a par with South Africa, they had caved.

Later, I learned that a German farmer, who by all accounts was an alcoholic and a loner, once owned the Rock compound, then just Big Rock. 'He must have been a mechanic, too, because, in addition to the glass beer bottles that come up through the sediment after a heavy rain, we also get the odd carburetor or broken headlight,' the owner said.

That sealed the deal. I needed to live in Little Rock. Like Swaziland itself, the place was too weird, too wonderful. Adam came with me, although we had not planned it that way – he just seemed to sleep at my place more often than he slept at his own. He loved that late on Saturday nights, we could hear the Zionists' ghostly chanting from across the waterfall. He loved pulling avocados, grapefruits and guavas straight off the tree for lazy Sunday morning breakfast smoothies.

It was a time of planting roots, of consolidating identities, of becoming known in this new place, a subtle shift that manifested itself both at home and at work. Right around the time that I found a new home at Little Rock, our growing team broke rank from the Partnership Suite and secured our own office space in another part of Mbabane, taking over a former beauty salon in Cooper Center, across the street from Nando's and right down the road from the Ministry of Health. Goodbye, Partnership Suite, hello independence. We hung our NGO name above the door, took a team photo underneath it, and emailed it back to headquarters.

It was a calculated move of separation. What had previously been a friendly atmosphere of inter-organizational give-and-take became increasingly territorial as timelines dragged, rumors flew and cash dwindled. We were up to our eyeballs in preparations for the start of Back to School II and we still didn't have the 1,000 disposable circumcision kits needed for the campaign. We were short of nurses, counselors and support staff. We also hadn't heard a peep about the ASI award, which would have provided much-needed continuation funding.

Then, in July, we got news. Clara sent all of us NGO leads an email that read, 'I wanted to inform you that we have received a communication to respond to a sole source request to support the ASI. We will be in touch with you through your respective headquarters.' PEPFAR was finally moving ahead, putting the money where only its mouth had been, with the biggest, fastest male circumcision initiative ever attempted. And, confirming what the rumors had said for months, it would not be funded through the usual competitive process. Project funds would be directly handed over, or sole-sourced, to the NGO that Clara worked for. And Clara would lead the overall coordination. To say this was highly unusual would be an understatement, but I was way too far down the totem pole to know why this process would work this way. I just knew that the rest of us would support distinct scopes of work, with my NGO responsible for human resources, clinical training and quality of clinical services. The news of the award should have been huge. It should have been thrilling, or, at the very least, energizing. But Back to School II was weeks away. All of us were fixated on the target: 7,000 circumcisions.

To John, who had cut his nonprofit teeth running a refugee hospital in Darfur during the worst of the terror, this was manageable. He ordered diathermy machines, surgical beds, countless consumables, pharmaceuticals, hundreds of circumcision kits, vehicles to haul the surgical waste, vehicles to pick up the clients and vehicles to move all the stuff to the shifting outreach sites. He helped develop electronic recording forms for the collection and release of daily statistics – detail after detail, carefully mapped out in Excel.

From our new office, I contacted Clara on Skype to find out when we expected to hear back from Washington D.C. on our ASI plans. 'Yes, we did get some news,' Clara said. That was weird. Why hadn't she called me straight away? 'There's been a bit of a reaction from PEPFAR,' she wrote. 'They said our budget was way too high.' The price tag for the yearlong intervention now totaled 56 million dollars. 'You're going to need to cut back,' she told me. More than half this budget is for human resources. Do you really need that much headquarters support?'

Whoa, hang on just one minute here. We were bringing in hundreds of international volunteers, contracting hundreds of local nurses and support staff, securing hotel rooms, caterers and *kombis*. Yes, we needed back-up – from Baltimore, from Kenya, from Ethiopia, from India, from our local Swazi office. I needed, honestly speaking, a whole universe of back-up.

Apparently, PEPFAR's concern warranted a face-to-face discussion. Solomon, our D.C.-based donor, flew to Mbabane where he requested a dinner meeting with Clara, me and Remi, who was in town for a periodic check-in. We met at Café Lingo, a sandwiches-and-coffee place with faux leather chairs and Wi-Fi for purchase by the hour. It was no social call.

'The time for dialogue is over,' Solomon told us. He was particularly upset by setbacks with our Kenyan nurse swap, a development that seemed to have fueled a frustration with the increasingly under-assertive Kingdom. 'Let me be very direct with you, the Swazi approach to the ASI has been backward. We need to think differently. We need to start from our bottom lines' – in dollars and foreskins – 'and work back from there.' He told us that we also needed to reframe the discussions we were having with the government. 'American taxpayers are not writing a blank check for this.'

This quickly became very clear: Solomon was in Mbabane to give us new marching orders, what he termed 'project parameters.' These non-negotiable terms would be the conditions upon which funding to this particular group of individuals, in this particular country, with this particular government, would depend.

'The ceiling amount will be ten million dollars,' he said, less than 20 percent of what we felt we needed to carry out the ambitious project. 'That amount, coupled with the HIV incidence survey, is more than PEPFAR's total annual budget in Swaziland.'

We absorbed this information. What exactly was the funding allotment? It seemed to change by the day. Each of us wondering which critical aspect of the work would be shortchanged. Solomon observed our reactions carefully.

'Remember,' he said, 'the ASI is not about strengthening Swaziland's overall health systems. It is about a one-time effort to complete 152,000 circumcisions. That's all.'

Then he looked directly at me. 'Laura, think about the implications for human resources. How can we increase efficiency? South Africa has already demonstrated that one provider can easily perform forty circumcisions in a single day.

Go ask your colleagues in Tanzania. They did much more than that every day of the last campaign in Iringa.'

I was starting to develop an allergy to comparisons with other countries.

But Solomon saw things in black and white. This would not be a dialogue. 'Thirty-five teams working for six months should be able to circumcise 166,000 men. There, that's the ASI – done!' How simple he made it sound. 'I don't care about what the implementation pattern looks like' – here he looked at Clara – 'as long as the whole thing is finished by September 2011.'

The last part wasn't exactly true. He did care what the implementation pattern looked like. 'You'll need to use the South African model to reach these numbers in this time frame. You'll need to operate on four beds, not three. You'll need to reduce your teams to six nurses total.'

So who would perform the two- and seven-day post-op reviews, which could number up to eighty per day? Who would cover the recovery room?

'If they don't need them in South Africa, you don't need them here. Go to South Africa. See for yourself. I'm sure you can figure it out.'

He sat back in his chair. 'You know, guys, we can no longer support a Cadillac circumcision program in this country, not when it's been proven that more cost-efficient models work. Swaziland is the only country right now that pays to transport clients for procedures. We cannot continue like this. It's too expensive. The ASI requires economy of scale. Our goal is as many circumcisions as possible – safely, of course – but I don't think I need to explain to all of you that the only way we get population level benefits from this intervention is with real numbers.'

Solomon was an evangelist. His spreadsheets and color-coded graphs were impressive, but it was his imposing body language and his commanding voice that left us nodding our heads in silence like a bunch of rapt congregants.

But once the tough love was doled out, Solomon eased up. A hard face relaxed. He counted on us, needed us, cared about us in his own peculiar, dictatorial sort of way.

'You are a valuable team,' he continued, 'skilled, highly trusted, supported at the top levels. Many, many people,' he told us, 'are invested in your success. I will be here often, to make sure you get the help you need. You should expect daily communication with us. A sense of team unity,' and here again Solomon looked at Clara, 'will be of extreme importance. Okay, it has been a long day. I appreciate the late meeting. Let's continue the discussions tomorrow.'

I started to pack up my laptop, desperate to get out of there and dying to pee, when Solomon pulled me aside.

'Laura, what's going on with the negotiation for the Kenyan nurses? The next Back to School is starting soon. You are not going to be ready.'

I assured him that we were doing everything we could, that we were almost done with the nurse quantification exercise the Ministry of Health had requested before they would authorize the use of foreign nurses. 'It's looking a lot more promising than we expected, actually. It turns out that there is some untapped capacity here.'

'In the future,' he said, 'please consult me immediately if anyone tells you to stop moving forward. I will sound the alarm bell with WHO. I'll bring in the ambassador if needed.'

I imagined how that would go over with the Swazi Ministry of Health counterparts whose trust I had worked so hard to gain – Dr. Mamba, Charity. A move like that would destroy those relationships. But this was much bigger than I was, much bigger than any single one of us.

30

It was Clara who coined the mantra, 'Swaziland will not make me cry today.' I said it to myself often.

Days passed in a blur. Weeks before the start of the biggest campaign yet, we had a fraction of the nurses we needed, and our willing doctors were growing less willing by the day. I chewed my fingernails to bloody stubs. Because the funding still hadn't been released, there was no ASI project office. No ASI project vehicles. No dedicated ASI project support staff. All of that required cash that we wouldn't receive until the bureaucratic wheels of the US government went through the requisite creaky turns. I felt a constant pressure to be doing, doing, doing... A pressure exerted, an energy discharged, only in nonstop motion. Adam worried about me, could not understand my drive. Certain differences were just too hard-wired, too embedded in the twisted helixes of our cultural and familial DNA, to explain.

Each day presented another sharp poke from the beak of some logistical complication or screw-up. For example, customs officials were holding a massive supply of penis models hostage at the Matsapha airport. We needed them for our staff trainings. Clara and I did not see eye to eye on how to resolve the situation.

'Those models have been holed up in a warehouse through at least four clinical trainings,' I said. 'Why can't we just pay the tax, liberate the models and get on with it?' I mean, honestly, we were talking about a few hundred bucks. For several hundred plastic penises, I thought we – as a multimillion-dollar project – could probably spring for it.

'Because customs tax is not an allowable expense according to our contracts with the US government,' Clara countered. 'We have a waiver with the Swazi government. If this project gets audited, which it will, the fact that you paid the tax will be a very big deal.'

These models had been a thorn in my side almost since my first day on the job when Erin had asked me to work with an American supplier to design the perfect low-cost training tool. They had gone through dozens of revisions – wrong skin color, wrong consistency, urethral opening too small. Then, our contracts department had caught wind of it and reprimanded me for failing to recognize that we should have patented the models. Personally, I didn't feel that we needed to be too concerned with someone else making a mint from our plastic penises. I felt that we had more important things to worry about, which was pretty much exactly how I felt about the tax issue. Seemed to me the goal was to get the plastic penises into the hands of hundreds of on-leave nurses before those nurses got their hands on Swazi dudes.

This was not an isolated case of conflicting viewpoints. Increasingly, Clara and I were clashing. At a Back to School planning meeting in a conference room in Manzini, still smarting from the absence of our Kenyan cohort, I presented the challenges we were facing with recruiting enough nurses with such short notice.

'What are you going to do?' Clara asked me, agitated.

'Pray for a miracle?'

No one laughed.

My cell phone rang. It was Adam. I hung up and sent a text message, 'In a meeting.'

He texted back. 'It's urgent.'

'Excuse me, guys. So sorry. Give me just a minute.'

'Saved by the bell,' Clara muttered.

I walked out onto a busy Manzini road at midday, stopped in front of RFM Hospital and dialed his number.

'What is it?' I asked.

'I have to tell you something you aren't going to like, angel,' he said.

I tensed.

His ex-girlfriend had just called him from Matsapha Airport. After two months, she had returned without warning. Now, she was here – less than an hour from Mbabane – pleading for Adam to pick her up because 'she didn't have anyone else.'

His voice broke. 'I can't leave her there alone. I'll just take her back to the old house.'

A scalding iron rod worked its way through my intestines. 'I don't have time for this bullshit,' I said, and walked back into the meeting to field more questions I didn't have answers to.

After that, Adam's returned ex delivered a ten-page letter to my office in which she argued that Adam was 'a gold-digger.' Then she confronted us one day at lunch in the Plaza. Adam and I were eating at a corner shop, a cramped spot with organic juices and vegetarian specials, during a rare break from the office. I spotted the ex in a yellow summer dress, examining some handbags that hung from the door of a shop across from the café. Her face looked pale and gaunt, the suffering obvious. It wasn't that I felt a lack of empathy toward that suffering – I

202

knew I'd contributed to it – it was just that the whole thing felt so cheap.

Adam said, 'Relax, angel. Just ignore her. She's not here to bother us.'

He was wrong. When she sauntered over to our table, her blonde hair pulled up into a severe bun, hands on hips, she directed her words toward Adam. 'After our talk the other day, I've decided that I can't go with you to India. It's just not right for me to buy you a plane ticket.'

Adam looked down at his plate. He did not speak, did not engage: a Swazi-style rebuttal.

'Well, I just wanted to tell you my decision,' she concluded. Then she walked off in the direction of the Mr. Price shop.

I felt like I had been slapped in the face, which was certainly the point. Adam looked cornered, panicked and pained. 'Don't let her mess with your mind,' he said. 'We'd talked about going to India long before we came to Swaziland.'

What should I believe? 'Did you meet up with her and not tell me about it?' I thought about all the hours that I spent at work. Did I always know where he was? Did I need to track his movements? Check his phone, his email, just as his ex had learned to do? Jesus, what was happening to me?

'She's been coming to Serendipity crying, asking for me. I'm so sorry about all this, angel.'

Perhaps life was trying to teach me what it was like to be a part of this culture from the inside, to feel the sting of a concurrent partnership in the first person. It was not a lesson I wanted to learn. I wasn't someone who had public confrontations with jealous exes. This was at unfathomable odds to my self-image: that I was a gladiator for good, an observant, sensitive person, and superior to all of this.

Deep down, I felt like Adam should see that he'd obviously scored to get a woman of such substance. And to keep said woman, he should know how important it was to remove us from this muck. He should want to be my white knight, spare me this demeaning nonsense.

But he was not a white knight. He was a flawed man. And I was not a gladiator of good. I was a flawed woman. And we were locked in the dance of a new relationship, that heady elixir of desire where one sees the projection of an imagined, best version of the other.

At that café table at the Plaza, our projections started to crumble. A flimsy pedestal faltered as I realized we were part of an all-too-human drama that knows no tribe and does not award passes for privilege.

***

A few days later, Adam found out that someone he had worked with for decades had just died in an emergency room in Florida. A week before the start of Back to School II, he flew to the States for the funeral.

As Adam left, a coworker and friend of mine arrived from Baltimore. My boss Erin had talked Remi, the infectious diseases specialist from headquarters, into fully relocating to the Kingdom to serve as clinical services director for the ASI. I had known him since my earliest days with the organization, when he had made such an effort to make me feel welcome. A freakishly bright surgeon from West Africa, his emotional intelligence was matched only by his cognitive capacity. I'd never seen him flustered in either a social or a work situation. Remi was three years my junior, but ready for leadership. He was presidential, warm and compassionate. I was enormously relieved when, in his distinctive glasses and bright tunics, he finally landed in Swaziland. With his help, our team stepped it up a notch. We'd never worked so hard.

With Adam gone, I could be hyper-focused. I battled

budgets, dealt with headquarters, with the government, with other organizations. I also dealt with the endless stream of Back to School II staffing questions: *Do I qualify for overtime when I work after 5 p.m.? Will I receive holiday pay for working on the king's birthday? Will I get a separate on-call allowance (the Swazi government gives me one!)? Will I get free meals on my days off?*

Meanwhile, one of our two program assistants, sweet and hard-working Thandi, handled all the volunteer doctor logistics. For Back to School II, we would have eleven volunteer docs this time, coming in from the US, Tanzania, Ghana and Lesotho. They needed visas, insurance, plane tickets, registration documents, accommodation and communication devices. She worked around the clock to arrange everything, leaving her baby with a helper.

Roberta, meanwhile, employed previously unknown powers of persuasion to attack our Back to School nurse deficit. She camped out at the Nursing Council where she intercepted new nurse graduates as they came in for their registration paperwork. She pleaded, wheedled. Most often, she won them over when she told them the daily $77 per diem rate. Meanwhile, more registered foreign nurses started to appear in Swaziland. At least a handful turned up at our office every day. The 'bush telegraph' did our work for us. Since these nurses came of their own volition, we could hire them with clear consciences.

The doctors, Remi and Morris, were in charge of all things clinical. They struggled to clear the delay with the circumcision kits, led quality assurance checks at all sixteen sites and prepared the circumcision teams. That was our deal. Thandi, Roberta and I lined up the people; Remi and Morris trained them. For weeks, they ran back-to-back circumcision trainings for these short-term hires. They organized sessions on evenings and Saturdays in a kind of circumcision ultramarathon.

Slowly, the master Back to School II staffing whiteboard in our Cooper Center office, grouped by site, team and position, started to fill. The sea of names flooded me with pleasure. Mostly I reveled simply to see their number, but the novelty and playfulness of the names delighted me too. Listed there – a Petunia, a Savior, a Napoleon, a Girlie, an Eggie, a Memory, a Beauty, a Perfect, a Mona Lisa, a Fortunate, a Sympathy, a Jennifah and an Elvis. Also listed there, a nurse at Litsemba Letfu clinic, was my mom.

My mother, bless her, signed up the minute I asked her to volunteer for the three-week campaign. We had to keep this concealed due to the ban on foreign nurses, but I figured that Charity, a mother of four, would probably let it slip. Not that I was planning to tell her. My dad would come along for moral support. They would do some sightseeing at the end of the trip, check out the vineyards in South Africa and take in the Euro-African vibe in Cape Town. But I knew they were not coming for the cause, or the tourism. They needed to find out if I was okay.

Still, this circumcision gig was right up my mom's alley. A born nurse, she possessed the two traits that defined the best of the profession: a profound wonder at the perfectly synchronized operations of the human body and a deep empathy for what those bodies endured over the course of a lifetime. I was in second grade when she returned to work full-time as a hospice nurse, the year she took care of a boy named Danny who was exactly my age and dying of leukemia.

My dad, on the other hand, was a former naval officer who made a comfortable living in smart investments and plastics. Throughout my childhood, he was a suited, briefcase-carrying executive who flew to foreign countries business class. I devoted a wall in my childhood bedroom to the postcards he brought home, stoking an early appetite to see the world myself.

Now they were in their sixties, and not quite as energetic and resilient as they had once been. My poor parents: immediately after deplaning at Joburg's O.R. Tambo airport in August 2010, drugged and disoriented from a sixteen-hour flight, they witnessed a paramedic team failing to jumpstart the heart of a dead man lying in the middle of the concourse. Right afterward, my dad's ATM card number and PIN code were stolen by an eagle-eyed thief who'd watched him withdraw a fat chunk of South African rand in anticipation of the five-hour drive to Mbabane.

Around four, I rushed to Café Lingo, as planned, to meet my parents. When they stepped out of their rental car in matching zip-off cargo pants and sneakers, they looked exhausted. As we hugged hello, they probably thought the same about me.

That first night I took them to Finesse, the restaurant tucked away in the back of the new mall, overlooking the Mbabane River, where Adam and I had had our first 'date' and where I'd welcomed our first batch of volunteer doctors so many months before. I thought it would be perfect for Mom and Dad – a bottle of wine, a soup starter and a crackling fire in a wood-burning stove.

However, the minute we walked in, I regretted it. Clara was at a back table, wedged in next to the stove with the South African ASI marketing director. Stephanie Silva sat with Dr. Mamba at the table next to us. It was claustrophobic in the extreme. In other places, people are connected by six degrees of separation. In Swaziland, you're lucky if you can stretch it out to two. I pulled a piece of paper and pen from my bag and scribbled notes and diagrams to explain who was who to my jet-lagged parents. My mom made the mistake of asking, 'So, what's a typical day like for you? Take today: what did you do today?'

'Oh, I had a meeting with some journalists about the program. It was interesting, actually. The journalists were late – you'll get used to Africa time soon – so I was chatting with some government officials. They'd just come back from a trip around the country meeting with chiefs and traditional leaders, getting their blessing for the ASI.'

In retrospect, this would have been inaccessible, bewildering information for them straight off the plane. I was in so deep that I couldn't see that.

'Apparently some of the chiefs were skeptical. One of them asked, 'How do we know the *mlungu* scientists won't decide a few years from now that we actually need our foreskins?' Some of the chiefs offered tips for us NGO workers. They said that HIV counselors should not ply their trade in their home communities.'

'Why?' asked my dad.

'Well, blood is a powerful tool for traditional medicine here. If you have an argument with your neighbor, and you drew his blood, you could use that blood for magic against him.'

My dad shook his head in a sort of 'yikes, really?' gesture. We Americans like to think we're well beyond sorcery and superstition.

My mom changed directions. 'So what did the journalists want to know from you?'

'I talked about the evidence behind circumcision for HIV prevention. There are many myths out there. One journalist asked, 'So, how long does it take before a newly circumcised man uses up his 60 percent HIV-prevention protection?' A lot of people just don't get it.'

I looked at my mom, carefully lifting a forkful of salad and paying close attention to my words. She wanted to demonstrate how much she cared to learn about the world her daughter occupied. But my mom was also nervous. She had been preoccupied since their arrival with what she called 'the exam' she'd be taking at the volunteers' orientation the next day. 'It's been twenty-five years since I was tested on any kind of nursing knowledge.'

'Mom, you aren't going to fail.'

'How about you give me the answers now? I'll destroy them immediately afterward. No one needs to know.'

I rolled my eyes. 'I'm not doing that, Mom. Look, we just need to ensure that all the volunteers have the same information and are doing things the same way. With such an international group, it's important that the preparation is standardized.'

It was a rigorous process, one that we'd been refining for nearly a year. First, all our volunteers completed an online training course. This was followed by a half-day session in-country, led by Morris. Then, a sequence of skills stations in which new volunteers circumcised our plastic models. After that, we would have the so-called 'exam' in which we would ask volunteers to match a dozen photographs of magnified penises with various conditions – cancers, congenital anomalies and sexually transmitted infections – that rendered a man ineligible for surgery.

After I brought my parents back home that night – we'd rented Big Rock during the conveniently timed month when the owners took an annual trip to Europe – guilt crept in. My mom had signed up to spend twenty long days on her feet tending to teenagers in a foreign country where her teammates wouldn't speak her language. Hadn't I been in pretty much the same boat at Kibo? And how well I remembered the anxiety I'd felt as a midwifery student rotating through a similar set of skills stations.

A memory flashed through my mind. Me, performing my first breast exam on a slender 'gynecological teaching associate.' I'd moved my fingers in careful rows up and down her breast tissue. 'You aren't breathing,' she'd said. 'Your tension is making me tense. I'm holding my breath because you are. Try again.' Other students watched as I tried again. 'You still aren't breathing,' she'd said. Again and again, until I could breathe and touch at the same time.

I called Remi. 'Can I pick up the photos for tomorrow's orientation? I think my mom needs some extra study time.'

'Of course,' he said, seeing no harm in encouraging a diligent student.

When we arrived at Esibayeni Lodge for the orientation the next morning, my bedraggled team seemed revived. This was the fun part, where the work started to feel real and immediate and rewarding.

I greeted the first volunteer to arrive, a doctor from California. 'I googled you,' he said while shaking my hand. 'Oh yeah?' I asked. He grinned, leaving it at that. He wore a baseball cap and long shorts. It was his first trip to Africa. I introduced him to my parents and listened to the rise and fall of their lively conversation as I tacked penis photos on a wall. While the volunteers circled the skills stations, my dad programmed the group's cheap cell phones and internet modems. All seven volunteers aced the photo–disease matching quiz.

The next day, dozens of *kombis* transported dozens of surgical teams across the country to various Back to School II sites, and the circumcising started. Every night, I got a text message with the day's numbers. And, my God, they were solid. Better than solid. Solomon, our donor back in D.C., sent us an approving, encouraging email, letting us know that

D.C. was very happy, but reminding us that this was just the beginning.

After that, I hardly saw my mom and dad. I clocked fourteen-hour days. When I wasn't working, I just wanted to sleep. I yawned constantly. At meetings, I propped my head up with my hands. My heart hurt. My head ached. My limbs were strangely swollen and tight feeling. I was both too heavy and weightless at the same time, ungrounded.

I called Adam in the US but had nothing to say. I should have been cheered by the turn in client demand, but a deep, unnamed dread appeared, a fear that success would be fleeting, perhaps. When I slept, like the girls in Cindy's art therapy group, I dreamed of the dead. My great-aunt Ruth a revenant, her small sapphire eyes glinting, urged me to come home.

31

In the Kingdom of Swaziland, in September 2010, nerves ran raw. Clara's baggy button-ups and pants fell off her. John, our logistician, snapped with minimal provocation. He chain-smoked and paced. I started to feel uncomfortable around him, sensing that he had no more patience for me, for Swaziland, for this circumcising work. We were told that the president's office – as in the office of the President of the United States – was watching our progress. ABC's Diane Sawyer planned to come to southern Africa once the ASI was fully up and running to cover it.

But on the ground, it was another setback every day, another impossible deadline. Solomon's non-negotiable terms... Such rigidity in a place where nothing went according to plan was crazy-making. Our instructions – circumcise 152,000 HIV-negative boys and men in less than a year – were branded onto our brains.

I started to wish for an illness, something severe enough to send me home, but not life-threatening. Maybe a touch of malaria from a site visit down to Lobombo, or an infected bite from one of the bony, snarling dogs that picked at street garbage at the end of my road. 'Some days I wish that I would get hit by a car… just a little bit. Just enough to get me out of Swaziland but not enough to do permanent damage,' I told Clara.

She found that hilarious. 'Hit by a car… just a little bit!' She slapped her leg, guffawed.

Back when I still called myself a nurse-midwife, penises were just not my department. Now, my world had shrunk to the size of one adult foreskin. Brown and bloody, less than an inch long – post-surgically, the thing resembled nothing so much as a shriveled slug. My life, reduced to this – an evolutionary vestige, a primordial invertebrate.

Adam found this decidedly weird. Perhaps part of it was because he himself was not circumcised, but I think a larger part of it was because he felt icky that his girlfriend had such a constant and unrelenting professional preoccupation with men's privates. The program messed with our minds, too, gave us all the sense of humor of eighth-grade boys. Immaturity eased the tension. The marketing guys came up with dozens of catchphrases we could never use.

Don't be silly, snip that willy!
The revolution is in his pants!
Cut the flappy pappy, make mama happy!
Be a cut above the rest!

In the midst of this absurdity, my private life continued as if it was the trashy reality TV show I often felt it to be. Two weeks later, when Adam arrived back in from the funeral, he said that I looked haggard. 'If I didn't know better,' he said, 'I'd think you were pregnant.'

Turns out that he didn't know better. Three tests confirmed it.

My first response was neither happiness nor horror; it was deep shame. How could this happen? I should have known better. I did know better. But in the wake of two negative HIV tests, we'd pitched the condoms. There are good reasons why condoms are not the HIV-prevention solution they could be: condoms can feel at odds with a committed, caring relationship; a relationship like ours. By then, we nodded off at the end of a long day, naked and holding hands. Sometimes, as warm and cozy couples do, we made love half-asleep in the morning's dark hours. Under such situations, we didn't fiddle with dresser drawers and boxes.

However, even though condoms were no longer part of the routine, I certainly knew all about contraception. I'd been on the pill myself for years. In my work as a midwife, I could recite the effectiveness rates of each method and their respective pros and cons automatically. I had given countless Depo Provera injections, slid small-bore needles into the upper-right quadrant of buttocks of every size and description. Back in New Haven, women just emerging from terminations, crampy and confused from intravenous sedation, pretended to listen as I showed them a sample pack of pills and told them to set their cell phone alarms for the same time every day so that they wouldn't forget to take them.

Now, this. I'd been irresponsible with my own contraception. Was part of my absent-mindedness caused by my aching desire to be mother? I couldn't shake the belief that I'd brought a pregnancy upon myself with all the hand-wringing that I'd never have kids. Into that obsessive preoccupation – the mismatch between a life's true prosaic circumstances and a soul's fondest wish – a spark of life found an opening.

What to do? Here was my chance to ensure that I'd never become the eccentric global single lady. There was a knife-like wrenching in my solar plexus. I searched the internet. I tried to focus on the facts. A dozen websites, created to feed moneyed,

Western women's insatiable need for expert answers, spun the days into images – today the splitting cells were the size of a period at the end of this sentence, tomorrow a fully formed spinal cord, in two more weeks a lima bean with a heartbeat.

'We will figure it out,' Adam assured me. 'We can make this work.'

He held my cold, blue-veined hands in his warm brown ones. He was okay with this news. In this part of the world, perhaps in most of the world, a relationship is not sealed until a baby is made of the union. But I wasn't looking to use a pregnancy to stake a claim on this man, and Adam knew it.

It was still early in our fraught relationship, much too early to be considering children. It was also too early for Adam to grasp the depth of my chronic indecision. He didn't know that he would be the third man to propose to me without a ring, because he, like the other two, intuited that I didn't have it in me to say yes, knew that to me the idea of permanence – of person, of place, of profession – carried with it the cloying stink of a life frozen mid-stream.

There wasn't a kinder man. Absent-minded? Yes. Drifting? Yes. Dreamy and impulsive? Yes. But also deeply good. And an extended family that accepted me from the first meeting. Still, I craved choice, and change. I wanted one thing with all my heart today and something entirely different tomorrow. It was a relentless sprint away from the death grip of monotony, a race to keep just ahead of depression.

It was also more than that.

'You don't want to keep this baby because its father is an uneducated African,' he said when I didn't leap to agree that we could, indeed, figure it out. In our small, rocky kitchen, with a clock issuing an ominous tick-tick-tick from the cement wall, he dropped my hands. For the next few days tidal swells of anger rolled between us.

'Can't you see what this program is doing to me? The baby will stew for nine months in a bath of stress hormones,' I said. 'How can we have a baby when we are so unstable? I could barely keep up with the drama when I wasn't pregnant.'

The latter statement was meant to cut. It was meant to remind him that if we'd started without all the sneaking around, then maybe I'd feel differently about the whole thing.

But it was more than that, too.

What I did not say, because it was too painful to say, was that I felt that I had to choose between a not-yet-officially-begun one-year project to prevent 88,000 HIV infections and an imperfect, unprepared motherhood. It seemed impossible to do both, and the chance to be part of something this big, this important, came once in a career and only if you were lucky. The chance to bear a life, on the other hand? Well, just a few missed pills and I had gotten pregnant. Wasn't it safe to assume the chance would come around again? The next time, I'd make sure that the timing and the circumstances were the product of careful planning.

On Skype, I told Erin that I was pregnant because, weirdly, at that point I had a closer personal relationship with my boss than I did with my friends from home. I emailed Human Resources to find out about the maternity package for staff living overseas. Meanwhile, my parents were in Swaziland, in the house next door, totally unaware.

It should be said that while I've never for a moment doubted their love, my mom and dad don't exactly get my craving for a storybook, swashbuckling life. I hadn't exactly been an easy kid. In yearly conferences, teachers told them that I was bright, but vulnerable. Perpetually big-eyed and blushing, I sucked a pacifier until age five when my dentist outlawed the habit. Then, I began biting myself. Angry or hurt, I chomped down so hard on a curled pointer finger that the inflamed digit grew to the size of a hot dog. The swelling did not subside for the whole of elementary school. There I was, learning to stuff things down. There I was, trying to render an invisible, nebulous pain visible and specific.

By adulthood, I found other tools – healthy and otherwise – to manage suffering and sensitivity and shyness. In Swaziland, I found Adam, who was perhaps the best shield yet against daily assaults of judgment and competition, stress and insecurity. However, to reduce Adam to his accepting nature and generous spirit – to what he did for me – is to oversimplify a complex man with cultural and experiential wounds of his own. The situation with his ex had carved fault lines in our dynamic and those lines rumbled and quaked under the strain of the pregnancy.

Adam, whose reputation as a genius in the kitchen was growing, offered to make dinner for my parents one night. Prior to their arrival, my parents knew very little about him, let alone that I was living with him. I'd talked about him during the early days of their visit, while Adam was still in the US. Now that he was back, it was time for an official introduction. I didn't worry about the interracial issue – I'd crossed that line years before. I worried about other things: commonality, education, class.

We walked half a dozen aromatic pots and pans in oven mitts right from our back door in Little Rock to the front door of Big Rock, where my parents were staying. During dinner, Adam was quiet. I was moody and drained. My mom, as ever, tried to fill the space, ease the tension. An accomplished cook in her own right, she immediately saw food as a common language. 'Is this lamb?' she asked Adam. 'I don't think I've ever had lamb prepared this way. It is delicious. Honey, do you eat like this all the time?'

It was meant to be a compliment to Adam and to engage me,

but I felt so sick. 'Not hungry,' I said. The truth was that the smell of the roasted lamb made me want to vomit.

I struggled to stay present and was relieved, somehow, when my dad entered into a long-winded commentary on his experience of Swaziland so far. He summarized conversations with taxi drivers and neighbors, recited various statistics he'd read online while my mom worked at the clinic. I realized my dad was probably getting a more authentic picture of the place than I was, locked up in my circumcision echo chamber.

After we got back to Little Rock, Adam asked me why I was so afraid. 'It's not as if you're a teenager,' he said. 'They are good people, your parents. Couldn't you try to talk to your mom?'

Adam remembered being nineteen years old, and the hangdog feeling of telling his mother that Dotty was pregnant. How at first Lisaya was horrified – what would this mean for her golden boy and his bright future? She had half-expected this news, had been bracing herself for it; only she had expected it from her other son. Eventually, she came around. Then, Adam told me how Lisaya had doted on her pretty granddaughter.

'You need to give your parents more credit,' Adam said. 'You don't know what they've been through in their own lives, all the things they've never shared with you.'

I drove to Litsemba Letfu one Wednesday morning to check in on the circumcising and to lift team morale. I was ashen and sick, and not just from the pregnancy hormones. When the clinical team took a quick lunch break, I asked my mom if she wanted to get some fresh air. She wore the same handmade flowered scrubs that she'd donned to volunteer at the New Haven clinic where we'd once worked side by side on Fridays, abortion days. We sat on the landing at the top of a dirty stairwell in the Big Tree Shopping Complex, where my mom pulled the lid off a yogurt she'd purchased at the Pick n Pay just below.

When I delivered my news, she stayed alarmingly even, lifted a spoonful of yogurt to her mouth and stared out onto a lot full of parked cars and the highway beyond. I watched her face in profile. How worn-out she looked. 'Well, this is not the life I foresaw for you,' she began carefully.

I had expected, I realized, a flicker of excitement. By my age, she'd already had all three of her own babies. Unsure what to say next, I let the silence hang. Eventually she said, 'Of course, we would love any child of yours.'

She felt about a million miles away from me then, even though, after so long and such distance, we were finally sitting right next to each other. My head pounded. In the parking lot below, a harried woman swatted her whining child. There on the step, my mom still smelled like perfume and body heat, exactly as she had when I was a six-year-old finger-biter with lopsided blonde braids and she was the leader of my Brownie troop. Back then, she told my Brownie friends that the 'RN' pinned to her white uniform stood for 'really nice,' which made them laugh and made me crawl into her lap like an infant so that everyone would know that she was *my* mom. Here she was, the person who loved me most on this earth, morphed into a stranger. I watched the subtle movements of her facial muscles as they contracted. I watched her straddle a tightrope between love and fear, between love and judgment.

Afterward, as if not a thing had changed in twenty-five years, I got back into my car, big-eyed and pale-faced, and sobbed the entire death-defying way back up the Malagwane.

32

There was little time to waste in idle contemplation or self-indulgent obsessing. Two days later, a second batch of Back to School II volunteers arrived and cycled through the ritualistic circumcision orientation. Although the campaign was only three weeks long, most doctors hadn't been able to leave their home practices for the full duration so they came in two waves.

The now-veteran first batch of volunteers swapped clinical tales. My mom – who'd also managed to sublimate whatever she was feeling about my disclosure – passed along some tips. 'You can really reduce your team's resupplying needs by pre-preparing circumcision packs,' she told them. She brought one such pack along for show and tell.

She wasn't the only one who'd blossomed in the Kingdom. Our volunteers were celebrities in their communities. After his three weeks were up, the Cameroonian volunteer could not wait to pitch up for the fully fledged ASI. Local teenagers badgered our Ghanaian volunteer with questions about circumcision and sexuality. The hotel receptionist knocked on his door half a dozen times in the evening, apologizing for the repeated disturbances.

After the orientation sessions for the new volunteers,

everyone piled into a rented *kombi* to go to the *Umhlanga*, the Reed Dance. The well-known Swazi tradition symbolically promoted Swazi cultural ideals about fertility, chastity and womanhood. Only virgins could take part, dressed in special costumes to dance, sing and walk great distances to gather reeds for the queen mother. My parents, an American urologist from New York, the Cameroonian, the Ghanaian and three other southern African doctors stood side by side snapping digital photos as the *timbali*, or flowers of the nation, performed their annual harvest dances for the king.

I decided not to join in. Given everything, I could not bear to be surrounded by countless joyful, topless girls. I told the team I needed to rest and drove past the royal grounds in Lobamba as the volunteers' *kombi* turned in. From the road, I watched a tremendous dust cloud puff out and spread across Ezulwini Valley, presumably from the tens of thousands of bare feet stomping the earth. The car window open, I heard the low vibrating hum of all the girls singing in unison. Later, a *Times of Swaziland* journalist wrote that the girls sang of circumcision, praising the boys who had been brave enough to go under the knife.

My mom loved it. To her, the Reed Dance was an unselfconscious delighting in the beauty of the female form, a celebration of all its shapes and sizes. As American women barraged our whole lives with a very specific ideal of thinness and conformity, we had no cultural equivalent. I found her interpretation touching and chose not to tell her that many (generally urban and educated) Swazis kept their girls far away from the *Umhlanga*, and that every year the soldiers tasked with protecting the *timbali* were rumored to assault them. Plus, during this annual event, the king sometimes chose a new teenage bride.

These customs did not sit well with me. I was aware of the need for cultural relativism, but I was also a women's health practitioner and a feminist. I could not help but observe how rough it was to be a female in the Kingdom, and not just because, once a year, you might be expected to dance topless in a tiny beaded skirt before your king, a flower for the plucking.

For starters, as a Swazi woman, your life expectancy at birth is forty-seven years. There is a 30 percent chance that you will grow up an orphan and the same likelihood that you will be sexually abused by age eighteen. By the time you're married, lots of people will think that your husband has the right to beat you at will (according to one study, about 40 percent of Swazi women and nearly as many men believed that there were circumstances under which hitting a partner is justified). According to customary law, the only acceptable reasons for you to refuse sex in marriage are sickness, menstruation, or imminent or recent childbirth. Also according to Swazi law and custom, as a woman, you cannot acquire land; only your husband, male relatives, or male children can do that. You cannot divorce under any conditions, but you can be legally evicted for a host of infractions including adultery, witchcraft, or the inability to produce sons.

Then there's the whole sharing-your-man-with-other-women thing. Adam's older brother Jaco, who wanted me to understand all things Swazi in order to most effectively do my job, tried to explain it. He walked me through the Swazi idioms meant to illustrate men's natural, normal need for more than one woman. The list was lengthy.

Indvodza ayihlafuni ngamhlatsi munye. Men don't have only one side of the jaw for chewing.

Umfati ukhetfwa eliningini. A wife is chosen from among many women.

Indvodza lichatsa kuyalunyiswana. A man is like meat – you share it.

Shukela wekwebiwa umnandzi. Stolen sugar is nice. (The 'sugar' here was a euphemistic reference, per Jaco, to 'a wife's pussy.')

It didn't stop there. To the lot in life for Swazi women, add the frightening risk of HIV. The epidemic disproportionally affected women. Of the 200,000 Swazis living with HIV, 110,000 of them were women. By the time you were pregnant, you had a 40 percent chance of being infected. And if you didn't want to get pregnant in the first place, you wouldn't have much of a choice about how to handle it. Abortion was illegal.

I wasn't a Swazi woman.

***

I had unfair advantages and extra resources. I could make a decision. And I did. My first stop was a private clinic, the Mbabane Clinic. Once ushered into the consultation room, I told the doctor exactly what prescriptions I needed: mifepristone and misoprostol. I listed the dosages. I thought that if I spoke the language of medicine she would see me as a colleague. I thought that maybe she knew what it was like to beat her own head against a rock and a hard place. I was wrong. The doctor – a South African woman with a buzz cut – glared. 'I cannot give you those drugs,' she said. 'It is illegal.' She scribbled something and closed a file. She handed me a slip of paper to take to reception. It was the bill for my visit, which had lasted all of about four minutes.

I remembered something I'd heard as a midwife in Kibo Hospital in Tanzania. There, women knew how to mix the root of the henna with the root of the papaya to make a concoction that pulled the fragile tendrils of a fetus up from the loamy lining of the womb. But if a woman was caught – literally red-handed – digging up the roots of the henna plant, she would be imprisoned. Then there was something that I'd read in the *Mail* and the *Guardian*: a South African midwife wrote that it was easier for her patients to say that they are living with HIV than to admit that they'd had an abortion.

Of course, that didn't mean that abortion didn't happen in Tanzania. Or South Africa. Or in the Kingdom. In Swaziland, you needed only to look in the classified pages of the *Times of Swaziland*. Among allegedly successful treatments for 'job lack,' 'weak erection,' 'enlarging the bull,' 'virginal fluid,' 'bring back lost lovers,' 'return bewitches to sender,' ad after ad promised ambiguous 'womb cleansing' services. Unsurprisingly perhaps, in Swaziland, abortion-related complications were one of the leading causes of death for women of reproductive age. The newspaper ran a story about a young mother who had died after inserting weevil tablets into her vagina, trying to rid herself of an unwanted pregnancy. It made me think of bloody crochet hooks. It made me think of the issue of *Newsweek* magazine that showed up at our house when I was a kid and the troubled look on my mom's face when I asked her what the word abortion meant. I can still see the cover in my mind's eye: a picture of a floating fetus.

I would need to go to South Africa. I called to make the appointment from the frigid bathroom in the back of our new office. 'Do you offer terminations?' I asked. When I was helping to provide them, we never used the word abortion outright.

After being led on a wild goose chase of private providers who did not offer what I sought, I reached an NGO in South Africa well known for the service. The woman on the phone told me that I did not need an appointment. 'We close at three, just get here before then,' she said.

During the two-hour drive to Nelspruit, South Africa, on the Saturday morning after the big Back to School circumcision campaign ended and my parents left, I asked Adam if he'd ever read the J. M. Coetzee book *Disgrace*. My situation, and the landscape, made me think of it: the parched dirt and brambly shrubs of the savannah, the lightning that flashed across an entire horizon. Adam hadn't read it. Nevertheless, ever a patient man, he waited while I presented the basic plot outline. 'The professor's lesbian daughter gets raped by three local guys and ends up pregnant. And she decides to keep the baby,' I summarized.

With his soft brown eyes on the road, Adam knitted his forehead, puzzled. I guess the words had a ring of hope. They suggested to him that maybe I would still change my mind. I had been conflicted for days before making a final decision to terminate, a decision he didn't agree with. But I'd made up my mind, and now I was caught up in the improbability of certain decisions: a raped lesbian farmer has reasons to get an abortion, a thirty-three-year-old foreign aid worker with a decent paycheck and a supportive partner does not.

We were silent for a long time after that. Out the window, the reeds swayed gently as the wind blew over them. I took in the hills and the distant lakes, the spectacular scenery of Africa, and, as happened sometimes, grew overwhelmed. How had I arrived in this place, with this man, my life consumed by this impossible project? Of all the outlandish possible futures I'd dreamed of as a fanciful kid, even I didn't possess the imagination to come up with this one.

The clinic was in a part of Nelspruit that I had never seen during our weekend shopping trips out of Swaziland. We had to stop several times to ask for directions. Each turn led us deeper into a noisy, dusty, burglar-barred maze of back streets and hawking vendors, the cluttered sidewalks dotted with the shapes of homeless bodies lumpy under polyester blankets. When we finally saw the modest clinic sign, I panicked. 'Do you think it's safe to leave the car here?' I asked Adam. He told me to bring my bag and anything else of value inside.

Adam held my hand as we walked into the reception area where a bored receptionist was filing her nails. She barely looked up when we entered, did not make eye contact as she handed me a clipboard. She asked for the money up front. I told her that I wanted the pills, not the surgery.

She said, 'You can only make that decision based on your ultrasound.'

'Fine,' I told her, 'but I know that it's been eight weeks since my last period.'

She did not think pills were the way to go.

'It's a very minor procedure. It will be done in ten minutes. You can go back home and everything will be over.' This was nearly identical to what we told prospective circumcision patients.

'But you don't offer pain medication on a Saturday afternoon,' I said. I'd done my research; without a physician on-site, they only gave something called vocal local, which was supposed to be analgesia by way of a soothing voice and a soft touch.

'You've had a pap smear, haven't you? It's no worse than that,' she countered. 'All these girls today, they did it.'

'Then they must be stronger than I am.' Given what I had seen and heard in the course of my professional life, I knew that what she had just told me was complete and utter bullshit.

'Well… you cannot be a child for this,' she replied. 'For this, you must be a mama.'

The statement gave me chills.

A young Indian pharmacist at a chemist down the road, a place we'd stopped while searching for the clinic, had told Adam in whispering confidence, 'This isn't like where your girl comes from. They'll be rough with her. Here... give her this. I won't charge you for it.'

When he got back to the car where I'd been waiting, Adam handed me a tiny white tablet. Valium. I put the pill in my mouth. Before the hard gulp of a dry swallow, I thought – irrationally, given what I was about to do – 'Wait, which drug class is diazepam? Might this hurt my baby?'

Adam and I sat down on two plastic chairs in the cramped waiting area. The clinic gave the impression that it was still under construction. The drywall did not fully meet the ceiling, leaving a six-inch margin at the top over which sound freely traveled. Everything – the structure itself, the furniture, the minimal decorative touches – looked cheap and impermanent, yet a photograph of the clinic's founder hung front and center above the receptionist's desk. She was a London lady, prim and proper in the century-old black-and-white photo. In my mind, she claimed her place in a pantheon beside Clara Barton, Mary Breckenridge and Margaret Sanger – nursing legends. I was supposed to be on their side of the fence, I thought – glossed in a patina of modest reserve, quiet industry and fearless compassion – not on this side, cold and miserable in a cost-contained clinic, listening to stereos blaring dance music and the polyglot shouting of faceless men outside an iron door.

It was nearly three o'clock. There were twenty-three names above mine on the sign-in list. The trashcans were full. A thick red plastic bag, knotted at the top, sat beyond the waiting area. From my time on the other side of this equation, I knew the extent of the gore inside it.

We were not alone in the waiting room. Two girls sat

directly across from us. I put them at fifteen or sixteen years old. One was leaner than the other, but they both wore skinny jeans and sparkling eye makeup, and they absently flipped through glossy magazines picked up from the low-slung table in front of us.

Adam rubbed my hands to warm them and stared straight ahead. I felt nauseous. I asked him if we had a bottle of water in the car. He seemed ignore me, until I realized that, aided by a perfect ear for Zulu, he was absorbed in the girls' conversation.

I had mistakenly assumed that one girl was a patient and the other a supportive friend. Not so, Adam told me later as he recounted their conversation, they had only just met and they were both at the clinic for terminations. I wondered at the circumstances. However difficult I felt mine to be, I calculated theirs to be worse. Perhaps because they didn't know each other, perhaps because they were nervous and needed to fill the air with talk, the girls were discussing us. 'Do you think she is really here for the same thing?' one asked.

'It has to be. But look at her. She's so old, why would she need to do this? Maybe she is having an abortion because she knows it will not be a white baby? Maybe her family can't accept that?' hypothesized the other girl.

'But how do you even know that's the father? Eish, *sisi*, he's probably just here to escort her.'

'But he's holding her hand. He has to be her boyfriend.'

'Okay, you might be right. But can you believe he would come here to support her? Colored men must be different. A black man just gives you the money and says, "Deal with it."'

They both giggled when she said this. At the time, I didn't know why they were laughing, but it felt inappropriate, irreverent, the way it used to when the doctor and nurse-anesthetist in New Haven played their favorite oldies, 'Sitting by the Dock of the Bay' and 'Bernadette,' humming along throughout an entire morning of abortions.

When it was my turn, a Zulu nurse-midwife led me to an exam room. The metal stirrups, on thick metal poles, were raised so high from the table that the set-up had an air of gymnastic equipment. The apathetic midwife, dressed in a uniform of navy sweater and a white skirt, limited conversation to the facts. After twenty-three cases, her vocal local was wearing thin.

A vaginal ultrasound confirmed that the dates were as I expected. She agreed to the pills, telling me I must take the first one before I left the clinic and the other three – which would melt into the mucous membranes of my gums slowly over a half an hour – after I got home.

The six hours in which I passed the 'products of conception,' or POCs as we used to call them, were surreal. I vomited so profusely that I brought up the paracodeine tablets they'd given me whole and untouched. The chilled tiled floor of Little Rock's palatial bathroom was my only source of relief. When I wasn't doubled over cramping, emptying liquid shit into the toilet, or puking into a trash can, I lay on the tiles in the fetal position, feverish, convulsing and stripped naked. When Adam tried to give me a smoothie, I barked that I would just puke it up. He retreated to the porch, rejected and grieving. I counted the passing seconds. The pain required a concentration so fierce that I could not speak. This, the midwife in me thought with absolute clarity, is labor.

A week or so later, I Skyped Erin. 'Sad news, I miscarried.' It didn't feel like a lie. I chose to remember it as an involuntary loss.

'I am so sorry to hear that,' she responded. 'Remember, it's really common. You can definitely go on to have a normal pregnancy. I'm sure the stress isn't helping.'

I sent my mom an email that said, 'I am no longer pregnant.' I asked her not to speak of it again, to anyone. By then, my parents were home, wowing other suburban retirees with stories about Swaziland, the weird, the wild and the wonderful.

'You make the best decision you can with the information you have at hand,' I would tell those few New Haven patients racked with regret at their two-week follow-up visit. Anchors of grief lodged upon their hearts. Now I had my own. It's an indescribably complex tangle of emotions. I'd be lying if I didn't admit that the most pronounced thing I felt in the immediate aftermath of the abortion was relief. It simplified things, returned life to the status quo.

In the midst of this, another birthday passed. Thirty-four years old – the same age as Florence Nightingale when she hired up a crew of thirty-eight nurses and elbowed her way into the hellhole of the Crimean War to save soldiers and revolutionize a profession. What was I doing with my life? Had I really done this for the ASI? For the cause? For my career?

Somewhere along the line, I'd decided the splitting cells were female. Would she have had Adam's cupid bow lips or my thin ones? Would her eyes have been my green or his brown? Who would she have favored with her pronunciation of tomato, or potato, or water? Would our child have been an analytical introvert like me or a gabby friend-to-all like him, or something entirely brand-new at which we could only marvel in amazement? Was letting go of the possibility of her life a plausible trade-off for the lives we would save with the ASI?

I sat on Little Rock's veranda, sipping Earl Grey tea and taking in the woodsy smell of brush burning. Just on the edge of the westerly horizon, a blazing bushfire licked the violet sky. It was cold, now, and dark early. I watched the ball of sun descend and imagined her seashell fingernails and the springy curls of her hair. Eventually, Adam asked me to stop talking about it. 'It hurts too much that you didn't want our baby,' he said. The word 'our' broke me. For someone so deathly afraid of permanence, I had finally done something irreversible, something that could not be corrected or erased clean.

'We'll have another chance,' I told him. 'When the ASI is over.' Yes, when 152,000 foreskins were eradicated and 88,000 lives saved, after I had done my part, proved my worth. Then I would put my own real life first.

33

Although I couldn't forget, I also didn't wallow. Adam and I used different devices – mine work, his weed – to cope. Still, slowly, over the next few weeks and months, we found our way back to each other. Things started to settle. It had been so tumultuous: the return of the ex, my parents' visit, the forgotten pills, the trip to Nelspruit, a wildly successful campaign that circumcised over 7,000 Swazi boys in three weeks. By the time October arrived, we held hands as we waited in line to buy steaming coffees at the café in the new mall. A careful optimism appeared, a hopefulness, like the first springtime daffodils after a particularly brutal winter. And, in fact, it was spring in the southern hemisphere. October: when the sun intensifies and the first rainclouds gather, when a dry, burned earth readies herself for relief.

Finally, Adam and I had the energy to make plans, to address decisions as two levelheaded adults. We were ready to laugh again, to get excited about something. Adam's usual levity returned. I kind of thought he was kidding when he told me he wanted to get circumcised himself. I thought it was part of the new, tentative jokiness.

But no. He was completely serious. In fact, once he had

made the decision, he talked about it all the time. Like he'd decided to get a piercing or a tattoo, like it was a body modification statement. But he also talked about it like he was taking up recycling or buying Fair Trade coffee: circumcision as virtue signaling.

In our lives, dominated about 90 percent of the time by the surgical removal of foreskins, I guess the state of his own was bound to come up eventually. I genuinely did not care one way or another. That extra tissue neither grossed me out nor turned me on. But long before he'd met me, and long before any research supported it, and despite the fact that the overwhelming majority of Swazis were uncircumcised, Adam didn't like the way things looked down there. Relentlessly hygienic, somewhere along the line he'd picked up the idea that it was better, cleaner to be without. Now the perfect opportunity had arrived; our relationship promised him the safest, highest-quality circumcision that a tad of influence could get.

He stuck his head into the office of my colleague Morris one afternoon when picking me up from work. 'Hey, Dr. M, I'm finally going to do it!' Adam told him.

'Do what?' Morris asked, looking up from his keyboard.

Adam turned two fingers into a pair of scissors and made an air snip.

'Hey!' Morris said in his chuckling low growl, shaking Adam's hand in a manly way. 'Tell me when, and I'll do the procedure myself!'

'Wow, babe,' I turned to Adam, 'Take him up on that offer. This man is a veritable plastic surgeon.' Which was true. By then, Morris had surgically severed thousands of southern African foreskins.

In his whirlwind of circumcising enthusiasm, Adam went straight to his brother in Manzini, Jaco, a forty-one-year-old cop with the rare reputation for being incorruptible, and got him on board the circumcision train. Like Adam, Jaco said he had always wanted to get it done. Now was the time! They whooped and hugged. If you didn't know any better, you'd have thought they were planning some testosterone-fueled boys' bonding outing – a Karoo hunting trip or a Maputo beer-and-strippers Bro-zambique weekend.

The fact that Adam and his brother were getting snipped was something of a circumcision coup. We'd struggled to get anyone over the age of twenty anywhere near a surgical bed, and here were two 'mature' Swazi guys, and brothers at that, ready and willing to serve themselves up as poster children for the circumcision campaign in the critical days leading up to the start of the ASI. I thought for sure we could get some press coverage. I called our National Male Circumcision Coordinator, Clara's right-hand man and our link to the Swazi Ministry of Health, to give him the scoop. He immediately contacted both national newspapers where we got no traction whatsoever.

In New York, a person in my demographic – college-educated, mid-thirties, left-leaning – might take a few minutes during her subway ride into work to swipe through the *New York Times* on her iPad. In Mbabane, a person in that same demographic rubbernecked from the window of her own car or a *kombi* to catch the newspaper headlines posted on telephone poles alongside Golf Course Road. It was a parade of scandal: 'Deaf Miss Swaziland falls pregnant!', 'Man accused of raping sugar mama's daughter!' In a country of a million people, there was likely a shortage of both hard-nosed journalists and serious news topics. In response, both papers took the tabloid route.

'Sorry, Laura,' our MC Coordinator reported back, 'they claim that there's been too much circumcision coverage lately.'

Yes, there had been a lot of coverage, just not particularly objective or balanced coverage. For example, when we'd delayed paying our nurses from the Back to School campaign by ten days – due to a glitch in accounting back at headquarters – you'd better believe I got contacted by a *Times* reporter. I had immediately notified our MC Coordinator, to warn him. Then, I woke my boss Erin at 4 a.m. Half a dozen HQ staff went into a tizzy of frantic untying of red tape to expedite the payments. I spent a harrowing forty-eight hours wondering if I was about to lose my job and/or see my name posted on a Swazi telephone pole. Thankfully, the article never ran. However, when, just after Back to School, three boys from the southern town of Nhlangano claimed that they were left high and dry on the roadside while suffering serious adverse events post-circumcision, it made the front page. And now? Two middle-aged biracial Swazi brothers psyched to lose their foreskins? Well, we just had to accept that this was not considered news.

Accepting such things was all part of the careful tiptoeing we foreigners practiced in the Kingdom. Our marketing guys knew these unspoken rules too. Everything needed to look, sound, and feel authentically Swazi. For instance, only a Swazified moniker would capture the hearts and minds of the nation. The ASI acronym had to go. So, while Adam prepped for surgery, our team met with representatives from the Ministry of Health and supporting government bodies at the out-of-the-way Maguga Lodge to hash out the communications strategy and settle on a suitable new name. The group came up with Soka Uncobe, which, loosely translated, meant Circumcise and Conquer.

Shortly thereafter, Adam and Jaco set their surgery dates, ready to be among the first in their age group to Circumcise and Conquer. In mid-October, when the day came, the brothers, so close in age and appearance that they were easily mistaken for each other, put on their game faces. We all headed out to the Litsemba Letfu Men's Clinic in the Big Tree Shopping Complex in Matsapha. Jaco came in his police uniform, official cap and everything, just in case the paparazzi turned up after all. Later, I learned that Jaco asked one of the surgical runners to film his circumcision with his cell phone, a gory clip he planned to post on YouTube. If the press would not come to him, then he would take his penis to the masses himself!

Adam and Jaco approached the reception desk to sign in. I felt puffed up and famous because I knew everyone. Well, at least most of the staff. 'Hi, Violet,' I said to the tiny woman behind the reception desk. 'Give these guys your most special treatment, okay?'

Litsemba Letfu was a shining beacon for circumcision in southern Africa. It was one of five 'baseline' circumcision sites that ran year-round. The clinical team was friendly and welcoming. They followed every infection prevention measure to the letter. There was TV in the waiting room. It was not 'sustainable.' Every penny for gauze, operating tables, forceps, autoclaves, salaries, uniforms, even the tea in the staff break room, was sponsored by an American foundation and, later, by the US government. If the donors pulled out, Litsemba Letfu's branded doors would close forever.

When Adam, Jaco and I walked in, the place was crawling with lanky teenagers, baggy jeans sitting way down on their hips and all manner of metal chains extending from belt loops and around necks. You could tell who was pre-procedure, and who was post. The distinctive shuffling walk of the just circumcised: a bow-legged, halting gait that made you wince.

We didn't have to wait long. Within about fifteen minutes, a shockingly young counselor stepped into the waiting room and called Adam's name from a printed list. I didn't recognize her. Must be new. She didn't make eye contact as she waved Adam and me to a back room, and she spoke at such a low decibel that I had to ask her three and four times to repeat herself. Maybe we, perhaps her first older couple, intimidated her. Perhaps her first couple, period, given how women rarely tagged along for the experience. I could also pretty much guarantee that I was the first white woman she had counseled.

I could feel the annoying, know-it-all tone creeping into my voice as I asked, 'What kind of HIV test kits do you use?' and 'How often do clients refuse testing?' Adam, on the other hand, was suddenly approaching the whole thing with extreme caution. He balled up his fists and shoved them into the pockets of his gray sweatpants. I watched the tendons on his forearms flex.

Then the counselor closed the door to our tiny exam room and prepared her materials for two HIV tests. Since we had both been tested only a few months earlier, this should not have provoked anxiety on either of our parts. Yet it did. When the counselor did not put on plastic gloves to prick our fingers for the rapid HIV tests, Adam gave me the stink-eye. I knew he was wondering about the quality of care he was about to receive. I was wondering the same thing. Was what I professed about the safety of this whole thing – the no-big-deal-ness – really true?

The testing done and the results given – thank God, no surprises there – the counselor commenced her automated circumcision speech. Again, I had to ask her to raise her voice, something she seemed physically incapable of. She stared at the painted cement block wall. From a small folding table to her left, strewn with papers and medical consumables, she picked up one of our plastic penis education models. It must have been part of the stash just released from the storage unit at the airport. Holding the model, she said in a child's whisper, 'The doctor will remove the skin over the head of the penis,' while she steadily drummed the model against the palm of her other hand.

'You must be sure to clean the area with fresh water and mild soap every day,' she said, still tap-tapping the penis against her palm, 'and you must refrain from sex for six weeks after the procedure.'

'What happens if it gets hard – you know, afterward? Won't that be terribly sore?' Adam asked her, all serious and focused attention.

The poor girl squirmed, increasing the nervous pace of her plastic penis-slapping. 'You'll have to ask the nurse.'

The nurse was Lucas, a gap-toothed Zimbabwean with ebony skin and the build of a linebacker. He was one of the best nurses in the program. He wore a set of spotless aquamarine scrubs and a stethoscope around his neck, every bit the first-class professional. Repeatedly, our visiting volunteer doctors singled him out as exemplary. It turned out that he was exemplary on multiple levels. In the downtime after Back to School II, Lucas was also circumcised. Adam took to him straight away and asked all the anxious questions that had so perplexed our model-slapping counselor: when can I go jogging again; when can I go back to work; what about stairs; what position should I sleep in; will I get medication; is it true what they say about the sex being better afterward?

Lucas carefully answered them all, but deferred on the last one. He was still in the six-week post-surgical window, but, he said with a mischievous smile, he certainly hoped the rumors were true.

'So, Lucas,' I asked him, 'what should I do for him to help him during the healing period? Cook him his favorite foods?'

Adam raised his eyebrows, as if to say, wouldn't that be a nice change.

Lucas said, 'Yes, you can cook.' And then he thought about it a bit more. 'And when he tries to get close to you,' he added, 'push him away!' Lucas laughed. 'This is the only time you are allowed to push him away!' Then Lucas, concluding his physical exam – having identified no signs of infection and/or malformation – cleared Adam for surgery.

We stepped out of our exam room at the same time that Jaco stepped out of his. Adam's brother was practically bouncing off the walls with his hands in the air. 'Hey, bru!' Jaco shouted to Adam. 'Negative, my brother!' he said. They hugged big bear backslapping man-hugs.

With the first big hurdle down, next up was the snip. Systems were finely tuned at Litsemba Letfu. A guy wasn't given a lot of time to sit around and deliberate once he'd been counseled and cleared. Adam and his brother were whisked away into conjoined bays in the surgical ward.

A part of me wanted to watch the procedure. A larger part of me did not. I had seen plenty of circumcisions and didn't need to watch this one for educational value. Plus, Adam didn't want me there. This wasn't like a delivery room, he said, where partners were encouraged to receive the baby and cut the cord. This was supposed to be assembly line surgery, as quick and emotionless as a Ford plant.

I imagined how it would go…

First, Nurse One would carefully wash Adam's groin before covering him with a green O-hole drape. Then, Nurse Two would make small talk with him while injecting a local anesthesia to deaden the nerves that fed his most tender flesh. Adam would shut his eyes tight through three, four, five bee-sting jabs. 'That was the worst part,' Nurse Two would tell him, and he'd relax.

They would wait a few minutes to let the drug kick in while Nurse One tore the sealed lid from the disposable circumcision pack and prepared the instruments on a tray. Then our Dr. Morris would step up to the plate, affix two forceps on either side of his delicate foreskin, and use the instruments to pull the thin tissue away from his body. Afterward, Morris would draw an incision line with a purple surgical pen, replace the pen with a scalpel, and start the careful sawing of the skin. Droplets of blood would form and grow as vessels opened.

Nurse One would dab at them, and then apply the hot tip of the cautery pencil. Adam would hear the quick buzz and sizzle. He would blink his eyes closed again. 'Almost done,' Nurse Two would say, as Morris tied the knots on the first four stiches, and then Nurse Two circled back around to add another couple of sutures between each of the doctor's. Finally, Nurse One would bandage up the wound with gauze and adhesive tape. She would unroll a pair of MoliPants and help Adam wriggle into them. 'All done!' she would pronounce.

It was starting to actually dawn on me – as stupid as it sounds – that this was real surgery. On someone that I loved. It wasn't like a routine trip to the dentist, which is what we often likened it to. I felt kind of nervous, and useless. So I walked to King Pie and bought the brothers some beef and mushroom pies and Cokes to wash down their painkillers in the recovery room.

I had an idea in the waiting room. What about wristbands to promote the campaign? I texted Clara. 'I like it,' she wrote back. 'A guy can't exactly whip out his wiener to show everyone how badass he is... but what if he could wear his circumcision status on his wrist?' She'd ask the marketing team in Johannesburg to place a massive order for bright orange wristbands. We'd litter the country with them, hoping the boys would do our advertising for us.

After we got home, Adam was sore and swollen, and he

moped around the house in a sad pair of holey sweatpants. Our shy housekeeper, Buhle, who normally never inserted herself into our personal lives, had pulled me aside to ask how he'd been injured. A few days later, when he went back to work, his friends teased him. Actually, they did more than tease him. They scolded him. These were the energy healers and homeopaths with whom he worked. They suggested that the circumcision was further proof that I had Adam, so to speak, by the balls. 'Why would you do that?' Annie, the waifish English Reiki healer, asked angrily. 'Don't you know that you've just handicapped your ability to experience full orgasm?'

These comments catapulted Adam into a period of short-lived regret. It passed and was replaced by something like pride. Healing well, Adam showed up at my office one day at lunchtime with my homemade lunch in a Tupperware container. Morris asked how he was feeling.

'I'm feeling okay,' Adam said with uncharacteristic shyness.

'So what made you decide to finally go for it?' Morris asked.

'You guys are doing so much for this country. I just wanted to show my support,' Adam told him.

At this, our Ugandan princess of a program assistant, Roberta, the one who'd camped outside the Nursing Council to recruit every warm body available for Back to School and who was prone to unapologetic eavesdropping, said loudly enough for the whole office to hear her, 'Laura, I hope you can see how much that man loves you.'

It was true, and it prompted a realization. Decisions that strike the cringe-tender flesh below the belt are not the result of cool, dispassionate deliberation. They are made in pursuit of the sweet forehead kiss of approval – from society, from family, from the object of one's desire. This is what Adam taught me as we rushed headlong into the ASI: men will not part with part of themselves for just disease prevention or health promotion.

Their reasons are more visceral than cerebral. They will do it for camaraderie, for belonging. They will do it to demonstrate courage, to fit in, to please. If Jaco's circumcision was a gesture of brotherhood, then I believe Adam's was a gutsy and wordless way to say... I am trying to do what is right. I am giving what I am able. I am here beside you and we are in this together.

Two weeks out, he and Jaco compared notes over the phone. Jaco was optimistic and enthusiastic. Jaco had never, in his entire adult life, gone fourteen days without sex. It was like a fasting ritual for a monk. He was having a spiritual experience, he said; his whole life had changed. He told everyone 'the car was in the shop for a tune-up,' that he was 'pimping his ride.'

Adam and I were pretty smug about the advised six weeks of abstinence too. We knew the rules. As one of my Swazi colleagues always said in reference to the healing period, 'You can't expect to eat meat immediately after you've had a tooth repaired, now can you?' I was sure that would be a breeze.

But after three weeks, everyone was getting antsy. Neither of the brothers lasted a month. I lied when people asked me about it. I had to – I was a nurse and a public health professional managing a circumcision program, you think I was going to admit to cheating on the mandatory abstinence period? I rationalized it. Six weeks was a conservative estimate for couples at risk of transmitting HIV. We felt that we did not fall into that camp. But it did beg the question: if we – who knew so much better – couldn't last, how did we expect anyone else to?

In our defense, part of the reason it was so difficult to go without sex for six weeks after circumcision was because of the killer curiosity. We were not allowed to say that sex was better post-circumcision. Scientists are squeamish. The marketing guys, on the other hand, were anything but. 'If we were selling shampoo or a health drink,' the marketers would say, 'we could play the sex card. How is this any different?'

But with HIV-preventative circumcision – an intervention that had everything to do with sex – promoting better sex was off limits. Still, conventional wisdom held that men 'lasted longer' after circumcision because of the toughening of previously protected tissue, and that women were more satisfied as a result. Now, we would be able to apply some real data to this theory.

I hate to say it, but from my end, I couldn't really appreciate a difference. The brothers Van Rensburg disagreed. Both of them claimed that, from a male perspective, sex was definitely better without a foreskin. When asked, Jaco would flex his bicep and say, 'Stronger than ever!' But Jaco's wife was with me. When her husband was out of earshot she said, 'It's a lot of fuss over nothing. We women have better things to think about.' Not yet thirty, she fought hard to feed the five kids she and Jaco were raising and to keep them in school. To her, all the circumcision nonsense was just so much background noise. HIV – the raison d'être of so many Americans in Swaziland – had surely affected her life in countless ways, but it was not her most immediate problem.

However, we knew enough to protect our men's pride. The ASI marketing guys were the first to ask. By then, they had resuscitated Jaco's bid at celebrity with half-page ASI advertisements, including a handsome photo, in both papers. Just in from Johannesburg, they leaned over my desk to maintain some degree of privacy around the subject. 'So, how is it?' they whispered and winked. I gave them the thumbs-up.

34

Christmas 2010 called forth basic questions of survival. The sun blazed with a relentless ferocity. Everything – insects, dogs, snakes, people – shifted from one shady spot to another, thirsty and unhurried. Build It sold out of electric fans. Adam and I lay on the tile floor in front of our veranda in the middle of the day, still and sweating, grateful for the inexplicable cool that the rocks in our house maintained year-round. The month-long 'festive season' and the extreme heat prompted a sort of nationwide stupor. Our office closed mid-December along with everything else.

Contractual delays had slowed Solomon's proposed ASI timeline in an American snarl of paperwork and approvals that contradicted the message of urgency our email proclaimed daily. The timeline for Clara's proposed 'surges' had long passed. But, on 30 November, Clara's organization finally signed a contract with the US government to fund the ASI. Her NGO, one that had never previously led circumcision work anywhere, would be the prime for this historic project.

Given the timing, Clara and I both decided that we would stay in the Kingdom over the holidays to work. Our Swazi colleagues were drinking beer and eating roasted meat with their families. And most Swazi-based foreigners were luxuriating on a Mozambican beach or riding around Kruger Park counting the Big Five. We didn't feel we could lose such valuable planning time.

Therefore, I spent Christmas Day with Adam and Clara, my stand-in Swazi family. In the polygamous Kingdom, Clara often referred to herself as Adam's second wife. When asking after him, she would say, 'How's our husband?' It was a little weird, but that was Clara. When we showed up at Clara's place on Christmas evening, Adam embraced her, as was his habit. 'You give the best hugs,' she said to him in a way that suggested she badly needed them. To me, she winked, and said, 'And how are you, doe eyes?'

By then, Clara lived in Ezulwini Valley, the heavenly green and fertile base of the Malagwane Hill. There, she'd found a huge building on a sprawling, flowered property that could be converted into an open-plan Soka Uncobe workspace. Clara imagined outdoor staff *braais* and working weekends spent by the pool. Once a furniture warehouse, the big building needed an overhaul – floors repaired, desks purchased, air-con installed, separate male and female toilets added. Now that ASI cash was finally flowing, workers were paid overtime to push through the festive season so that we could get down to immediate circumcising business in the new year. Clara lived about twenty steps away from the Hub's front door in a wooden cottage with a thatched roof. The arrangement would allow her to work constantly, something she already did, answering emails and Skype messages at 3 a.m. For her, there would be no separation between work and home. For the next year, the project would be her life.

When Adam and I arrived around dinnertime for our Christmas sushi feast – because, what the hell, two Americans stuck in a suffocating landlocked Kingdom and itchy with summertime insects can imagine a Christmas feast as they please – she was keen to show off the progress on the office space. She ushered us inside the swinging workshop door. I quickly realized, however, she actually wanted to reveal something else. On the far wall, taped against a spot earmarked for a massive whiteboard, she'd drawn a brick chimney onto a single piece of flipchart paper. Underneath, on the newly installed shiny floorboards, sat two sandwich baggies full of Christmas chocolate, which, by the time we arrived, had melted into a gooey mess.

That was typical Clara, but when had she had time? The day before, we'd put in a fourteen-hour workday. She'd picked me up before 6 a.m., handed me a peanut butter sandwich and said, 'You're the navigator!' as she dropped a map from a Swaziland tourist magazine in my lap. On it, she'd marked a hundred possible circumcision sites with little red asterisks. We'd been researching sites for months, but hadn't physically visited them. Our goal was to weed out the clear rejects – clinics with poor road access, without water or toilets, or without enough space. It was definitely not a task two American technical advisors should have spent their Christmas Eve carrying out. The government should have led the site consideration process. The problem wasn't that we didn't know this. The problem was that government activities were effectively suspended from mid-December through mid-January, and with the ASI now slated to start in February, eight weeks away, Clara didn't see any other way.

Driving through reedy green stalks of sugar cane, the backbone of Swaziland's agricultural economy, Clara thought aloud: 'We need to find a way to reach all these seasonal cane cutters. These guys are mobile. They are away from their partners for long stretches of time. And they're grouped together, so they should be easy to access.' By then, the map was damp from absorbing my chin sweat as I puzzled over it. It was impossible to escape the Christmas sun, and there in the lowveld it was especially intense. But Clara was not wilting like I was; she was strategizing. 'We've got to think beyond schoolkids. Get creative. Identify the sugar daddies, the older guys who are infecting the young girls,' Clara said. I wondered if it was too late. What we'd found at one of the sugar company clinics was unbelievable: close to seventy-five percent of the clientele in the register were already infected.

Clara had been in good spirits. I think it was satisfying to her to feel movement – literal and programmatic. While riding in the car the day before, we had had perhaps our most personal conversation to date. She'd asked, 'You know how much I like Adam, but the thing we're all wondering is if you guys are in one of those semi-fucked-up expat-local relationships – I mean, no judgment, we've all been there – or if you guys are the real thing?'

'Real thing,' I'd said, 'I think…'

But overnight, something had changed. The professional relationship was back in front. While in her cottage preparing our Christmas feast – Adam starting a barbeque outside (sushi was fine, as a side dish, he decided, but on Christmas we'd need meat too), and Clara and I chopping carrots and cucumber – she said, 'Guess what I learned after we got back from our little holiday road trip?' She worked a knife hard and quick against a cutting board. Her voice had its own sharp edge. 'The supplies and equipment team never placed the order. Some of that stuff has a lead-time of three months or more. It's going to blow our timeline.'

'What?' A dark cloud formed and closed in like a swarm of mosquitoes. I thought of all the international volunteer doctors we'd booked. And before the government offices broke for the holidays, I'd met with Charity, now the Director of Nursing.

Together, we had reviewed the ASI timeline with nurse managers nationwide. Stephanie Silva had secured an unprecedented arrangement whereby we could 'hire' government-employed nurses during their scheduled leave time. The deal had required a special high-level exception from PEPFAR; it essentially meant that the US government was doubling these nurses' pay during their leave time. We agreed that such a compromise was necessary to meet the project's demand for nurses from within the country. Nurse Managers had already started aligning hundreds of nurses' schedules with the new Soka Uncobe campaign dates we had provided.

I looked at the ridiculous sticks of Krab, red-skinned tubes of off-white near-fish product found in Pick n Pay's freezer section. 'Why does this project have to suck so profoundly?' I asked. We were doing exactly what we had been told to do. Yet, if everything had to be bumped back again, we'd be the ones who looked disorganized and untrustworthy.

'Oh, and that's not all,' Clara continued. I steeled myself. 'Looks like we're not getting the prefabs in time, either.' The prefabs were the ready-made clinics we needed to extend geographic coverage to places without functional clinics. Clara peered over the top of her glasses at me, to gauge my reaction. I wondered whether this was a crisis worthy of contacting Erin on a holiday.

'Swaziland will not make us cry today. Not on fucking *Christmas*,' Clara said.

Adam came back inside and sensed the tension. He looked from me to Clara, and then said, 'Hang on a second.' I heard him close the car door. A minute later, he bounded up the front steps, his hands behind his back. 'Christmas presents!' he declared, and stretched his arms out to Clara, fingers wrapped into fists, as if he was performing a magic trick.

Clara looked down, slid her glasses up the bridge of her nose, and tapped his left hand. Adam flipped it over and opened his fingers to reveal the prize. It was a dried, hollowed-out gourd the size of a golf ball with one circular cutout on top and a smaller hole at the bottom. 'It's an *umcadvo*!' Adam said proudly. 'Traditional Swazi underwear!'

In the program, there was lots of talk about the *umcadvo*, and whether it got in the way, so to speak, of pro-circumcision messages. Difficult to acquire at other times of the year, they were in plentiful supply at Christmas when the annual *Incwala* ceremony – a sacred rite for the king and his male regiments – was underway. One admired the original purpose of the *umcadvo*: modesty and containment – to keep the business end of a guy's apparatus safely covered. Also, its carved inner edges were hard, unforgiving, kept a person in line.

Clara was thrilled with the gift. 'How did you get this?'

'While you guys were driving around the country yesterday, I went to my first *Incwala*.'

First adopted in the early 1800s at the birth of a unified Kingdom of Swaziland, the ceremony marked the symbolic binding of multiple clans into a single military machine to protect against the Zulus. Some aspects of the *Incwala* were shrouded in male privilege and secrecy. Others were spectacularly public: tens of thousands of warriors – extensions of the king – dancing the history of Swaziland back into being, bringing together the living and the dead to top up the king's power, the nation's power.

Adam had never before attended. Each year, as December approached and teenagers in animal skins and bright red fabrics, called *lihiya,* clustered along the Malagwane, his mother had tightened her grip on her biracial boys. She had feared the bullying groupthink of hormone-fueled adolescents turned warriors. Now, at forty, Adam had a reason to attend the ancient ceremony at the royal kraal, or cattle pen, in Lobamba: to search out gourd underwear for circumcision–obsessed Americans.

'So what's it like on the... inside,' I asked Adam, as I piled a plate full of oddly shaped sushi and blackened boerewors sausage.

Adam explained how he'd pulled up to the main gate to begin his quest. Idle much of the rest of the year, the royal grounds were abuzz with activity. Groups of men clustered in their regiment groups – joined by age, community of birth and clan name. Those regiments closest to the king, older Dlaminis, loitered in the grandstand. The younger regiments sang the slow chanting songs they'd been perfecting over the past few days.

Six police officers, tasked with protecting the sacred ceremonies, had asked Adam, 'What do you want?'

'Officers, where might I find some *umcadvo*?' Adam asked, politely, in siSwati.

A self-appointed ringleader stepped forward and sized Adam up. 'Are you circumcised?' he asked. 'Because you know that you can't wear an *umcadvo* if you are.'

Adam, barely eight weeks post-op, proudly announced his status to the group. Then told them about me.

The ringleader cop grew defiant. 'This circumcision thing is another trick brought to our country by foreigners!'

The other officers snickered. One giggled, but they all watched Adam carefully.

The ringleader continued, 'Yes, these foreigners brought HIV to this country, and now they want to experiment on us. Okay, okay... so you say your woman is one of them... I don't want to offend you, my brother. But Americans and Europeans are always testing their drugs in Africa. Haven't you heard? AIDS came from a vaccine that went wrong! Then, when they realized what they had done, they created an industry to treat it. And this circumcision project? It is the same thing! All the money they are pouring into HIV in this country should be spent dealing with poverty and unemployment issues, our real problems. No, *bhuti*, as for HIV, there is only one thing we can do to fix this AIDS thing. We need to turn to God.'

Adam considered how to be tactful. He sat quietly at dinner parties while we foreigners decried a local ignorance that fanned the flames of an epidemic. He also listened as loved ones questioned lab test results while nursing hacking coughs. He would need to be subtle, smart and Swazi about how he approached this. Addressing the ringleader, he said, 'Well, even if foreigners did bring HIV to this country, why do we now have the highest infection rate in the world?'

Now the officer was outright angry. 'But circumcision isn't even one hundred percent effective. What is the point of getting rid of my foreskin if I still have to use a condom? If you stick to one partner, you do not need any of this anyway. I stick to my wife.'

To this, a colleague said, 'You don't have a wife!' Another said, 'What woman would ever have sex with you?'

'*Hau!* Men, listen to me. The only answer is to follow God and to abstain. Because here is what happens, you all know: you go to see a woman and you come with a condom because you plan to be safe. You take the condom out of your pocket and put it on the table. This makes the woman relax because now she thinks you are a careful someone. Then you get caught up in the moment. You never even open the plastic. You are in the middle of it, and meanwhile, the condom is still on the table and it is looking at you and it is saying, "Why did you even bother to bring me to the party if you were just going to leave me sitting here?"'

One of the other cops took pity on Adam. 'Don't listen to

him,' the cop said. 'He's very stubborn.' The sidekick cops, it seemed, were sick of hearing their buddy rant. They pulled out packets of cigarettes, turned out of the way of the wind and cupped the flames. The youngest, lit cigarette in hand, asked Adam, 'So, what was it like? How painful, honestly, brother?'

'I won't listen to this nonsense,' the ringleader said. 'You want *umcadvo*? Go there.' He pointed at a wooden structure to the far side of the field.

The darkened interior of the hut was littered with stacks of animal skins. Slices of sunlight streamed through gaps in the wooden siding and illuminated items on tables and on the floor – claws, horns and bones. A traditionalist operated the place, ready for consultation should any of the regiments require wardrobe assistance. The traditionalist, who may have been a chief or a distant member of the royal family, was plump and dimpled. He invited Adam to sit, and asked him what he needed.

'I can't just give you an *umcadvo*, nephew,' the man said. 'I have to measure you, size the opening, and adjust the fit.'

This was a serious matter, not a bit of tourist kitsch. Swazis said that if the seeds of the cleaned and dried *umcadvo* were not burned after removal, the wearer would die.

'Yes, but, uncle,' Adam said, 'I will be giving these *umcadvo* to white people.'

'Ah!' the traditionalist exclaimed and smiled. 'In that case, it's fine! Our *muti* doesn't affect *mlungu*.' He reached behind a pile of baboon skins and pulled out a handful of spare *umcadvo*.

Adam pocketed them. 'But why?' He had a particular curiosity about this topic. If white people were immune to the traditional medicine that could kill Swazis, then what happened to someone like him, a double-brain who possessed within him both cultures?

'Well,' the traditionalist said, 'they do not understand our culture. The reason our *muti* works on Swazis is because the medicines are made from herbs and plants that are a part of this soil, the earth and the water that are only found here, in the same way that our ancestors and our sacred lineage also come from this very soil.'

'But what if you are like me? Half and half?'

'My son, it is for you to decide. You must know what part of you is dominant. You must be careful. We as a nation must be very careful. In these changing times, we cannot lose our cultural identity. Without this, what is left to define us as Swazis?'

In a very real way, the old man was afraid his country was losing its essential uniqueness, the source of its strength, afraid that it was dying. And not in the way that public health experts thought it was.

35

Whatever the old man at the *Incwala* said, as a species, we are programmed to survive. Any midwife working in a warzone can tell you this: life persists even during the toughest times. Humans are conceived and born in concentration camps, during floods, earthquakes, and in the midst of epidemics.

And so I learned that Buhle, our timid housekeeper, was pregnant around New Year's Eve. This was also around the time that the gas-powered grass-cutter disappeared from next door and our neighbors fired Clement, Buhle's husband, who worked for them as a gardener, with a fairly well-supported accusation of thievery. Clement's gambling problem was well known; he had a reputation for pinching odds and ends from the houses where he worked and then pawning them off to settle his debts.

Well, I should say that everyone knew this about Clement except for us. Adam and I didn't know squat. Mostly, we kept to ourselves. We didn't even really know our neighbors' names, aside from a few notable exceptions, like George the Architect (a friend-of-a-friend of Adam's, not to be confused with Talkative George, a different English guy living out a different midlife crisis a bit further down Pine Valley Road).

Our interactions with our neighbors mostly consisted of half-hearted waves from the inside of our car to the inside of theirs as we both slammed on the brakes and skittered along the dry brush on opposite sides of our narrow dirt road, a former cattle trail barely wide enough for two modern-day vehicles and interrupted by sharp turns around gigantic boulders. Although I guess we did know that several houses on the street shared staff. This was how we came to know Buhle after we moved into Little Rock.

A thin girl about twenty years old, Buhle would have been quickly overlooked were it not for her exceptional face. Buhle was beautiful, and she and I avoided each other completely. In her first weeks and months with us, I am not sure that she even knew my name. On the very rare occasions when she needed to address me, she called me *sisi*, sister. Generally, I preferred that Adam converse with her. She was obviously so much more at ease in siSwati than in English, I reasoned.

In truth, I was deeply uncomfortable with the fact that this attractive soft-spoken girl scrubbed my toilet, hand-washed my running shoes until they gleamed, stacked even my underwear in perfectly folded color-coordinated piles, and noted and mentally catalogued each and every quotidian detail of our domestic lives. Anytime we moved anything – a toothbrush, a plant, a dish, a box of tampons – it would find its way back to its original location. She knew what we ate for breakfast. And dinner. She knew how much we spent at Pick n Pay on fancy food, fancy shampoo and organic cleaning supplies.

I, on the other hand, didn't know that she was married, didn't know that her husband worked as a gardener for several houses on our street, didn't know that she had a three-year-old daughter, and didn't know that, underneath that arresting beauty, her life was a daily struggle to keep her family afloat.

But I quickly learned all of this when her husband stole the weed-whacker from next door and our neighbor fired him, and our landlady knocked on the back door of Little Rock to see if I would talk to Buhle. 'You're a midwife, right?'

Buhle was supposedly six months pregnant and not showing so much as the smallest baby bump. 'Can you please assess the situation?' my landlady asked with worry. And by assessing the situation, I knew our landlady meant the whole Clement stealing-and-gambling situation as much as she did the invisible pregnancy situation. This was not a job I wanted. But I dug underneath Little Rock's rickety ladder staircase, behind a few hand-me-down novels and pirated DVDs, to find my stethoscope: a $200, barely used 3M Littmann. By Friday, when I couldn't put it off any longer, I came home early and staged an intervention. Buhle was upstairs in our loft bedroom, putting away clean laundry. I took the ladder one rung at a time, with my stethoscope hanging from around my neck. As my head peered above the floorboards, Buhle lowered her eyes and greeted me. 'Hello, *sisi*,' she said.

'Hello, Buhle, how are you?' I asked as I seated myself on the end of the freshly made mattress. The windows were wide open. A gentle breeze passed through the faded army-green curtains and set them aflutter. Fresh floral smells blew in.

'Eh, *sisi*, I'm fine,' she answered, dragging the 'fine' out in a girly, sing-songy way. She did not stop her work – still putting away, still looking away, and still smiling a careful white smile toward a fraying reed mat.

'May I speak with you for a minute?' I asked. Never before had we sat down beside each other and talked like two grown women.

'It is about Clement, *sisi*?' she guessed, sparing me the circling in. Like me, she knew she was being talked about. No doubt boredom and pettiness watered the seeds of behind-the-back gossip in all tiers of Swazi society.

'Yes, I heard about what happened. I'm really sorry, Buhle.'

'He's not a bad man. He has a problem. I pray that God will help him get rid of this demon. But he is not a bad man.' There was emotion in her words, carefully controlled, and the smile still there, still wide, disguising a world of secrets.

I thought about the gambling. I thought about the drinking. I thought about the violence that probably accompanied them. 'Buhle, are you safe with him?'

She looked me in the eye for a split second, scanning my face. The arm that held Adam's folded jogging sweats dropped to her side. The smile waned at the corners. I wondered if she grasped what I was suggesting.

'He is not a bad man, *sisi*,' she said again. I decided that I would not push this.

'I also heard that you are pregnant?'

'Yes.' She subtly turned her torso toward the wardrobe.

'Do you know how far along you are?'

'I was drinking the family planning pills they gave me at the hospital, but it happened anyway. They told me I'm five months.'

Buhle burned hundreds of calories a day, scrubbing our floors, beating our mats, climbing the rocky path back and forth to the clothesline. We told her that she could help herself to anything in our fridge, to anything she wanted in the cupboard, but we never saw her eat. Later, I wondered if this had to do with a persistent first trimester nausea that would have coincided with her initial employment with us. But I also never saw her use the bathroom, never once heard a flush while she was cleaning. It was an exquisite shyness.

'Would it be all right if I examined your belly?' I asked. She responded with a sudden and unexpected eagerness. A moment of worry. What if I couldn't feel anything but the squishy gurgling inner tubes of her digestive tract and her own fast and steady pulse? What would I say then? But she'd already put down the laundry and lifted the bottom of a pink T-shirt. She'd already lowered the fragile curve of her vertebrae onto the clean sheet. Ah, there! A small mound on her lower abdomen, firm and secure and holding strong to the slightness of her hips.

'Do you feel the baby moving?' I asked.

'Oh, yes, *sisi*!' Buhle giggled toward the cobweb of mosquito net tied in a knot above the bed.

I tried and failed to identify baby parts with my very rusty Leopold's maneuvers; I cupped the top of the baby mound with one hand – a butt or a back? – and reached down below, to the fraying elastic at the top of her underwear, hoping to find the hard ball of the skull in the head-down position. All the while, I cooed and praised. This fetus, small for its age, was starting out with several significant strikes against it. Barely getting by on two tiny incomes, the family was now down to one.

I got Buhle another gig cleaning our small office in Cooper Center two days a week. Even though we had moved in months beforehand, with Back to School and back-to-back trainings, and the 'soft launch' of the ASI set for February, we had never really had time to unpack and organize. Before she started, I worried that Buhle might be horrified by all the penis gear that littered the place. In the middle of our central hallway sat a cardboard box that could fit a grown person, which housed 132 uncircumcised plastic penises now liberated from the airport. If Buhle was offended, she concealed it expertly, dusting around the dozens of plastic penis models that sat on our desks like joke paperweights, like castoffs from a sex shop or the remnants of a raunchy bachelorette party.

My coworkers seemed to like her, although she said little, head down and beautiful. In response to the extra work, her gratitude was enormous. She left a note in careful block-lettered English on our spotless kitchen countertop back at Little Rock: *Dear sisi, Please buy for me more cleaning powder. God bless you for everything you have done for me.*

It shamed me. For a full day's work, she earned the emalangeni equivalent of ten dollars. Buhle would have known that we regularly spent more than that on wedges of imported brie. Back home, my working mom friends debated the merits of language immersion schools and science summer camps. They wondered if their children had attention deficit or sensory issues. Buhle had working mom problems of a different sort: my landlady pulled me aside one afternoon to tell me that Buhle's daughter was left soaked in urine for an entire day at a neighborhood daycare while she cleaned our house.

'Buhle, you are welcome to bring your daughter to work with you,' I told her the next day.

'I can't, *sisi*. That small person, she's too busy, she gets into everything. I cannot work if she is here. But I also cannot leave her at home alone. There, anything can happen to her. They can come and rape her.'

Who? Who would come and rape her child? I didn't understand, but I nodded my head. Such problems were so much bigger than I was.

I watched Buhle talk to Adam with a twinge of jealousy. He spoke to her as he did to everyone – with gentleness and consideration. For him, she aired a sassy side. Like one day, she had commented to him on the shape of my calves. '*Sisi* has such nice legs,' she had said in siSwati. 'Even though she runs up and down the road, she doesn't look at all like a man!' And about our new puppy, Pebbles: 'Why are you buying toys for this dog like it was a child? You should just have your own real baby.'

But Buhle and I communicated in other ways. One afternoon, I came home to find a doctor's note folded carefully underneath our electric teakettle. It was Buhle's prenatal record: her lab test results, her ultrasound results. A midwife's sequential comments about fetal growth.

The next morning, I waited for Buhle to show up at our door before I left for the Hub. She came dressed for town – immaculate in a long skirt, jacket and shiny patent leather flats. In a plastic Pick n Pay bag, she toted her work clothes – the loose skirt, T-shirt and bedroom slippers. Outside, at the doormat, she switched shoes. The rest of the transformation took place behind the white curtain of Little Rock's bathroom. While she changed, I played it casual. 'Buhle, I think you accidentally left your records here?'

Buhle stepped out from behind the curtain, stared at the ground, and whispered, 'Can you tell me if my baby is okay? The doctors do not say anything. They don't explain.'

Adam swiveled around. 'Of course,' I told her.

I reread the clinician's jargony English and shorthand. Adam translated. A part of me was slightly surprised to discover that her prenatal record was entirely unremarkable. By all accounts, this stubborn bit of a baby was progressing and growing normally. But then, that is what they taught us in nursing school: a developing fetus is a parasite. It will take for itself what it needs while the mother suffers.

At the office, colleagues started to notice. 'Is Buhle expecting?' Roberta, our outspoken Program Officer inquired. It was a Monday morning. Buhle was depositing a few bags of noxious-smelling, rotting chicken thighs in a dumpster beside the parking lot. With such a shortage of live human clients, we were now using the chicken thighs for suturing practice during our circumcision trainings. Someone had forgotten to return the stitched thighs to the office freezer on Friday afternoon.

'How can she carry that rotting meat? It'll make her sick.' Her tone was mildly accusatory, as if I was guilty of mistreating the pregnant lady.

Buhle heard us and turned shyly back in our direction. 'Don't worry, *sisi*.' She smiled. 'I am fine. This is nothing.'

I'm sure, in the grand scheme of her life, that was true.

36

In January, as the country slowly came back from holiday merrymaking, Soka Uncobe prepared for its official lift-off. Amazingly, the delivery of the prefabs had been successfully expedited by the Department of Defense, and we were able to work around the ordering delays with other supplies through some last-minute regional inter-program swapping. This was it. The ASI. Circumcise and Conquer. The famous first-ever accelerated national circumcision campaign.

Clara hosted a Partners Kick-Off Meeting at the Hub in Ezulwini, now ready for operations, to make it official. Adam dropped me off at the 9 a.m. start, and poked his head into the conference room to say hello to Clara. Immediately, I could see he felt out of place. Clara was engrossed in conversation with Stephanie Silva and barely nodded in our direction. He gave me a quick kiss and disappeared. I took a second to get my bearings. The room was filled with a mix of American and European program managers and higher-level Swazi NGO leadership, everyone seated before his or her neatly prepared file folder of essential program documents and a fresh pad of lined paper. Time to solidify our relationships with one another, to get on – in a phrase we overused to the point of comedy – 'the same page.'

Clara opened the meeting with the ASI origin myth, the story of an idea born at the Johannesburg MC Conference a year earlier, of a group of four donors and implementers sitting at a breakfast table, dreaming up the possibility of a circumcision campaign carried out at 'lightning speed' and on a national scale. Now, she said, was the time to make the dream a reality. And we were the dream team who would do it.

Stephanie Silva followed. 'The management of the ASI is notably non-typical,' she started. The project would cost a cool 30 million dollars – the revised budget for the yearlong implementation, she told us. Three different US government agencies would fund it through seven different funding mechanisms. By non-typical, I guess she meant exceptionally complicated.

'Let's talk openly,' Clara said, 'and early about what could crop up as rate-limiting factors to ASI success.'

People threw out answers. Waste management. Supply storage and distribution. Complications with the Department of Defense deliveries of our surgical tents. Other procurement delays. Provision of drugs and establishment of management processes for newly identified sexually transmitted infections. Administration and approval delays, given that the project would be co-managed between Swaziland and South African funders. It occurred to me only in retrospect that no one mentioned client demand, even though we were four months into a notable client dry spell.

As we wrapped up for the day, Clara checked in with me. 'How'd that go?'

'It's exciting,' I told her.

'Exciting and scary,' she agreed.

In the weeks that followed, we started preparing to launch

the new Soka Uncobe brand. The transition would be marked by an effort comparable to the Back to School campaigns. This was the idea that Clara conceived on our Christmas Eve road trip: the Back to Cane Cutting campaign that would target the largely uneducated, muscular men who performed the grueling, sweltering, health-stealing labor that fortified the nation's economy. The idea was to recruit seasonal workers as they signed on with private cane companies. We struck a deal with the sugar companies to circumcise guys when they reported for their mandatory pre-employment physicals. A win-win. It made sense. Here was an extremely high-risk, migratory group – the perfect demographic group for Soka Uncobe.

My team started recruiting the doctors, nurses and support staff – the thirty-four additional workers needed to run the four new sites in the heart of sugar country. Damn it, we were on top of it. As soon as the sites were selected, we started making phone calls, sending emails, making site visits, coordinating with the national nursing leadership. Roberta handled the nurses, the counselors, the cleaners and the data clerks. Thandi, along with our backstopping team in Baltimore, lined up the local and international doctors. By then we had a new system: a master three-ring binder, a page for each site, with a dizzying array of color-coded sticky tabs, each one designating a staff position within each team. Once the teams were set, we converted them to electronic files that we circulated program-wide. We were feeling pretty good about ourselves.

But as February arrived, some major and new operational problems came to light. Arguably, the worst of them was that the Swazi MC Task Force had not yet approved Soka's mass-marketing materials. The materials were ready to go; the Soka Uncobe logo ready to be rolled out, the catchphrases dreamed up, the computer-generated faces and figures for the campaign designed. But, two weeks before the first Soka circumcisions, approvals requests were still sitting on some desk at the Swazi Ministry of Health. Therefore, not one billboard had been erected, not one advert posted in either newspaper and not one recruitment poster hung on the door of so much as a single Back to Cane Cutting clinic.

Kristi's interpersonal communication agents, the IPCs, were out in rural villages attending soccer matches and community meetings, trying to drum up circumcising business, unidentifiable in their secondhand jeans, without brochures, without circumcision swag. Circumcision was a tough sell even in the best of times, with uniforms, informational materials and giveaways – the T-shirts, wristbands, pencils and backpacks that sweetened the deal. Without them, it was close to impossible.

The second major problem was that our baseline five sites, the circumcision sites that would run at all times throughout the year of the ASI, irrespective of specific campaigns, had next to no clients. As we approached early February 2011, the client dry spell had progressed into a fully-fledged drought. Since the end of Back to School II in September, a steady and reliable flow of clients into even the most popular circumcision sites had slowed to a standstill. Sites that were seeing a respectable twenty clients a day nine months before were seeing less than half that number. With clinics stocked, shiny prefabs ready, clinical and support teams hired, the men – our droves of eager clients – were conspicuously absent.

Kristi's clinical team reassured us. Peaks and valleys in demand were normal in the short life of the Swazi circumcision program. Things naturally slowed down around the time of the plowing of the maize fields, and then again during Christmas and the *Incwala*. Relax, they said, this is not a great mystery. No one wanted to nurse a wound to the groin when he could be out celebrating the holidays, getting loaded and getting laid.

But back in Baltimore, Erin didn't like what she was hearing from our US-based donors. 'What's going on out there, you guys?' she asked Remi and me. 'This is worrying. How do we know this demand problem is going to turn around in time for Back to Cane Cutting?'

Remi, our new Clinical Services Director, and I echoed our in-country colleagues: it was too premature to judge the campaign a failure or to panic about a lack of clients. We figured you couldn't call the client problem a 'crisis' when the program hadn't yet gotten a green light to actively advertise.

'I don't get it... why not have some focus groups?' Erin said. 'Ask around? It's just weird. Something must have sparked this change in demand.'

I brought this suggestion to Clara, who said emphatically, 'No, we have all the research we need.' I knew what she meant. Swaziland had long ago established its stance on circumcision with a documented 87 percent acceptability rate. Clara felt sure that things would change once the national media campaign started. Which is not to say she was feeling breezy and confident. The mismatch between supply and demand was a giant red flag to her too, but here she was: stuck between the pressures of leading a high-visibility multimillion-dollar award that promised to deliver 152,000 circumcisions in eleven months, and a government that didn't share the sense of urgency. In a private moment, Clara told me that she was involuntarily throwing up most mornings.

The anxiety was palpable in the Hub. Our supply chain partner had sent their version of a Kristi or a me, a skinny, sweet-faced guy named Tommy, to organize things on the ground. Listening to Tommy on the phone, which we all could because the place was a wide-open warehouse, was, well, distressing. Eventually, he'd get up and walk outside and we'd hear his trailing voice rise. 'I'm not authorized to sign these things!' or 'Did you know they're making us send all the permissions through South Africa?' or 'Dude, I just came here to assess the incinerators!' or 'I don't think you hear me, we need this *now*!' or 'I can't tell them that – that we only buy commodities, and not, like, toilet paper. They need toilet paper too!'

I empathized. By then, I was taking a beta-blocker daily. Even when I didn't have a stressful meeting scheduled, I took it on a prophylactic basis. Tossed it back with a chalky multivitamin and a dainty pink birth control pill. The beta-blockers made me tired and slightly spacey, but I preferred this feeling to being forever on edge. I knew that chances were high that at some point during any given eight-hour period I'd be asked a question I didn't have the answer to, or told that some unforeseen change and certain crisis was about to descend. I dealt so much better with these unwelcome eventualities slightly sedated.

I wasn't the only one who found pharmaceutical means of coping. Remi, at the technical helm of the project, overslept on the morning of a major project meeting. This was shockingly out of character. For hours, his phone went straight to voice mail. When I finally got through to him, he was frazzled. 'I took some Valium last night and must have overslept.'

'Really? That's not like you.'

'Laura, you live with a massage therapist. You get to de-stress at home. I was just doing the same thing with the resources I have available to me. It was, you know, like a chemical massage.'

That night, I told Adam the story. I thought the line about 'chemical massage' was hilarious. Adam did not agree. 'You guys have some really messed-up habits in your professional and personal lives. And because you all act the same way, you think it's normal.'

With less than two weeks to go before the start of Back to Cane Cutting, the Task Force signed off on the marketing materials, but there was no denying it now: if we didn't do something, anything, right now, we were screwed. For the entire month of February, the five baseline sites claimed only twenty-three circumcisions. A single site could easily do that many in one day. Meanwhile, we were flooded with a windfall of interest from international doctors. We'd figured out how to tap into the network of local private doctors, as well, who were all too willing to reorganize their schedules to support circumcision campaigns at the going per diem rate. Little by little, we were finally achieving numbers of clinicians that amazed even us. Nevertheless, what did it matter without waiting foreskins?

Clara called an emergency demand-creation meeting in the conference room at the Hub. We had to kick out a troop of Swazi women making circumcision paraphernalia: condoms stuffed into cardboard Soka Uncobe covers and earrings crafted out of Soka Uncobe cell phone bubble stickers. As the women shuffled out of the conference room, Clara outlined the problem. It was one of those rambling meetings with iffy leadership. I set about discreetly triaging email on my laptop, letting the others debate various client-enticement strategies.

I heard Remi's confident voice chime in every now and then and concluded that he had it well in hand. With less than my full attention, I heard the dozen or so people in the meeting consider how to capitalize on student availability during a university break. I made note of the suggestion, thought it a good one, and went back to my overflowing inbox: doctors from all over the world wanting to sign on to our yearlong campaign. I only tuned back in when I heard my name and looked up to see Remi's expectant face staring at me.

'What do you think, Laura, are you available to drive? Can you offer your car?' one of the marketing guys asked.

Victor, the Swazi point person for the Joburg-led marketing team, was standing at the head of the table, a fat blue marker in hand, writing down a plan for door-to-door client recruitment by Hub staff to local businesses and schools. Apparently, students had told him that, though they were interested in circumcision, they would only come for procedures if the program offered free transportation. The training could only go ahead in the next week if we had the students as clients.

'So, Laura, can you drive?' Remi repeated.

'Yeah, I guess so. Are you driving?'

'Absolutely,' he answered. 'This is a team effort.'

We were back to the transportation issue again. Before the final Soka Uncobe proposal was drafted, our D.C. donor, Solomon, outlawed free transportation for circumcision clients. No other country paid circumcision clients to travel to and from their snips. In Tanzania, our colleagues said that men walked without complaint for twenty kilometers or more for their circumcisions. Why should Swaziland transport healthy men for a preventative service when other clients, like women with obstructed labor, could not avail themselves of this life-saving measure? Talk about transportation, and tempers flared. So transportation became a lightning rod, a word synonymous with the evils of incentivizing. This pioneering project, once trialed in Swaziland, was meant to be replicated and rescaled elsewhere; paying for transportation would set an unrealistic and unsustainable precedent. 'Absolutely no client transportation,' Solomon had decreed.

Yet, as I took an ASI update call with my organization's leadership the next day, Erin was pressing me on 'challenges with client demand.' Beta-blocked, I was circling my back office in Cooper Center, affecting an anxious loopy flight pattern around my desk.

'We need to prepare ourselves for what will happen when the demand creation efforts are in full swing,' I explained. 'We need to be ready to dramatically ramp up our human resources. The logistics for the international doctors and the training of local staff require substantial lead times; we are going to look really bad if there are thousands of clients waiting, and we aren't ready. We need to be training those staff now. So we've come up with some innovative solutions,' I told her, and I went on to detail our resourceful and self-sacrificing client transportation plan.

I knew I had seriously screwed up when that statement was followed by pin-dropping silence.

In our quest to find willing Swazi men, we'd acquired a collective amnesia. Erin, who was on assignment in Lusaka, eventually recovered her composure. 'I want this to be clear beyond any doubt. No one in Swaziland will transport clients for this training. I am surprised at you. USAID has explicitly stated that this is unallowable. The only time it may be acceptable to transport a client in your own private vehicle is if he is bleeding to death.' She took a breath, and then added, 'And, even then, it's better to use a program car.'

Beta-blocker or no beta-blocker, I felt my entire blood supply redirected to my face.

Later that evening our organization's CEO would tell Erin, 'The thought of this Swaziland project is giving me an ulcer.'

I went home. I felt sick. Erin called me back, and we talked for almost an hour. She wasn't angry. She had had a few cocktails, and I think it helped. When we fucked up, Erin almost always took the heat from our higher-ups. Anger and shock were now replaced by concern. 'I worry that you guys are slowly losing your sanity over there,' she said. 'Would it help if I came out?'

I appreciated that she asked my permission rather than simply announcing that she was booking a flight. 'I would love your help,' I told her, honestly. 'This is overwhelming.' These were perhaps the most honest words I'd spoken in months.

'I know it is,' she said. 'Just do the best you can.' Before hanging up, she said, 'I know you have high hopes for the mass communication campaign, but maybe we should talk about a timeline for action if it doesn't work out.'

37

That was when a new, preoccupying anxiety took over. What if it *didn't* work out? The thought had genuinely never occurred to me. I thought the ASI would be messy. I thought it would be inordinately stressful and all-consuming. I figured there would be complexities and some substantial mistakes. I thought there was a good chance we would not hit the target. But I still thought we would do something amazing in Swaziland. I hadn't yet pictured a big global health program failing. I hadn't a clue what that would mean for careers or future funding or an intervention's long-view prospects, but I imagined the worst.

I started to talk in my sleep. I tossed and turned and had vivid, lifelike nightmares. The night before a PEPFAR delegation came back and we partners presented our sugar-coated updates, Adam woke me up from a distressed dream in which I'd been repeating the word 'Don't!' over and over again as if speaking to an attacker who held a knife to my throat.

We told the delegation that we had temporarily frozen the training plan. 'But once the mass communication campaign launches' – now a mantra – 'we expect the client numbers to rise and the trainings to get right back on track.'

A week later, Erin landed in Swaziland. She arrived at the office polished as ever in a wrap-around blue dress and open-toed red heels and said, 'On the way from the airport, I didn't see any Soka Uncobe billboards. I didn't see anything at all. What's going on?' Then, when she found out that four more American volunteer urologists were winging their way over from the United States to take part in the doomed campaign, her anxiety levels went through the roof.

See, I'd inadvertently neglected to tell her about them. Every week, we'd had these keep-us-in-the-loop phone calls and I'd somehow omitted what was perhaps the most politically charged information of all: the arrival of high-powered volunteer surgeons who could sink our program in a heartbeat, were they inclined to bad-mouth it to the right people in power in D.C.

We were at the Hub when this information became known. Quite composed, Erin said, 'Laura, can I speak with you for a minute?'

'Sure.' I dreaded what was coming. I brought her into the side room that served as the Hub's makeshift kitchen. Aside from the toilet, it was as private as it got at the Hub. Two Soka Uncobe drivers sat in bar stools beside a particleboard shelf, sipping milky tea and eating white bread with fat chunks of avocado piled on top.

'Let me get this straight. We have four prominent American urologists coming to Swaziland to circumcise forty clients a day, and we have no clients... *zero*... lined up?'

'Erin, I thought that I had the authority to make key decisions,' I snapped. 'I didn't know I needed to run everything by headquarters. Do you know how crazy things are here? I can't pick up the phone and call you every time something happens.'

'I don't want to fight with you,' Erin said. 'I'm just trying to understand what's going on here. I just landed and I haven't slept in two days. And we have a lot of work to do if we are going to pull this thing off.' She looked utterly spent but she kept her cool. Her voice softened. 'I've been doing this work a long time. I've learned a few things.' She studied me. 'I want to help you. I am not the enemy here.'

I was agitated, reactive and overly emotional, but I wasn't so far gone that I'd lost it entirely. I knew that things were not okay, that *I* was not okay. We hadn't even officially started this historic project yet, and I was attacking the people who'd fought hardest on my behalf.

By the end of her quick visit, Erin realized that her primary job was to 'support' the team on the ground. This meant that when I told her I needed to buy a pack of cigarettes, she didn't judge. I tried to put myself in her shoes. What a disaster this must have appeared to those who hadn't yet been subject to the hell of its daily punishments.

When the Swazi MC Task Force finally signed off on the marketing materials, less than two weeks before the Back to Cane Cutting campaign that would signal the first visible push of Soka Uncobe, the South African creatives went into overdrive. They contracted an army of workers to blanket the country with Soka Uncobe billboards and painted signs. Within days, you could go to the remotest corner of the Kingdom and find a Soka Uncobe sign painted on a wall of the only village store. The SU logo – a simple orange graphic that, to conjure Swazi culture and virility at the same time, resembled a bull's head with horns – was everywhere.

And yet client numbers showed little to no improvement. And absurdity reigned. Disciplinary issues (such as when one circumcision nurse sent her site manager a text message in which she threatened to have the 'ancestors deal with you for what you have done!') started to crop up. Staff quit or ventured off to HIV conferences in other countries with no notice. I got annoyed out of principle, but not because these things wielded a heavy impact to the program. With so few clients, it was hardly a calamity when an eight-nurse team dropped to seven.

As the chasm between supply and demand widened, Remi grew increasingly frustrated. He was ready to employ careful inter-organizational brinksmanship. I'm sure he felt some degree of personal pressure to protect his, and our organization's, reputation. Our only bargaining chip, really, was the staff we hired and paid. Remi convened a small internal huddle, with Morris, our two Program Officers and me. Both men, the rational doctors, wanted to force a decision, to make a clear, unequivocal statement. 'I think we should pull our staff if the numbers don't improve,' Remi said. Morris was in favor of laying people off outright.

'It's not fair to use newly hired Swazi clinical staff as pawns,' I argued. 'I agree that we shouldn't add more staff until the numbers improve, but it's unethical to fire staff we've already contracted.'

I thought about how painful it had been to recruit and train all our staff, to broker a deal for our on-leave nurses. I proposed a compromise. Write a letter outlining our concerns and present it to Clara.

'That is not a solution. That is more of your emotional swindling,' Morris said to me.

It hurt. Immediately and deeply. I knew Morris was not a fan of my conciliatory management style, my focus on detail, my hyper-flexibility, my over-allegiance to authority, but I did not know, until that moment, that he thought me insincere and manipulative.

A week later, Remi asked to speak with me privately. He did not look me in the eye. His hands, elegant slender fingers, usually so poised, vibrated slightly on the surface of the wooden picnic table on the Hub's manicured grounds. His voice, normally so controlled, wavered. 'It's becoming difficult to talk openly with you. We used to be able to talk honestly about anything.'

A second devastation. This one all the more painful because it came from a true friend. When had I become prickly and guarded? When had I stopped including Remi in meandering discussions about religion, or relationships, or what we are meant to do with our brief time on this planet?

That night, I left Adam's warm side and crept down the ladder to Little Rock's loft bedroom. I looked through the bars of the locked veranda door to a glorious Pine Valley lit by moonlight. The peaceful, perfect scene blurred with wetness. My throat squeezed closed. It felt like something was breaking inside my chest. The last time I'd stood in that place, feeling that feeling, I was grieving the loss of a life I'd created. Now, I was grieving the loss of someone else: the person I'd always thought myself to be.

When Remi said, a few weeks later, without malice, that he could not remain in Swaziland unless conditions improved, I was floored. Yes, the situation was untenable, but never once, in those many miserable months, had I thought I had a choice. Never once had I thought leaving Swaziland would signal anything other than a confirmation of personal failure.

38

After the flow of circumcision clients slowed to a Dust Bowl drought, an entire nation of government-employed nurses went on strike. In March, the government asked us to send our underutilized, non-Swazi circumcising nurses in as unwitting strikebreakers. As the Soka Uncobe Human Resources point person, I got the phone call. 'It's not like we can say they're too busy,' I told Clara and the national MC Task Force Coordinator.

By then, it was clear that the Back to Cane Cutting campaign was not working: cutters were primarily concerned about their ability to spend eight grueling hours a day slashing cane and taking home the wages, not with preventing HIV. They readily agreed to circumcision counseling and free health checks, and then opted out of the surgery. The numbers were appalling – one to three circumcisions at each site a day, as compared to Solomon's mandated forty. Meanwhile, upward of fifty men daily got the blood pressure checks and vision testing required by their potential employers. Program nurses and doctors complained bitterly about performing a function – namely, completing the private company physicals – that they weren't being paid for. We were, in essence, subsidizing the for-profit sugar industry while getting no closer to our sky-high circumcision target.

Remi was so furious about the wasted effort that he circulated a red, exclamation pointed email entitled: 'Cane Cutters Say NO to Circumcision!' He'd told Erin that if things didn't dramatically improve by 31 May, he and his family would leave.

In March 2011, the Nerd Circus booked their tickets to the Kingdom for a meeting with Clara we euphemistically called a 'Communications Meeting.' Erin agreed to come back to Swaziland to support Remi, Morris and me. Clara's team reserved the conference rooms at Mountain Inn for two days and came up with a glossy agenda. I braced myself for battle.

As the meeting opened, Victor, one of the marketing guys, said, 'We should not consider this a program failure. Remember, no one has attempted to do what we are now doing in Swaziland. Rather, we should view this an opportunity for education. Maybe these hundreds of cutters will come back later for their procedures, after they've had time to talk to their wives and think it over.'

Muffled voices reacted. Then, Solomon started in. 'I think it's pretty clear at this point that this program is being mismanaged. Who is in charge of leading client demand? Why is the US government paying for dozens of trained, contracted staff to lounge in program-procured recovery room chairs reading magazines? This is exactly what we saw on a site visit yesterday.'

I winced and looked at Clara. Solomon looked directly at Clara as well. 'You need to think about every possible option available to bring up these numbers.' He waited a couple of beats. 'It seems very clear to me that we need to introduce client transportation, given what your team just said about travel barriers.'

Was this a joke? Was there a secret TV camera somewhere capturing this? Had the last year been one cruel prank? Erin, sitting next to me, wrote notes and passed them under the table. The things she wanted to say but felt I should – things like, 'Should we cancel the campaign now???' I didn't have the heart to sell Clara out by so publicly bailing on her optimistic plan. I owed this group of people, this exhausted team I'd worked alongside all these months, my loyalty.

Then Solomon turned his head eighty degrees to address Erin and me. 'I believe your organization has sufficient funding to take care of that?'

Erin confirmed on the spot that we would take over the responsibility of picking up and dropping off pre-recruited circumcision clients. Part of me felt irate that the hard and fast rules could change that arbitrarily and that quickly, but another part felt vindicated. Now, these guys were actually getting it... now, they understood the desperation and grasping we'd felt for months.

After the meeting's unresolved deliberations and hostility, Remi, Erin and I returned to our little office in Cooper Center to debrief. Erin spoke first. 'Guys, it's time to set a drop-dead date. If things do not get better, we need to take this to senior leadership and consider pulling out. I'm beginning to question whether this program has the true backing of the Swazi government – and without it, this situation isn't turning around. It's clear that there is no correlation between effort and outcome over there. To me, this is looking more and more like a sinking ship. It's a waste of valuable talent. I look at Remi – his skills are squandered here. He's needed elsewhere.'

I listened to Erin, frozen in slack-jawed shock. Remi had been in Swaziland for a matter of months. I'd been there, toiling away on this sinking ship, for over a year. And no one had been overly concerned about my squandered skills.

I admired Erin's formidable brain, her political savvy, her approachability, her passion, her deft ability to think and speak articulately on her feet. But as I looked at her, such an asset to the organization, I felt expendable. I'd told myself, two long years before, that I would scrub the toilet to get my foot in the door. It felt as if that's exactly what I'd been doing with the endless workdays, the weekly calls with senior management, the constant reports and donor updates, the rivers of nausea... I'd done it all, in more than some small way, to please her, to please Remi, to please all of them back at headquarters. In a heartbeat, I moved past hurt and disillusionment and entered blistering fury.

My cell phone rang. I excused myself. Adam's calm voice told me that Buhle, our housekeeper, had sent him a text. She'd been leaking amniotic fluid for three days and was now having sharp, intermittent abdominal pain. She'd been turned away from Mbabane Government Hospital because the nurses were striking again.

'Come and get me,' I told him.

'You are doing the right thing, Laura,' Erin said as I packed up my laptop and file folders.

I probably nodded an acknowledgment, or said thanks, but I didn't want or need her permission to go. I didn't need anyone's permission. I was leaving – at least for the afternoon – to see if, in this one instance, with this one person, I could force some small correlation between effort and outcome.

I may have lived in Mbabane for over a year, but this was the first time I'd ever seen the side of town, a neighborhood called Msunduza, where our housekeeper Buhle – and thousands of others – lived. The Mbabane police station sat on the unmarked boundary between those with money and those without. Minibuses could not even navigate these back roads, footpaths really, that twisted and turned up rocky mountainsides. Formerly a hideout for both South African and Mozambican freedom fighters, the area was now run-down, unsafe and overcrowded. To go to work, Buhle must have walked a mile to the nearest pick-up point.

Adam drove as I gripped the grab handle on the top of the Pajero's passenger side door and we bumped over rocks and gullies. Adam knew the way. Before taking a sharp turn, we passed what was clearly a daycare or crèche for the neighborhood kids. On an uneven, splintery wooden fence, someone had painted the words 'No baby dumping' in jerky red letters. No doubt this was where Buhle dropped her daughter every day, where the child had been left soaked in urine. We passed a collection of tin-roof shack shops, each one selling exactly the same things – the usual assortment of dried milk and Lux soap.

I looked in the back of the car to see if we had any old copies of the *Times of Swaziland* lying around. Newspapers. One of my midwifery professors told us that, in a pinch, you should deliver a baby on newspaper. That, or on pages torn from a phone book. They were apparently the cleanest of household resources. And gloves… I reflexively unhooked the glove compartment. Shit. At home, I have a spare pair stashed in there just in case. How stupid is that? In Washington D.C., I was as prepared as a good Girl Scout with sterile gloves and a facemask. In southern Africa, I was without.

I had not delivered a baby in two-plus years. I closed my eyes and tried to visualize a smooth delivery, a midwife's hand skills – the crowning of the head, the gentle downward pressure with one hand to prevent tearing, the way the head spins as the body rotates before emerging. I mentally walked through each step. I imagined Buhle's baby – breathing, tiny ribs pumping like bellows up and down: healthy, pink and squirming.

Eventually, we had to abandon the Pajero and walk the

rest of the way. Armed with a phone, a pen, and a piece of paper, I was still wearing the same outfit I had worn for our Communications Meeting at Mountain Inn: a black knee-length dress with tiny white polka dots and black heels with little black flowers attached to the straps. I don't think I could have looked or felt any more ridiculous, locking my fingers into the crook of Adam's elbow, watching each step along the winding edge of a steep hill, ducking underneath the knotted bough of a pine and side-jumping a sad trickle of a stream.

Buhle lived in a one-room mud house. A single woven mat lay on the floor, and a single mattress had been pushed into a darkened corner. Everything she owned was folded and stacked in perfect color-coordinated piles, just like the piles she made at our house. A devastating tidiness.

Praise God, Buhle was not in active labor. She was composed, gracious, and smiling widely with not a hair out of place. Clement, her husband, wore a vacant expression as he shook my hand. He and Adam greeted each other, and then both of them instinctually stepped to the side of the house to make way for us to talk about womanly things.

'Tell me what's going on, Buhle,' I started. 'You are leaking fluid? And there's pain?'

'Yes,' she answered and stopped there.

'When did the leaking start? Are you sure it's not urine?'

It started three days earlier, she replied, and she was sure it wasn't urine. I put the flat back of my hand to Buhle's cool temple and I let it travel across the expanse of her wide forehead. No fever. I dropped the same hand to her tiny wrist, and felt for the pulse. I swung my cheap Timex wristwatch around so that it faced up, and counted for a full sixty seconds. Eighty beats per minute. Normal. 'What about the pain, Buhle… are you still having pain?'

'It is gone now. It was there earlier today, and yesterday.'

'Is it like contractions? Like when you had your first baby?'

'No, not like that, *sisi*. It is like the pain from menstruation and then it goes away.'

I searched deep in the files of my brain for this knowledge. 'Buhle, you need to go to the hospital. I'm worried that you might be getting an infection.'

We went to RFM, Raleigh Fitkin Memorial Hospital in Manzini, the only major hospital in Swaziland that – as a faith-based institution – was not hamstrung by the government nurses' strike. I trusted the place. In April 1968, King Mswati III had been born there. Our volunteers worked in a small circumcision unit on the eastern side of the hospital. At RFM, we were known and I would have some pull. I hoped.

Forty-five minutes later, Dr. Abdulla was the first to greet us. A tall, pale-eyed, mild-mannered Eritrean surgeon, he seemed pleased to bump into me in the outdoor corridor next to RFM's maternity ward. I explained what was happening. He directed us to the midwife on duty. Buhle was promptly examined, and promptly dismissed. When I questioned the dismissal, the midwife told me that there was no evidence of leakage and no signs of labor. If Buhle wanted to, the midwife explained, she was welcome to stay in the maternal waiting hut until something more definitive happened.

We went to check out the waiting hut. The floor was a patchwork of flimsy foam mattresses. Bored pregnant girls lounged on them in wrapped cloths with cheap plastic combs sticking up like feathers from their hair. Several of them were coughing. I thought about how quickly TB would spread in a place like this. 'Buhle cannot stay here,' I whispered sharply in Adam's ear, as if she was a child and I was her mother, as if I had a right to make decisions for her.

Dutiful and silent, Buhle hauled her pregnant belly into the backseat of the Pajero and we headed back to Mbabane. I tried to explain to her why she was better off at home.

'Call me anytime,' I said, and I ran through a laundry list of danger signs to watch out for. She sat silently, her head ricocheting off the glass of the side window. 'Just buzz me,' I told her. 'Anytime.'

The next morning, Erin left. Her departure followed a tense 7.30 a.m. meeting with Clara, Remi and me at the Hub. As the partner with the fattest budget, Clara had come to us first for a sit-down about her dissatisfaction with certain elements of the human resources and clinical management. The dynamics had totally changed since my first arrival to the Kingdom. I saw little of Kristi, now back from maternity leave but no longer the prime. This was Clara's show now and, with all of us under the gun, finger-pointing had started.

Erin had spent the previous day on site visits. She'd texted me constantly throughout to report things like, 'Did you know there are no sick notes?' and 'Everyone is just sitting under the trees doing nothing' and 'Why don't the teams have petty cash?' With seven organizations working on seven aspects of the program, most of what she was reporting was outside of our control. Still, I read the messages as personal critiques.

During our early meeting with Clara, Erin was diplomatic but clear, her experience lending her authority. 'We cannot, in good conscience, keep staff working and circumcision sites open with so few clients. You need to scale back. I suggest we close the Back to Cane Cutting sites until you've regrouped and have committed clients lined up, and that we do not open another new site until we have the demand to justify it.'

I couldn't accept this. 'Erin,' I said, 'I hear what you're saying, but to coordinate the volunteer doctors and the on-leave nurses, I need three months' advance notice. Two at the very least. I can't just snap my fingers and produce fully trained teams once our demand partners give me the green light. I'm not comfortable sitting back until further notice – to wait, for how long? You heard Solomon – we only have eleven months to do this.'

'Laura, please understand what I'm saying. There will be no more volunteer doctors and no more on-leave nurses.'

In that instant, I did, in fact, finally understand. A year of round-the-clock planning to figure out how to staff thirty-five simultaneous circumcision teams. It had been tremendous. Amazingly, remarkably, it had all come together. We'd cracked the case. We'd tapped into a global sentiment of medical goodwill. More volunteer doctors than, even in the best of times, we would have needed. And after painstaking planning, countless meetings and delicate negotiation, we'd scheduled hundreds of on-leave nurses. We'd been told it was impossible. We'd proved that it wasn't. All of it rendered, in a half-hour meeting, a complete waste.

I drove Erin to the airport. 'I can't do this anymore,' I said to her, my voice cracking and girlish.

'I am supportive of whatever decision you need to make,' Erin answered, clearly uncomfortable. Remi sat stone silent in the back seat, certainly also uncomfortable given his evolving plans to move on. 'I just ask that you give us four weeks' notice.'

When I got back to the Hub, Clara seemed defeated. 'You know that deal you brokered with the Director of Nursing, to recruit on-leave nurses and pay them during their scheduled leave?'

Yes, of course I knew it. PEPFAR had garnered special permission to authorize it. It had been the only way to secure the nurses we thought would be necessary to make Soka Uncobe happen after the Kenya deal fell through. Now I was going to have to put a freeze on it. I dreaded the fallout.

Nurses who'd been promised supplemental pay throughout the circumcision program – nurses already striking for other reasons – would certainly feel deeply misled. How to frame this so that it would not appear yet another false promise from scheming foreigners? But damage control in the wake of canceling the plan to hire on-leave nurses wasn't what Clara was referring to.

'Yeah, well, word spread. Now government employees from other ministries are refusing to support Soka unless they get a top-up.' A top-up, a little gravy, an added financial incentive to help push a program forward. Long-term, the strategy was poisonous. What to say? Such were the unintended consequences of an all-out, once-off intervention. Risks we'd considered worthwhile trade-offs for success. Now rendered not only heartbreakingly pointless, but potentially damaging.

I confided in Clara. 'Our headquarters is getting increasingly worried about our association with this project. Remi wants to leave, and Erin supports him because he's so valuable to our MC work globally. I'm another story. I feel like I've slaved away on this thing for a year, but I'm not a loss.'

Clara said, 'Your leaving would be a huge blow. Remi may be exceptional, but you would be harder to replace.' It soothed my ego more than it should have.

A question struck me: why had I felt such an irrational need to prove myself and stick it out when others clearly didn't? 'Clara, why are you still here?'

'Because I'm too exhausted and lazy to look for the job I really should have in Chicago.'

That day, we made a deal. We would give it four weeks, set an appointment in our Outlook calendars. Together, we would make a decision to stay or go.

39

Utterly impotent within the program, I felt I could at least do something positive for Buhle. Nothing happened for several more days. When labor pain kicked in, government nurses were back in business, so we took her to Mbabane Government Hospital. At first, they didn't want to admit her, so I insisted on speaking with a doctor.

'The doctor is performing an emergency caesarean,' one of the midwives informed me.

'She's been leaking for almost a week,' I said, temper flashing. I was aware of Buhle next to me, staring at the linoleum floor and gripping the underside of her basketball belly. 'I'll wait.'

Then, to my incredible disbelief, Buhle spoke. 'I need to use the toilet,' she said.

The surly midwife heaved herself from a wooden stool and strolled to a file cabinet. From the pocket of her navy scrubs, she pulled a key and proceeded to open the top drawer. 'Bring it back to me when you are done,' she told Buhle as she handed over the half-roll of toilet paper. Buhle's hand shook as she accepted the roll.

What? In Mbabane Government Hospital, the toilet paper is

locked up? Nurses make $100 a day, but the government can't afford toilet paper? We walked by a labor room with at least twenty prostrate women in apparent agony. All of them had to make their way, many of them pushing an IV stand, to this unfriendly woman when they needed to pee? Lord have mercy on the poor woman afflicted by a bout of diarrhea. I couldn't help but think of all of our empty, well-stocked circumcision suites. All the toilet paper we'd procured.

Buhle disappeared behind the curtained, wooden door of the labor ward, sucked into an acrid darkness. It was almost dinnertime. I walked back out through the swinging double doors that led to the maternity ward. Adam was leaning against the Pajero, smoking a hand-rolled cigarette.

'Do you have to do that here? This is a hospital.'

He gave me a look that said, *Must you be so relentlessly American?*

Then my phone rang again. It was Remi. He was worked up about something, but first he wanted to know about Buhle. Remi had young children. I assured him she was being cared for. 'Good,' he said, then: 'I have to tell you something. I want you to hear it from me before you hear it from anyone else.'

These are not words you wish to hear in the parking lot of the national referral hospital of a developing country. These are not words you wish to hear anywhere. I stepped away from Adam. I don't know why. I needed to focus, maybe, to tunnel into the labyrinth of bureaucratic confusion and power struggles that defined my working life.

'The numbers got out. Someone leaked them to Washington and then the email went viral.'

'Okay.' For a moment, I failed to grasp why this was such a dire emergency. We were miles from meeting our set circumcision target in Swaziland. This had been the case for months. Didn't anyone who cared already know this?

Well, it turns out they knew it conceptually, but they didn't know the exact color, shape and weight of the shortfall. To quantify it turned it from scurrilous rumor to substantiated, irrefutable fact. Also, this was a gross breach of protocol. The data was owned by the Swazi Ministry of Health, not by an NGO.

'So what does this mean?' I asked.

'PEPFAR is putting the daily and weekly statistics on lockdown. They aren't going to share the numbers anymore. We will have no idea how many circumcisions are happening in Swaziland after today,' Remi said.

So now we were supposed to manage the program blind? I was trying to follow what Remi was saying as I paced the hospital parking lot. The thought momentarily occurred to me that Remi had forwarded the email himself, as a wake-up call to D.C., but I could tell from the way he was speaking that he hadn't. He sounded worried, vulnerable.

'Thanks for the info, Remi. Let's talk about it tomorrow.'

'Good luck with everything there, my friend,' he said. Something pricked my heart, something in his voice. The affection mixed with exhaustion.

We needed to kill time until the doctor came out of the OR, so Adam and I ducked down the hill and over to Nando's drive-through for some veggie burgers and fries. Anxiety had stoked a powerful hunger. We got a can of orange juice and another box of fries for Buhle, but I wound up giving Buhle's French fries to the midwife on duty when the smell alone made Buhle sick. It worked like a charm: a box of French fries allowed me access to Buhle's file.

'She's possibly been leaking for a week now,' I repeated to the midwife, who rolled the end of a crispy fry in a packet of salt and then inserted it between her lips in small increments, like a log pushed through a woodchipper.

'Aside from risk of infection, we should be concerned about loss of amniotic fluid from a slow leak,' she said while chewing, 'and the only way to measure that is with an ultrasound.'

'Okay, great,' I said, finally starting to feel like we were getting somewhere.

'The problem is that the ultrasound technician knocks off at five.'

'So what do you do if you have an emergency at midnight and need ultrasound confirmation?'

She said, 'It's a problem. The government won't pay overtime, so the technicians refuse to take call shifts after hours.'

'So what happens during emergencies after hours?'

She looked at me like a burned-out customer service rep. 'You could try the private clinics. They might have someone they can call in. Is she your house-girl?' the midwife asked.

It was a logical assumption. Why else would a bossy white lady be there? I bristled at the way she'd said 'girl' until I realized that, in my head this whole time, I'd also called Buhle, a woman with much more real-life responsibility than I had, exactly the same thing.

When the government doctor, a grandfatherly Zimbabwean, emerged from surgery, he confirmed that an ultrasound was needed. He wrote the referral for the private Mbabane Clinic. Once again, Buhle squished herself into the backseat of the Pajero. When I glanced up the rearview mirror, I could see misery pinching hollows and creases into her delicate face.

At Mbabane Clinic, an ultrasound tech, another Zimbabwean, prepped Buhle's belly with clear, cold gel. The ultrasound results were reassuring. Buhle's small baby had plenty of amniotic fluid, but, still, her labor was not progressing normally. We waited for Adam to bring the car around. Buhle slumped in a chair in the empty clinic waiting room.

'Buhle, do you want to call your husband? You can use my phone.' I thought that speaking with him might be a comfort.

'Thank you, *sisi*, no,' she summoned the strength to say. 'He cannot help me with this.'

When we got back to the hospital, the doctor agreed that the situation was now serious. Buhle gave birth by caesarean the next afternoon. Two days later, Buhle and her healthy baby were discharged. She called Adam. 'Please tell *sisi*,' Buhle said, 'that I have chosen a name. The child is Noncobile.'

'What does it mean?' I asked Adam, although I should have known, as similar as it was to the name of our circumcision program.

'The one who conquered,' he said.

Buhle wanted a girl who would make it through the tough times. Like the Swazis themselves, a peaceful warrior. An endurer.

40

By May 2011, something elemental had changed. The whole ethos of the endeavor had shifted. After the Communications Meeting at Mountain Inn two months earlier, after the public shaming and the drama surrounding the statistics, something broke. The very soul of the undertaking took flight. The spirit with which it started, the excitement of 88,000 infections prevented, the build-up, the coalescing of global energy and interest, gone. Diane Sawyer would never visit the beautiful African Kingdom. My calls with senior leadership stopped. No more marathon MC Task Force meetings. Swaziland, a mountain Kingdom besieged by a deadly virus, lost its moment on the global stage as the public health world moved on.

By then, Clara had left, a departure prompted by a health scare. It didn't surprise me, given the tremendous stress she'd been under for months. I envied her. God, I also wanted to leave. I just couldn't bring myself to shatter the glass and sound the alarm. In the month or so beforehand, the two of us had stopped hanging out after hours and stopped spending time together on the weekend. It wasn't deliberate; we were both shrinking into ourselves. The date of our decision appointment came and passed without mention.

A letter to the editor appeared in the *Times of Swaziland* about Soka Uncobe titled 'Circumcision Campaign an Admission of Failure.' The author wrote, 'To advertise [circumcision] and air it on national radio is very degrading and embarrassing to the nation at large (South African tabloids have made big fun of this).' It continued, 'Our country has, over the year, become very vulnerable to all forms of manipulation and this is obviously due to our dependency on donor funding. The issue of circumcision is more of a culture change.'

A part of me could not help but agree. We were applying a technical intervention to an adaptive problem, a need that required years if not generations of changing behavior and patience. However, that wasn't the whole story. The timing had also been unfortunate. Swaziland was having a terrible year. When the global recession hit, Swaziland saw most of its funding from the southern African Customs Union, upon which it depended for more than half its national budget, disappear. The King's parliament cut the salaries of the huge civil service. Scholarships dried up. A contrite Swazi government looked to South Africa for a loan and balked when South Africa attached democratic conditions to it.

Meanwhile, King Mswati's personal fortune stood at a cool 100 million-plus dollars, and a suffering country watched as his government give him a raise. The king's eldest daughter was named the tenth richest princess in the world. And here we were, ploughing on ahead with the US-funded circumcision program.

It reminded me of a story an infectious disease doctor friend had told me about the early days of the epidemic. A patient, a single, struggling mom from West Baltimore, had told her during a visit, 'You know, HIV isn't my biggest problem.' It changed the way my friend practiced medicine. It's hard to care about preventing anything when you're focused on feeding your kids *today*. Swazis could likely relate. For many, poverty was the norm. In 2011, that was true of an even greater number of the Kingdom's population. A deep-seated frustration was simmering.

On the 18 April anniversary of the ruling that outlawed political parties, peaceful Swazis took to the streets in a Facebook-organized protest. In response, police sprayed them with tear gas and beat them with batons. Texts and phone calls started pouring in. Our staff in Manzini and Matsapha were marooned, the streets outside their clinics impassable for hours. Two weeks later, the king flew to London with a fifty-person retinue to celebrate Kate and William's wedding.

The unrest settled into a low-level tension that was near impossible to bring into open discourse. In Swaziland so much happened under the surface. A constant flux of energy passed at a subterranean level, with much communicated in gestures, in tone, in hints.

It was something I had been thinking about a lot, how Swazis didn't seem to share their most intimate and urgent problems with even their closest friends and family. Instead, they sought the help of *sangomas*, the powerful fortune-tellers and healers who outnumbered the Kingdom's doctors fifty times over. Despite the economic crisis of 2011, *sangomas* were still flush with customers.

Adam and I among them.

Adam and his brother had history with traditional healers. I'd learned of it many months after I'd first accidentally discovered the white marks on his chest, after Adam knew that I wouldn't judge him or his family for using 'witchcraft.' The story was this: their mother brought them to a *sangoma* a few years after the accident that left the boys fatherless and their mother penniless. At the time, visions of her dead husband regularly tormented Lisaya. Adam often woke to his mother's voice in the middle of the night, pleading from the bedroom next door. Through the wall, a young Adam could hear her addressing his father still, a full five years after he'd been buried. In the mornings, Adam saw the empty whiskey glasses on the bedside table. Lisaya swore that she'd watched in disbelief as she argued with a ghost, as the liquid in the glass drained.

Lisaya was thirty-one when she took her children to the *sangoma*. She was beautiful and still young enough to hold onto a steady optimism that things could change for the better, that fortune could favor her again. And she wanted to protect her children, position them for that better life.

She brought the boys to a wizened old man who lived simply in a mud house. Adam sat, frozen, while the old man rubbed a dark paste onto two razor blades. Then, two assistants pinned the boy's arms and legs to the hut floor as the *sangoma* went into a trance-state. He grunted like an animal and ordered the dead Van Rensburg to leave Adam alone. Chanting, otherworldly, the *sangoma* brought the blade down to Adam's chest and made two quick incisions above the breastbone. Adam and Jaco were left with marks, two centimeters in length and glowing a ghoulish white. They called them their elevens.

Three decades later and once more living in the Kingdom, Adam learned of a healer named Gladys. Around Mbabane, she had the single name recognition of a celebrity. A nurse, an academician, a woman with a PhD from a European university who sat on the board of half a dozen organizations, she could easily have escaped the provincial confines of Swaziland, but she was called by the ancestors to take on the mantle and the headdress of the *sangoma*.

'Let's go see her,' Adam suggested. He'd come to believe that the healing session he had as a child was a botched job, and according to his logic, only another *sangoma* had the power to release him from what he saw as the curse of his eleven. I was eager to tag along. Gladys practiced Western medicine and Swazi magic. I thought a visit to her might help me get some insight into the Swazi mindset. That it might help me understand how Adam looked at the world. I thought it might also provide some insight into what happened with Soka Uncobe, help me decide whether the idea of the project was at fundamental odds with the Swazi worldview.

We circled the roundabout and pulled off the highway and onto the Tea Road. Adam, on his phone having a back-and-forth with Gladys about how to get to her place, took a hard left and skirted the Pajero between a one-room shop and a one-room home. As we turned in it was clear that the homestead was a work in progress, that Gladys was building it bit by bit as the money came in. Goats and chickens milled about. Two dusty men – presumably helping with the construction project – sat next to the concrete pillars on the porch of the main house. The smaller one lifted himself from the porch and showed us to Gladys's treatment room. With a shyness that surprised me, he asked us to remove our shoes.

The place had been prepared. Two straw mats faced each other. A stick of incense burned in a glass jar, leaving a tiny anthill of ash falling on the cool, smooth floor. A single candle flickered. Adam and I were told to sit. I tried to tuck my legs underneath me in the modest way of Swazi women. It was awkward and uncomfortable, a state aggravated by the flies buzzing around our faces. I looked around the circular space. There was a humming fridge. Squares of cloth and blankets were draped over a foam mattress on one side. Stacks of candles and papers and more glass jars formed separate piles elsewhere around the perimeter.

We waited.

When Gladys stepped inside, she was, aside from the fur headband, a normal-looking middle-aged Swazi woman in a shoulder-length wig and a striped button-up shirt. She wore a *lihiya* as a man might wear a bath towel – wrapped around the waist, with one corner tucked – and she curled herself onto the mat across from us.

We told her our names. To each, she gave a dignified nod. Then she spoke. She did not make direct eye contact. I was mesmerized by her headband, worn like a tiara across her forehead, brown with a tuft of white escaping from a side part like a cowlick.

After the introductions, Adam stayed inside the rondavel with Gladys, while I sat on a plastic chair under the shade of the thatch roof. A few kids played in a homestead across the road and a cow issued low bellowing noises. Gladys's house was at the end of the line, the last plot before the Mbabane River made its snaking way toward Matsapha. The cattle shambled aimlessly along the banks of the river, mucking up the black earth with their heavy hoofs. Half an hour passed, then an hour. Eventually, the rondavel door swung open and Adam slipped his feet back into his leather shoes and sauntered across the yard. He was wearing what Clara called his J. Crew model outfit – linen pants and a pressed T-shirt, an all-white getup that harkened back to our first meeting – and he was clearly pleased.

'That was impressive,' he said once he got within earshot. Adam, the Swazi, conditioned to believe until proven otherwise. Me, the American, conditioned to doubt until proven otherwise, and skeptical as I made my way across the yard.

Once inside, it felt awkward and intimate. Exactly how I'd felt as a kid going to mass with my Italian Nana, my father's mother: the standing and kneeling, the call-and-response, and me, too gangly in this year's flowered dress, looking around, attempting to mimic the motions, the mouthing of words I couldn't discern. I thought of my Nana, now ninety-eight years old, a woman who, in the early 1930s, delayed marriage and motherhood to work first in an orphanage and then a tuberculosis sanatorium. If she could see me now, here in this incensed rondavel, she would have been equal parts horrified and proud. Horrified by the sorcery, proud of my independence. I hadn't seen her in two years.

Gladys leaned forward to collect from her mat an assortment of objects – a snail shell, dominos, colored glass droplets, tiny vertebrae, other small animal bones, and a miniature white plastic doll. She scooped them up, what healers call their bones, from where they'd been thrown for Adam's reading, and shook them inside a lidded basket. She closed her eyes. She called out pressured prayers. Words fell on top of each other. They had the repetitive sound of a worn and practiced incantation into which she had inserted my name and the maiden names of my mother and both grandmothers.

She wasn't quite done when her cell phone rang, but she went ahead and stopped mid-prayer to answer it anyway. Just as rude as our program doctors, nurses and counselors who took phone calls in the middle of HIV tests and circumcisions. And, just like them, by the time Gladys hung up, she'd lost her groove, fallen out of the zone. She closed her eyes and shook her head quickly. Then she lifted the lid from the basket and asked me to blow on the bones. Finally, she sprayed them out across the floor in front of her.

For a few minutes, Gladys studied the spilled bones. She looked at the shell, the size of an orange and bearing a tiger print. She picked it up and put it down again. She said that it represented home. She clicked the dominos together, and every so often said 'hmmm' or 'ah, yes.'

She said, 'Your grandmother is coming through very strong. She's not well, I think?'

'That's correct,' I told Gladys.

'I see now... Yes, someone needs to keep an eye on her.'

Strange how I'd walked into Gladys's hut thinking about my Nana, and here she was, speaking through the bones.

'Also, there is one ancestor in your house, a foreign ancestor, not a relative, but someone who is very close to you. This person has been looking out for you, has made opportunities for you,' Gladys said. This puzzled me, but after some critical thought, I decided my foreign ancestor had to be Ruth, Provincetown grande dame, my great-aunt. She'd been good to me throughout my life, took a special interest in me. The wheels turned in my mind, but I said very little aloud. I didn't want to provide any leading material, aware that the line between ancestral perception and observant psychology could be a thin one.

'Think about coming to Swaziland,' Gladys continued, slicing into my thoughts, 'about meeting Adam. Life has been easier for you than for most people. Don't you ever wonder why that is?' That made me start. Had it? 'But the problem is that now you're getting complacent, ungrateful. Things are getting very painful for you. This is because your ancestor wants to be thanked. He or she – I can't see the gender – is blocking your luck.'

My game-faced resolve faltered. 'So, what do I need to do?' I asked. 'Is there something I'm supposed to change?'

'What you need to do to correct the difficulties you are facing,' Gladys said, 'is hold a ceremony to honor the foreign ancestor. Show your gratitude.'

Well, that ruled out Great-Aunt Ruth. While she appreciated

recognition, she didn't go looking for it. And she wasn't spiteful. It must be someone else... But I could think of no one.

It was close to five o'clock when I finished with Gladys and the final departure discussion closed. We paid up, climbed in the Pajero, and moved on to Timbali, just beyond the roundabout, for an adult beverage and a chat.

I'd been underwhelmed by my reading, but cold beers in hand, Adam began a rapid-fire verbal download of his. Basically, Gladys had confirmed every one of his fears. There was a dark force thwarting his success. He was bewitched when he was a child, but not just by the *sangoma* who gave him the eleven, also again in early adulthood. A wicked mother figure had tied a metaphorical knot around Adam's waist to stymie him.

'So what are you supposed to do to fix it?' I asked. I was trying to reconcile the Swazi way and the American way, to come to a point of understanding between worldviews. Why did Adam feel amazed by the nurse-*sangoma*'s skill whereas I thought her an opportunist?

'I need a cleansing,' Adam answered. A weeklong regimen of purification and de-cursing for 1,500 emalangeni. He had already committed to the five-day affair, set to start the next day. Gladys had given him strict instructions: buy a black chicken, buy several packs of multicolored candles, buy a pack of razor blades, bring an old T-shirt and return at sunset.

Adam agreed to let me tag along throughout the week of sweat, vomit, blood and prayer – starting the next day – if I could help fund the near-$200 price tag. It seemed like a fair exchange. We drove to the Manzini market to buy our black chicken, the death of which would represent the death of darkness and the passing on of bad luck.

The chicken was the scrawniest of the Manzini market lot, clearly a runty, bullied bird. We brought it home in a cardboard box that we inserted into a crate. It spent the night in there, silent and unstirring. It was hardly moving at all by five o'clock the next day when we parked the Pajero inside the gates of Gladys's homestead.

We waited in the rondavel while Gladys wrapped a leopard-printed *lihiya* around her waist and got a fire going. She did this efficiently, each movement measured and purposeful, like a surgeon's. She was up against the sun now, a fiery red ball already making its downward descent toward the horizon. She and one of the construction workers, who I now realized was a spiritual apprentice in the disguise of a day laborer, were walking toward the fence. The sky was a dusky orange as we set off behind her out of the gates of her compound. I was carrying the box with the chicken as we scrabbled down to the river.

When we arrived at the riverbank, the apprentice dug a hole in the wet ground. Gladys quickly worked a knife across the black bird's throat. As the body dropped to the hard ground, she tossed the head into its freshly dug grave. I watched the headless chicken flail. The wings flapped in a horrible feathery cloud while the body moved like a violent twister across the ground.

Adam, stripped to his boxers, didn't so much as flinch when Gladys nicked first the crown of his shaved head with a razor, then each temple, then each shoulder, reopened the original eleven on his sternum, and lastly, grazed each elbow. Pinpricks of bright red blood marked the spots of the loose cross. I'd never seen him like this before – so reverent, so stoic. Gladys asked Adam to straddle the hole containing the decapitated chicken. He did as he was told, stretching one leg to either side as if preparing to start a series of jumping jacks, and then he stood stone still. The *sangoma* poured herbed water over him to wash away the released blood to be absorbed by the black chicken.

Afterward, Adam picked his way up the stony path, and I followed. The moon reflected off a white cloth draped over his shoulders. It felt beautiful and ancient. From somewhere up ahead, Gladys told us to slow our pace. 'Some of the ancestors are very old,' she scolded. 'They will not be able to keep up.' I thought of the African proverb splashed across a lower wall at O.R. Tambo airport: *If you want to go fast, go alone. If you want to go far, go together.* As we walked, the fireflies started to flash. They were everywhere. It occurred to me instantly that these were the ancestors, dozens and dozens of them, making their presence known to us.

The next day, Adam continued the purification process at home by downing two liters of a noxious black liquid and retching into the toilet, while I had to go back to the reality of my working life with our weekly Soka Uncobe Technical Meeting. We were in the process of a 'program rethink.' What this meant was that Clara's replacement, Kate, perky and under thirty, was attempting to repair relational fallout, revamp the organigram to create some new demand-oriented and site-coordination positions, and scale way back on site and staff numbers. In my estimation, the 'rethought' version of the ASI looked an awful lot like the pre-ASI MC program that Kristi had led, albeit with a lot more players and a fatter price tag. I didn't know what Kristi thought of this. Since her organization was no longer our prime, and our organization was no longer her sub, we didn't see much of each other. With a scale-up pretty much out of the picture, meetings were rather run-of-the-mill program management stuff, so Kristi sent her support staff over while she worked on other things. I often sat through these discussions in a checked-out daze, even though I was treated with deference, a now-senior member of the group.

The contrast between these discussions and those just a few months prior, when the Hub practically vibrated with an expectant, nervous energy, was jarring. I thought about Gladys and Adam. It seemed to me that the important work of understanding what had happened and why was more likely to be found with them than it was in the Hub's now-sedate conference space.

I left work a bit early to get to Gladys's place in time for the sunset session. This time, Gladys prepared a huge three-legged pot with boiling water, herbs and one of Adam's old T-shirts tied in a knot. Then she led us behind her house where a makeshift sauna was constructed out of draped cloths. Inside it sat two milk crates and the largest two-handled synthetic woven bag I'd ever seen. Once unclothed and inside, we hunched under the sack as Gladys introduced the boiling concoction. In short order the situation grew uncomfortable. I was drinking air. I tasted the boiled herbs in it as if sipping tea.

Meanwhile, Adam was lost in a siSwati prayer, his eyes closed. He was into this. I, on the other hand, had never been so hot in my life. Because I was so hot, because the entire surface area of my body was slick with perspiration, and because I was adjusting the bag-ceiling so that it didn't glue itself to my wet hair, I was not really feeling it. Adam could tell. He opened his eyes quickly and said, 'You don't have to be in here, angel. You can leave.'

I stuck it out. At the end of the session, we emerged from the steaming as if stepping from a hot spring. I wrung cupfuls of perspiration from my hair and then rinsed in a bucket of river water. Adam doused himself, per instruction, with the herbal brew, the one that contained the knotted T-shirt. Gladys retrieved the scalding T-shirt from the cauldron, untied the metaphorical knot in his spine, and used the freed T-shirt to wash his torso.

'Loving a Swazi man isn't easy,' Gladys said, leaning over to pat my damp back. It was an unexpected gesture. Until then, I'd felt like a tolerated voyeur. After, I still felt the outsider, but at least one who was making a credible effort to understand our substantial differences.

I had a late conference call on Thursday and needed to stay at the office until well after sunset. Adam went for his daily session on his own. My absence gave Gladys and Adam some time to talk about our relationship. She told him that we were a good match. 'Everything will change after this,' Gladys reassured Adam.

Friday was the last day, the day in which the activities of the week culminated in a final session of prayers and healing. Adam fasted in preparation. I lasted until about ten that morning when I had a banana. And some toast with butter. And finally a bowl of leftover lasagna because there was really no such thing as partial fasting and I'd already blown it.

When Gladys told us that we were to go 'up the mountain' to talk to the ancestors, I had something very different in mind. I did not imagine piling into her 4×4 vehicle, alongside her daughter, two nieces and the two construction workers to drive twenty minutes up the windy Tea Road. I imagined a multi-hour death march up a sheer rock face with pebbles in our shoes in search of a sacred precipice. Which is not to say that I was disappointed in the change of plan.

Once at the designated spot, a rocky overlook in the bend of the Tea Road, we stood out in the starry dark, the tight circle of us – Adam and I wrapped in green and white cloths – with lit colored candles in our hands, singing Swazi hymns. It turned out that the shy, muscular apprentice had an unspeakably tender voice. The hair on my arms prickled as I listened to the rise and fall of his harmonizing. I didn't know any of the words so I mostly hummed along. Hot wax dripped on my hands and on the green cloth. Closing my eyes, I tuned into the cool winds of a quiet, peaceful night.

The group of us drove back to Gladys's homestead in silence and waited in her rondavel while she mixed our final potions, uncapping tins of brightly dyed powders and mixing them with a white base. She gave us identical packets of this mixed powder and instructed us on how to use it: for steaming or for direct ingestion. I wasn't about to swallow any of the neon stuff, so Adam and I agreed to a compromise: we would create our own steam room in our shower.

Adam heated water and gathered buckets while I unwrapped my packet. The scrap paper used to hold the powder contained a draft academic article about diabetes in southern Africa. I pinched a bit of the pinkish material into the palm of my hand. The grains were sticky. It smelled familiar. I brought the packet to my nose and took a long whiff. Yes, definitely familiar, but what? A clean smell. I sniffed again and it hit me. Sunlight washing powder. This stuff was laundry soap.

Adam did not need to know this. He believed a positive change was happening, and I wasn't about to burst the bubble. Besides, we had different ideas about cause and effect, Adam and I. I remembered what the *Incwala* traditionalist had told Adam: *muti* couldn't harm white people because we didn't believe in it.

Here was the fatal flaw in our circumcision program and a growing problem in my relationship. Difference. So alluring on the surface, so desirable genetically, it is a constant and frustrating practical problem when it comes to two people, or two nations, attempting to reach the same place with wildly different ideas about how to get there – Swaziland's indirect wiliness versus America's brutish brawn, Adam's focus on the present versus my obsessive goal-orientation – and with an inability to even articulate those differences in ways that could be understood by the another. Adam really lived each day, treated every conversation as an unexpected gift. I moved single-mindedly toward a clear, pre-designated endpoint, and tried to minimize encounters that took me off track. Who's to say which way was better? But I could say that if happiness and contentment are what we seek, Adam's approach was the more effective.

That night, we steamed in buckets made neon pink and slippery with laundry powder, bathed in candlelight, and completed our week of purification. Afterward, we climbed to our bed in our house built into rock that had sheltered humans for thousands of years, and slept.

41

Disillusionment seemed the order of the day. Faced with the sad numbers (by the end of June, five months in, Soka Uncobe had achieved just over 3,000 circumcisions), each of us had to figure out how to resolve the lofty dream with this new reality. So much planning, so much build-up, and no lift-off. I was left questioning myself, my capabilities, my character, my career.

Clara's replacement, Kate, was a skilled program manager and more than competent enough to carry out the vastly scaled-back, business-as-usual strategy that replaced the all-guns-blazing approach of the ASI. But the old guard was gone. I missed Clara, who still sometimes checked on me by Skype and definitely was not returning to Swaziland. John, the logistics guru, had given notice and taken his wife Cindy to Iraq. Remi had formally announced his departure.

It was weird, how little the remaining group talked about what had transpired over the past year. I felt so weary, so worn out, but who remained to help me make sense of it? Sure, there were some, like Stephanie Silva, our donor, who'd endured the same drama, but we weren't close, and somehow, it didn't feel safe to ask the obvious questions when we were all still trying to work in circumcision in the Kingdom. Perhaps internally she was also reeling, but externally, life went on.

It therefore wasn't even strange when Stephanie sent all of us NGO leads an invitation to participate in an art exhibition. At least now we had time for such diversions. She explained that each of us would be paired with a local artist who would get to know our work, and then would prepare a unique piece that illustrated the spirit of our projects. The collection would be revealed in June at a local gallery.

Jay, our matched artist, specialized in 'recycled material.' He was a handsome, wiry Zimbabwean with excellent English, a Rastafarian flair and a persistent, disarming manner. He was also a walking advertisement for his products – he'd made all of his clothes from recycled cloth bags, the shoes and jaunty hat once green and orange plastic bottles.

At first, we were nervous. Just what 'used material' does one recycle from a circumcision program? But, thankfully, Jay had no interest in foreskin art. He had something else in mind. He hadn't slept in over forty-eight hours when he showed up at Yebo Gallery on a Friday evening in June to unveil his masterwork. He called it *60% Safer Avenue*. After Stephanie got a sneak peek of the artwork, she'd reported that Jay's piece was 'arresting.'

I popped a beta-blocker and arrived at the art gallery halfway into the ambassador's remarks. From where I stood in the hallway in front of Yebo's main display room, Jay's sculpture beckoned like a lighthouse in thick fog. At well over seven feet tall, it dwarfed everyone and everything else in the room. It was a whimsical beast with three legs, a vagina, pubic hair and an overarching penis, including a dangling glans-chandelier with a foreskin. From inside the glans-chandelier glowed a red light. All of it constructed from thousands of previously used, sterilized, disposable metal scissors and forceps.

It was difficult to do anything but stare in wonderment. Even the American ambassador was awestruck; once the milling about began, he made a beeline for Jay's creation. Stephanie joked that it was the most successful waste management strategy employed in the male circumcision project to date. From there, a side conversation ensued between the ambassador, Clara's replacement Kate, and me.

'This is Laura. She supports the human resources side of the Soka Uncobe campaign,' Kate said to the ambassador. A plate of cheese cubes stabbed with toothpicks was making the rounds. I reached for one and addressed the ambassador, a greying, reserved man, tall and academic-looking. 'How are you enjoying Swaziland?' I asked.

We talked for about ten minutes. 'I'm optimistic about Soka,' he said. 'The possibility of an official Soka Uncobe launch by the royal family looks extremely promising.'

'Great,' I said. Inside, I thought, *really?* We've been hearing that for nearly a year. And, moreover, isn't it too late?

It was quiet for a few awkward seconds until the ambassador said, 'That sure is some sculpture.'

'It certainly is,' I agreed.

After the showing, no one ponied up with the full 9,000 emalangeni to buy the incredible sculpture. (That's right; *60% Safer Avenue* was a bargain at $1,200.) So I organized a collection. We got only just over 3,000 emalangeni, but Jay settled for that, and the seven-foot sculpture took up official residence in the corner of the Hub's conference room, next to boxes of Soka brochures and penis models.

A week or so later, surprising us all, the *Times of Swaziland* ran a photograph of Stephanie, the ambassador and several other PEPFAR officials with King Mswati III. In it, all of them, including the Ngwenyama, stretched out their arms to display their rubber orange Soka Uncobe wristbands.

Honestly, a part of me – the stomach part, to be specific – lurched when I saw the image. Envy, maybe?

The *Times* photo rapidly circulated to inboxes in the States. Half-heartedly, but with stubborn optimism, everyone speculated on its significance. After all the rumors and false assurances, would the king finally publicly endorse circumcision and instruct his men to return to the ancient practice? Was there still reason to hope that the campaign could be revived?

Stephanie reassured us. 'The ambassador is totally committed to Soka Uncobe. He's willing to fall on his sword for it.'

Someone – I think it was Tommy, our waste management expert – offered a liberal and anatomical interpretation of 'his sword.' We laughed. We'd been dealing with the double-talk around Swazi 'spears' forever. But according to the photo in the *Times of Swaziland,* the game wasn't over yet.

Neither was the debate. Some people said that, although it had been a goal since day one, the king's launch simply could not take place; it was far too undignified for the king to reduce himself to a political talking head or to be the mouthpiece of a safer-sex message. Others said that he couldn't do it by Swazi law and tradition; his namesake, King Mswati II was credited with banning the practice of circumcision somewhere in the mid-1800s because the recoup time incapacitated too many of his warriors. The second Mswati could not undo the edict – it would be like contradicting himself. Historians, however, said that this was bunk.

'Swazis do what they are told. Just remember,' our Swazi program assistant Thandi said, 'that when King Sobhuza I told the nation over the radio that they must open their ears, meaning really listen to him, the Swazi people literally did just that.' And it was true that among the older generation of Swazi you could see the sagging slashed openings in their earlobes. 'The king is the only one who can get people to act.'

The amount of energy devoted to preparation for the king's Soka Uncobe launch was impressive. A royal events team came to the Hub and set up shop in the conference room. Hundreds of formal invitations were prepared, a menu set, dance troupes booked, dozens of little details anticipated and accounted for.

Meanwhile, the circumcision team at one of our best sites, Mankayane, led by a mild-mannered nurse whose siSwati name meant thunder, was beside itself with the honor and the expectation of hosting His Majesty. It didn't resemble anything so much as planning, inside of three weeks, a high-class wedding for a thousand, give or take, of your closest friends. Certainly, the cost, borne by the US government, was comparable.

A few words about hosting a celebration for the king of the Kingdom of Swaziland, the queen mother, and a handful of his wives and children. Firstly, the royal family does not use the same toilets as the guests; a special set of port-a-potties had to be purchased. Secondly, in keeping with a time-honored tradition, an honorarium in the form of live cattle – three, instead of the usual five, in deference to 'austerity measures' – was a minimum requirement for the king's participation in a public event. Thirdly, for the sake of preserving his spiritual purity, the king could not walk in a place of death. The last requirement posed an interesting logistical challenge since the circumcision unit was housed within a fully operational hospital. We devised a workaround. So that the king could observe the impressive flow and function of the various steps in a comprehensive circumcision for HIV-prevention process, the clinical team set up a mock circumcision unit on the fairgrounds. They ensured that the unit was outfitted with every diathermy machine and scalpel that a real circumcision site would need, and an official tour of it was added to the day's agenda.

On the morning of 15 July, two groups left the Cooper Center parking lot before eight to drive to the sleepy southern town of Mankayane. We were dolled up in our Swazi finest. Skirts for the women, of course; no pants in the presence of the king. When we pulled into Mankayane, a town so small that its only real landmarks were the hospital and the police station, the main street was strung with streamers of blue, yellow and red triangles. Police security swarmed the area. We parked in a vast field beside the grounds and made our way toward the mock circumcision unit beside a set of stadium bleachers. Remi was there, going through last-minute preparations with the Mankayane team.

The buzz in the air was palpable, the excitement unmatched in the year and a half I had lived in Swaziland. Suddenly, enthusiasm for Soka Uncobe returned. Solomon flew in for the occasion with a huge smile on his face and a camera slung around his neck. Stephanie beamed in a navy suit, pearls and black heels – Kate, too, in her sleek ensemble. Everyone had been waiting for this moment through the slog of an unspectacular campaign. Clara should have been there to see it.

Our very own Soka staffers handed us official agendas and directed us to a special roped-off section where we would be sitting on folding chairs under a canvas tent. For the first hour, the excitement built. For the second hour, impatience set in. During the third hour, the prevailing sentiments were hunger and thirst. It was nearly noon, and still not a trace of His Majesty.

When the royal entourage finally drove in – a cavalcade of twenty-plus vehicles that included shiny black BMWs and a gold Hummer crossing the grounds before us – we were awash with relief and giddy with expectation. Women in beehive hairdos netted in black mesh gracefully stepped high-heeled legs out of rear doors opened by drivers. A gaggle of teenagers followed them. The queen mother materialized in bifocals and her own beehive, a small, rotund form enclosed in a high-necked animal skin cape wrapped around her shoulders. It is one of the many paradoxes of Swazi culture that ordinary women may have had few rights, but the queen mother, the *Ndlovukazi,* the She-Elephant to the king's Lion, was nearly as spiritually mighty as he.

Adam's father, the man they called Ugly, told Adam's mother years before the death of Sobhuza that the child named Makhosetive would be crowned the next king and become Mswati III. Makhosetive is siSwati for 'King of Nations.' Adam's father saw how his monarch friend talked to the gentle boy. 'Just wait,' Adam's father said, 'that boy will be king.' To this prediction, Lisaya said, 'Nonsense.' How could her husband know the outcome of traditional decisions made behind closed doors years and years hence? But sure enough, that very boy was now a kind-faced, burly, middle-aged man who ruled the Kingdom of Swaziland – and in 2011, that boy-now-man had lived through what was probably the most difficult year of his reign.

He came under intense scrutiny from a critical international media. Maintaining so many wives in the face of a raging HIV epidemic did not endear him to journalists. They were unamused by stunts such as the one he pulled several years earlier when he had tried to reintroduce traditional chastity pledges for teenage girls and then took a seventeen-year-old girl for his ninth wife. For ignoring his own pledge, he fined himself a cow. A UK-based journalist writing for the *Daily Mail* wrote, 'He clings to antiquated traditions that promote rampant promiscuity in a land ripped apart by AIDS, where elderly princes take child brides under the cloak of culture, corruption is rife, and fawning courtiers feud for favors as their country falls apart.'

But when the king arrived at the Mankayane fair grounds, he was soft-spoken and smiling, dressed simply in a traditional red *lihiya* tied at the shoulder. During the US ambassador's introduction, the crowd swelled with whooping cheers when he successfully pulled off several siSwati words.

Then the Ngwenyama took to the microphone. I expected a politician. I expected a salesman. That was not what I got. He did not shout. He had no clever oratory gimmicks. He did not need the pyrotechnics that come from the pulpits of mega-churches. He commanded attention in a way I've never seen from a crowd of Americans. But then, Swaziland was not a place of equity, not a meritocracy. And this man, the king, was preacher, healer, leader, father, all rolled into one – a weight he'd worn around his neck for more than a quarter of a century. He spoke in the local language. The entire audience, including at least a hundred dancers and performers, was entranced. A translator converted the siSwati to English. On a screen, we saw his words.

'Circumcision has been identified as one of the many initiatives that we are using in the country to fight against HIV/AIDS. The virus, I shall liken it to a terrorist because it is here to finish our people. I therefore urge the nation to address and stand against the virus. In seeking funding, the Swazi government found the American government to partner with us in order that we may initiate the process that we are here to launch today.'

This was great. The king was verifying that the Swazi leadership was treating the HIV threat with grave seriousness and that it was proactive in its partnership with the US. The Lion went on to reassure the audience that circumcision in

Swaziland would be professional, with services delivered only by the most qualified medical care providers. He then said, 'I would like to send a word of caution to all of you here with us today. Being circumcised does not mean that you are entirely free to live as you please. Circumcision only reduces your chances of contracting the HIV virus. The terrorist determines that each and every one of us here has to lead his or her life well and use protection [...] so that the Swazi people can live without this terrorist... My desire and prayer is that as a Swazi people, you may grow old and be of a good age without this disease, and when your time comes to pass on from this life, you will do so in victory, declaring and saying: I have fought against this virus and kept myself from it.'

As I was watching the words on the screen, I got the feeling that something was amiss, like in pirated movies when the actors' lips moved ahead of the soundtrack. An audience full of Swazis laughed, but the English version we were reading wasn't funny.

Headlines the next day read 'King Endorses Circumcision.' Kate, our new Project Director, taped a blown-up copy on the door of her office at the Hub. Doubtlessly, for her, for her organization, for the US government, the day symbolized a sweeping victory.

I waited for the spike in circumcisions that we all hoped would follow the event. One day, two days, three, a week... It never came. Figures actually dropped the following week. And the week after that.

The next week, as Adam drove up Mountain Road toward Pine Valley, I stared out the passenger-side window at the roadside by Sifundzani High School, which was alight with zigzagging lines of flames. The bushfires extended all the way up the mountain on either side of Pine Valley. Plumes of windblown smoke filled the air.

'You know, love, what happened with that launch was really unusual,' he said, kind of out of nowhere.

'I know! Wasn't it amazing?' I said.

'Yes, it was amazing,' he agreed, never one to be overtly critical. 'But there was something about it that wasn't exactly...' He struggled for the word before landing on 'Swazi.'

'What are you talking about?' I said, looking at him. From what I could tell, the Swazi royal events team planned the day down to every detail. There were female traditional dancers, male traditional dancers, a Swazi gospel band that performed a song and dance routine dreamed up especially for the occasion. The National Correctional Services marching band was there. We ate catered Swazi food, and followed all the customs about who was supposed to eat in what order. Everyone observed the dress code. The proceedings were almost entirely in siSwati. Really, what was he talking about?

'I can't really explain it,' Adam continued. 'But something about it felt off. It was as if the king was accommodating the Americans, saying what they needed to hear... and everyone but the Americans understood that.'

'What do you mean?'

'Well, there are certain rules you must follow when it comes to the royal family. You can always tell from the king's dress. If he wears a suit, there are certain, more Western expectations. If he wears the traditional gear, then there is a certain Swazi formula that must be followed.'

God, he drove me nuts sometimes, the way he took the most indirect route to arrive at his point.

He went on, 'Swazis understand that if you want the king to say something, you don't plant him in front of the cameras. You do not turn it into a spectacle. In this country, decisions are made at 2 a.m. behind closed doors by a group of

316

handpicked men. Sobhuza and the *liqoqo* always visited my dad in the middle of the night for their serious discussions. The king goes to the chiefs, and the chiefs go to the people. I guess Americans would never trust that. Too stealthy, too secret. And, of course, when things work that way, you can't clip and quote the headlines.'

As I lay in bed that night, I sought counsel from two rock-splotches on our bedroom wall – mineral variations, like cloud formations, that I'd named The Olympian and The Spitting Lizard – while the winds lifted anything that wasn't tied down. These were the extraordinary winds of the Swazi winter. We were now living in Big Rock, a fortuitous move prompted by the owners' relocation to the Caribbean. And as soon as we'd left Little Rock, a howling gust tore the tin roof right off and deposited it in a bare tree where it dangled for days like a Christmas ornament. Another ripped a staked counseling tent right out of the ground at our circumcision clinic at Matsanjeni and sent it flying through a windscreen of a client transport *kombi*.

Our new project director was not the least bit embarrassed when our donor Stephanie witnessed the uprooted tent and smashed windscreen on one of her site visits. 'Let her see the kind of ridiculousness we have to deal with on a daily basis,' Kate said. Oh, honey, I thought, you just got here. Have a seat. Let me tell you a thing or two about ridiculous. But who even cared anymore?

On the day he left, Remi said, 'I know you can handle it. The worst is over,' and he gave me a hug. He also hugged Adam, bequeathed him a woolen scarf and said, 'Take good care of her.'

42

'What is the deal with this place?' a skinny, dark-haired New York fresh out of a Masters' in Public Health program asked. 'I mean, are Swazis just spoiled? Living in this peaceful kingdom, disempowered by an absolute monarch whose circle of advisors makes all the big decisions for them?'

He was sitting at our dining room table when he posed the question. With Soka Uncobe in slow motion, we decided to host a get-together at our place. A dozen folks, mostly twenty-something Americans, came to Big Rock with bottles of wine and compilation CDs. Adam busied himself with the grill and fancy marinades while I listened to the stories of their misguided hook-ups and their eye-opening discoveries about the Kingdom.

'I don't know,' another chimed in. 'I think the Swazi entitlement issue is a byproduct of extreme donor dependency.'

We'd all read the books. *The Crisis Caravan. The Wisdom of Whores. The End of Aid.* A new one seemed to come out every year or so, trashing aid policies, calling NGO approaches into question. Were we naïve, complicit cogs in some twisted geopolitical machinery? I'd heard that there are three types of people who bushwhack into foreign lands: missionaries, mercenaries and misfits. Who were we?

I glanced in the direction of the kitchen, where Adam was toiling away with the carcass of an impala. How did he feel during these conversations? What did he think when we bandied about words like 'entitlement' and 'spoiled'? His life certainly had not been one of entitled privilege. Widowed, his mother had fought mightily to provide for her two young sons. Probably one day our housekeeper Buhle's daughters would say the same of their mom.

Yet, alternately baffled and infuriated by what seemed to be an epidemic of hand-outstretched complacency and fatalistic opportunism, I seemed to have lost all cultural relativity. After a year and a half, I was no closer to answers.

Instead, I was frustrated by the attitudes I dealt with on a daily basis. From clients: mothers, alerted to the availability of free circumcision and free transportation to and from the clinics, called up our campaign emergency hotline and asked, 'If my child comes in for a circumcision, what will you give us?' MoliPants had been only the beginning. When we had introduced snack packs for clients who'd endured long wait times during the school holiday campaign, the feedback was astounding. Clients complained. They wanted locally baked Swazi buns, massive pastries, instead of the packaged biscuits we provided. And teenage clients were offended by the cartoon drawing on the juice box cartons, finding them too childish even to drink.

And from service delivery staff: the free hotel rooms, the free lunches, the free transport – carefully planned, coordinated and paid for by my team, they complained about it all. Never mind that most surgical teams – a collection of seventeen medical and support staff – were seeing fewer than ten clients a day, many fewer than five. When we asked them why they weren't using the free time to venture out into the community to rustle up clients, they feigned apologies. 'We want to,' they said, 'but unfortunately, it is not in our scope of work.'

I heard in my own voice, as I talked to the new American arrivals, how jaded and cynical I sounded, and I hated myself for it. But eventually, as bellies filled and stars shone and the dancing started, serious conversation faded. Then the New York arrival asked about Adam and me.

I guess I was aware of the interest we engendered – the yin and yang-ness of our pairing – and, on a certain level, I understood it: the speculation and whispering. I remembered Clara asking if we were the real deal or just another fucked-up expat-local thing. I liked the idea of us still, but increasingly the everydayness of our togetherness was growing difficult.

Adam had recently said to me, 'You are a robot. You just tick me off your to-do list. Schedule time with me like I'm one of your meetings.'

To which I'd replied, 'Well, someone has to worry about the bills, the groceries, about putting gas in the car.'

The truth was that our relationship was starting to wane in perfect parallel with Soka Uncobe.

I wanted out of this job, out of this country, out of this complicated situation with this well-intentioned man. What was I planning to do when the funding ended? Bring him back home with me? A forty-one-year-old man without a college degree and with a US work visa that expired in a matter of months? Did I believe we could make a go of it there? I knew the odds against us, had seen Peace Corps relationships crumble under the searing culture shock and social scrutiny.

I mean, how exactly would this work? Would Adam get by as a massage therapist, dabbling in yoga, shopping for his favorite overpriced gourmet ingredients while I covered the rent and the bills and the health insurance and the retirement savings? How would I ever find the time or space or freedom to write, to raise kids? I conjured the word *breadwinner* in my mind and spooked under its yoke.

We had entirely avoided that conversation as he delivered lunch to my office, kneaded the knots out of my shoulders, cooked for my parents and colleagues, was circumcised, and served thanklessly – month after month – as my cultural interpreter. We never had a honeymoon period, he'd said. And it was unlikely that we'd ever get one. Like the hope of 88,000 HIV infections prevented, I started to see us as a pretty idea that just couldn't stand up to the complexity of real life.

But, at the same time, a life without him was entirely too painful to confront. I couldn't even manage more than a few hours without hearing his voice. I called him half a dozen times a day, to reaffix my grip on the earth, to steady my life with the rudder of his kindness.

Drunk and spent after the heartiest of our partiers left with a Tupperware of impala, I scanned the upturned wine-stained plastic cups that littered our tile floor. I sat down, exhaled, and said to Adam, 'What a mess.'

43

It was an ugly fight. I'd just said the words, 'Deep down, underneath the New Age bullshit, you really are just another African man.' And by that I meant three things: jealous, insecure and proud. He countered with the accusation that I was only biding my time until I found a better-suited partner. An intellectual. An academic. A doctor.

Adam was an unreadable mystery half the time. The Kingdom's motto was, after all, *Siyinqaba*: We are the fortress. After more than two years together, we seemed less, rather than more, understanding of our cultural differences. Lately, work trips tended to provoke such arguments. This time, I was on my way to Durban for the triennial meeting of the International Confederation of Midwives. 'You should come,' I said. 'Then you can see exactly how well I behave with my colleagues.' I don't know where Adam got the impression that young, attractive men in their thirties turn up in droves for jobs in public health, or with anything involving birth, but I was pretty sure that this trip would set him straight.

From Mbabane, it would be a straightforward five-hour drive. Adam did all the driving, all the worrying about directions, all the sweet-talking of police officers and border patrolmen. So when we cruised through the Ngweya-Oshoek border, I wasn't in the least surprised to find him buddying up to a uniformed man who'd taken a concerned interest in us.

The border guard asked Adam to get out of the car and open the trunk. The two of them reviewed the inventory: two pieces of luggage, a trash bag containing empty juice cartons and Nando's boxes, and a random assortment of travel snacks in a broken cooler.

In Zulu, the South African guard asked Adam where he was going. The words were simple enough for me to follow. Adam explained that we were on our way to South Africa for a workshop. 'My wife works in HIV prevention,' he said. 'Have you heard about the circumcision program?'

To this, the guard responded, 'Where are you from? How do you know Zulu?'

Adam stopped sifting through his stuff and looked the guard dead in the face, flashed a smile, and said, 'Swaziland. I grew up there.'

The guard grew puzzled. 'Your parents are Swazi?'

'My dad was from South Africa but he got kicked out of the country because he liked black women. Then he came to Swaziland and met my mom.'

The guard, taking this in, joked, 'Sorry for your dad!' I think it was a reference to being booted from his homeland, rather than to falling for a Swazi woman.

Now Adam slid into his comfort zone. 'Oh no, it was great for him. In Swaziland, men can have as many wives as they want.'

'And how about you? Are you taking as many wives as you want?' the guard asked.

'Ah no, just one for me,' Adam bantered. 'My wife would cut my dick off!'

This was, I thought, a reference to the circumcision program. At least, I hoped it was.

Then the guard came back around to my side of the car and made a weird smirking face while slicing his fingers down each wrist in a gesture suggestive, to me anyway, of suicide, before he waved us off. Was that supposed to mimic a scalpel on a foreskin? Adam and I sat in silence as we drove toward Ermelo. I'd had enough of this place. The creepiness. The losses in cultural translation.

Once we arrived in Durban, the air between us improved: ocean swims, a nice hotel room, all-you-can-eat buffet breakfasts and fancy dinners charged to my travel per diem. I attended conference sessions on topics I hadn't thought about in years – ultrasound dating, group prenatal care, updated medication regimens for treating complications in labor. My brain was buzzing, in a good way. I felt full. Satiated.

At the end of the second day, I walked across the terrace on the way back to our hotel room and focused on my feet. They looked terrible. A Serendipity pedicure from a couple months back had grown out into chipped crimson half-moons, the crevices between digits dirty from yesterday's walk along a hot beach. Then there was my outfit. It traced back to an American life lived three years beforehand. Subject to Buhle's rigorous washings, all vibrancy and elasticity had long since disappeared. This, I thought to myself, was exactly the image of a midwife I'd formed as a student: leather sandals, shapeless clothes.

But in Durban, South Africa, during those few days in August 2011, I was surrounded by midwives who utterly defied that stereotype. The day before, I'd sat in a room jam-packed with thousands of them. They hailed from everywhere. West African midwives came in their tailored puffed-sleeve tops and fitted long skirts, their turban wraps. Asian midwives in trim pants and conference T-shirts. At the end of the welcoming ceremony, when the South African midwives broke out in a Zulu song of kinship and hope, the hair on my arms stood on end and tears filled my eyes. Gone were the penis politics; here was my sisterhood.

In that moment, I felt myself snapping awake from a two-year dream of bloody foreskins and cigarettes and mountain runs and a cave house built into a mountainside and a rain-god of a king and a handsome lover with a soft heart and a complex past. That storybook life. I'd tasted it. And I just didn't want it anymore.

Walking across the slate tiles from the conference hall back to the adjoining hotel to meet Adam and prepare for an NGO dinner, I felt myself alone and free to traverse these various trails of thought ... What next? Should I stay in Africa? Should I stay with Adam? Or should I finally admit defeat? Pack my bags, close this chapter, go home, start again?

I must have heard her footsteps first, the smack-smacking of thongs against stone. Or maybe I caught, from the peripheral vision of my downward-cast eyes, the terrific blueness of one of her beautiful saris. Whatever it was, some subtle sensory event caused me to lift my head and to take in this figure strolling toward me, a woman equally lost in thought. Her face looked tired and older than I remembered. The familiar red bindi on her forehead, marking the gateway to forgiveness and compassion, bleeding at the edges with perspiration.

Funny, the things that spring to mind in such situations. When I saw her, for the first time in five years, the image that flashed to the surface of memory was of the entrance to her homebirth practice in the basement of a three-story Connecticut colonial. On it, she had pasted a bumper sticker: *Well-behaved women rarely make history*. This was the professor who had taught us that if we found ourselves in a pickle, we should deliver a baby on spread newspapers.

I was sure that she wouldn't remember me. Even though I'd been a troubled student in my last year of the program, she must have had dozens of such hesitating, overly analytical young women in the years before and since. At graduation, she told my mom, 'You daughter is extremely bright, she just lacks confidence' – a reworked version of the parent-teacher conferences from twenty years before. By then, I already knew that I wouldn't slap my framed diploma on an office wall and make my living catching babies.

Living in Swaziland now for over a year and a half, something about seeing my professor catapulted me back to a previous self and a soft tug of homesickness pulled at my insides. In Durban, I saw this homebirth midwife and clinical instructor and remembered who I was supposed to be. And wasn't.

'Vidya?' I began tentatively as I pulled alongside her. I held out my sweaty hand. 'You probably don't remember me, but I was a student of yours about five years ago. Laura?'

'I remember exactly who you are,' she said. Taking my hand, she gently pulled me down for a back-patting hug. 'How nice to see you.' My right hand snagged her still-thick, waist-length braid. More grey in it than I remembered from my sunny graduation day.

'Where are you practicing now?' she asked.

'I'm not,' I told her, unsure how to explain that I had hung up my size 6.5 gloves for good. Carefully, I chose my words. I told her that I was living in Swaziland working on an HIV-prevention program. I told her the name of the organization I worked for, one synonymous with reproductive health. I told her that, although I wasn't entirely fulfilled professionally, I was happy in other ways. She looked at me as though I was the one who had aged. We stood there, me a head taller, and mirrored each other.

'You know, there's a lot more to life than work.' She studied me. She was calm. Her wide brown eyes were discriminating and intelligent, with a hint of youthful trouble-making underneath. 'You were a wonderful midwife, you know,' she said.

So many things I wanted to tell her. I wanted to explain that when I signed on to her program I hadn't known what it would feel like to be haunted by tight cords wrapped around purple infant necks, as hypersensitive and anxious an adult as I'd been as a kid. But while I may have rejected deliveries, I still felt myself akin to midwives, still felt myself a member of their tribe.

I didn't have the words to explain. Instead, I gave her my business card, and told her to call me when she was passing through Swaziland with her family en route to a safari in Kruger. 'No one ever visits Swaziland,' I'd said. 'It would be wonderful to show you around.'

Unless you counted my parents, no one from home ever did visit me in Swaziland and I certainly didn't expect her to be the first. In fact, I never thought she'd call until she actually did. I was sitting on a dirty rock in a littered field near Cooper Center, watching a scrappy teenager dump buckets of river water on my filthy Pajero, when I felt the vibrations of my phone inside of my workbag.

'Sorry, who is this?' I asked several times into the phone, blocking out the honking traffic with a palm covering my free ear. Durban already felt lifetimes away. The voice was talking about animals, and asking me to help sort out accommodation and a potential itinerary for a couple of down days in Swaziland. Vidya was made for this kind of travel. Between midwifery and motherhood, the woman thrived in a climate of chaos.

When Adam and I went to pick her up for a traditional Swazi meal, it was early September, the start of spring in Swaziland, and the country was just beginning to burst into a bright cloud of electric purple jacaranda blossoms. As she ushered us into her hotel room, fussing over keys, it became the most normal thing in the world for my once-professor to be visiting with my Swazi boyfriend and me in an African kingdom.

Vidya wanted to ride to eDladleni Restaurant with Adam and me. 'So Laura and I can catch up!' she told her husband. I slid past the folded passenger seat into the back and Vidya sat up front. In the cup holders on the Pajero's dashboard were two empty bottles of Castle beer. Vidya pretended not to notice. 'So,' she said, 'tell me about the project you're working on.'

As Adam pulled onto the roundabout bound toward Malagwane Hill, I tried to explain what we were doing with the circumcision program. She listened for a minute or two and then interrupted. 'You don't seem happy,' she said. 'This isn't the right kind of work for you.'

Once we got to the restaurant, I shifted into questioning mode. It was just easier. We drank wine and talked about the midwifery program Vidya was starting. As she spoke, I guessed at the struggles, the long hours, the plate forever too full. With her children out of the house and a husband who worked in another state, there was no safeguard on her time. This was the woman I never wanted to be, drained and fighting a constant uphill battle for her ideals. And yet, deep down, I feared that this was the only kind of woman I could become.

On the subject of my work, Vidya held her tongue until we piled into the car on the way back to Timbali. 'You know,' she began, 'the foreskin actually does serve a physiological purpose.'

Vidya, like many people, including all of Adam's holistic colleagues, opposed the removal of anything Mother Nature installed. To Vidya, it was simple. Like an episiotomy, don't cut if there isn't an immediate medical indication to do so. 'I just don't think you can solve a cultural problem with a surgical solution,' she said.

The next day, Vidya asked if we could meet quickly on her way out of town. I suggested she swing by the Hub. It was a quiet afternoon. Most of the staff was gone, either in the field, or working from other locations, or checked out for the day. By this stage of the program, most of the staff spent their workdays on Facebook or downloading movies and clogging up the server. With so few circumcising teams, and so few clients, what remained was routine administration.

'Things are winding down now,' I said, as a way of explaining why so many desks were vacant, why corners and tables were littered with cardboard boxes. In the beginning, the office space had been cluttered because we were too busy to properly organize it. Now, we'd run out of steam. An overflowing volcano of rejected or unclaimed paper poured from a box underneath the photocopier. Soka Uncobe pamphlets, buttons and cell phone stickers were scattered around and attached to various surfaces. A wide-screen TV, once intended to give up-to-the-minute information about the hundreds of circumcisions performed each day, was black and silent. A trio of staff stood before the open back doors and laughed and talked loudly about something probably not work-related.

I showed Vidya to the back, glass-walled conference room where our penis models were stocked ceiling-high. I introduced her to Jay's *60% Safer Avenue* sculpture with its red glowing penis. Next I took her to the boxes of promotional materials. I reached in and pulled out a handful of orange rubber Soka Uncobe wristbands.

'Here,' I said, giving them to my professor, 'a reminder of Swaziland.'

'You know I can't wear this!' Vidya joked, accepting them anyway. 'But could you show me to the toilet? I should probably go one more time before I hit the road.'

I brought her to the back of the once-workshop where two side-by-side doors displayed cartoon graphics of a male and a female. The woman now sported a moustache and beard. No one cared. Vidya stopped outside the door. She reached over and held my arm. 'Laura, I just wanted to say a few things to you before we leave.'

My heart beat faster.

'It's been so good to see you. I hope you know how much I really would like to stay in touch. I know you will be fine, but I really think you should take some time out to focus back in on yourself. Trust in life a little bit more. When I met my husband, we had absolutely nothing. Not a dime. I had no idea my life was going to turn out like this.'

I listened...

'I know you have doubts about Adam. But he's a good man. A kind man. You have something here. Make a go of it. Have I ever told you about my former student who married a Sherpa?'

I'd heard about the Sherpa at least three times. I smiled. 'Yes, Vidya, you have. Thank you.'

'Don't worry so much,' she said and raised her arms, making her gold bangles musically clink against each other. I bent my knees for the embrace, so that our soft bodies could find each other.

44

By November, after living in Swaziland for nearly two years, no one seemed surprised by my decision to leave. Leadership asked only that I stay on long enough to tell about one hundred people that they wouldn't have jobs after the festive season. So, slightly hungover, I embarked on a bookend whirlwind tour of Swaziland. Every day for a week, I told teams of a dozen-plus people that their contracts would not be renewed. I'd set out to make my career on the back of this program, and this is how it was ending.

But you know what? While I'd expected the worst, I didn't get it. Instead, amazingly, unbelievably, I got gratitude. A counselor from Siteki sent me a text message that read: 'Hi Laura, how are you? May I take this chance to thank you guys for all that you've done for us, and also going out of your way to tell us to fasten our belts in time... You guys are really worth our trust. It's sad to lose a job but it makes us all feel at ease that we were told in time. Thanks so much for taking on a drastic and challenging initiative. All the best in your future plans.'

It was counterintuitive. It made no sense. Why were these nurses, counselors, cleaners and theater runners not incensed?

Well, maybe this is what they had expected the whole time

from us crocodiles. Maybe we'd now arrived at the showdown of scientific reason in the Western tradition and indigenous belief systems. On one side sat North American or European academic experts scratching their heads, wondering why people weren't lining up in droves for the latest and greatest life-saving intervention – proven effective on thousands of people under tightly controlled conditions. On the other side sat groups of people with very long memories who'd watched trends come and go. (Another African proverb: *The axe forgets, the tree remembers.*) The graveyard of public health failures is chock-full of cautionary tales in which brilliant ideas were foiled by cultural ignorance. Or impatience. All the time, projects start, and end, and publicize what they wish. But people remember. And people have the power.

I was prepared for everyone to be as disappointed as I was. I wasn't prepared for the acceptance and the gentleness that marked this final phase of the program. The general sentiment from our staff on the ground, our nurses and theatre runners and cleaners, was 'Hey, we tried. I had a job for the last six months, and that's something. Tomorrow will come and we don't yet know what will come with it. We will deal with it in time.'

I hoped this signaled something: a shared understanding, a shared disappointment, and some sort of shared humanity. I hoped it meant that I'd been an *umuntfu*, a true person, to them, not just a *mlungu*, a white foreigner.

By then, the program totaled 9,730 circumcisions, less than ten percent of the ASI's original lofty target. Now, finally, conversation grew circumspect. Everyone agreed that the planning phase had been too tight. Gaining approval – from both the US and the Swazi governments – had been slow and inefficient. So many players made for a lack of clarity on roles and responsibilities. Then everything got further complicated by the unanticipated and unfortunate economic situation in the country, by the political striking and the generalized unrest.

But of course the biggest issue was a massive underappreciation of the fact that Swazi men didn't appear to want to part with their foreskins, and no one on the inside – that is, on the Swazi side – had managed to convince them, suggesting that they themselves were never sold on the idea. Not enough time, effort and resources had been allocated to figuring out what it would really take to get through to Swazi men.

The pressure to 'do it fast!' had been so ill-suited to this context. The American approach was never going to work in Swaziland; I saw it in my own relationship. Many times Adam commented on it: 'Your busyness, your structure, is an avoidance of really feeling anything.' Many times, I told him, 'Your disorganization, your magical thinking, and the quickness with which you blame external factors when things don't work out, keep you from making real progress in your life.' How much did these opposing mindsets destabilize Soka Uncobe?

Then the revisionist history set in. A newly arrived NGO whiz kid told me that he'd heard the truth about the ASI from his Swazi colleagues. We Americans had gotten it all wrong. 'Did you know that Soka Uncobe is a misinterpretation of siSwati? That it implies that there's a link between circumcision and sexual assault?' It infuriated me. The majority of the participants at the Maguga meeting, those who decided on the slogan, *were* Swazi. Swazis who'd selected the very name now disowned it, unwilling to be associated with the project in retrospect.

Then Stephanie left and so did Kristi. The original cast of characters, those of us sent to cut our teeth in the Kingdom, disbanded. All of us, lifelong overachievers, sent to Swaziland too early in our careers for us to be able to apply the perspective of experience. We craved praise and operated with a constant terror of screwing up. But, shit, had Soka Uncobe taught us a thing or two. The focus of our work may have been public health, the science of populations, of the collective, but the fallout of the program was absolutely individual, specific and personal.

What had previously been a distanced, academic discussion was no longer distanced and academic at all. At a certain imperceptible point while I was embedded in the work of circumcising for HIV prevention, the conversation about gender and relationships in southern Africa, about mathematical models versus reality, stopped being about *them* and became about *my* relationship, *my* attitudes, *my* cultural baggage, *my* vulnerability, *my* behavior. And, let me tell you, there's nothing that teaches you faster, that offers up such a dizzying array of hard-won lessons learned, than picking a careful path through the landscape of your own heartbreak.

I felt like I'd aged a decade, though I'd only just turned thirty-five. On my birthday, my workmates gave me a long, slender, surprisingly heavy gift. I shuddered when the veiny, soapstone shaft came into view: a stone carving of an oversized penis. More eighth-grade Soka Uncobe humor? It always featured into birthday celebrations at the Hub. I had a sick feeling as I held the heavy stone.

'Where did you get this?' I asked Kate.

'We found it on the way to Pigg's Peak. You know those stalls on the side of the road where they sell the same stone ashtrays? With the pot-smoking carvers? I was headed up to our MC site at Pigg's Peak last week and we stopped to have a look. I couldn't believe it when I saw this! One of the carvers told us that a white couple specifically ordered it years ago to spice up their sex life, but they never came back to pick it up. Great, right?' I had a sudden flashback to those early days of the project, the early days with Adam, when we were so enamored of each other, when we wanted to try everything.

When the Kingdom later went into its festive slumber, I pulled the Pajero out of the Hub's gravel parking lot for the last time. Adam and I had spent a few months bumping up against each other in Big Rock, both of us lost. I filled page after page with drivel about the circumcision program, convinced I would eventually write a book about it. He talked about vague business plans. We made half-hearted attempts to keep up with the social scene until things went drastically wrong on a boozy weekend in Maputo, when in response to the question, 'What's the one thing you want to experience before you die?' Adam had said, 'A real, lasting love.'

My jaw dropped. Others looked at me in horror. No one spoke. Adam attempted to backpedal. 'I meant a relationship that was equal. Angel, everyone knows you have one foot in and one foot out.'

His words became a legitimate reason to take those feet and walk.

I licked my wounds in Provincetown, the three-mile spit of land that welcomed one and all, boasted 800 year-round inhabitants and possessed a tendency towards pettiness and drama, just like Swaziland. I sat on my great-aunt Ruth's back porch, spotted a skittish coyote in the brushy saltwater swamp, thought obsessively about Adam and fretted over what to do now.

Swaziland was with me, every waking minute. In a world becoming increasingly homogenous and molded by social media, where was the magic of chance, of ritual, of mystery? They'd been alive and well in the warped fairyland I'd just left. I was homesick for a place I'd never understood. *PBS News*

Hour ran a short snippet entitled, 'Why a US Circumcision Push Failed in Swaziland.' I called Adam.

'Come home,' he said.

I was crying too hard to answer him.

45

I am thirty-six. I've moved to Washington D.C. to start a new job working with international midwives. Every day I walk to my office off Dupont Circle from my apartment on 15th and Q. I often grow teary for reasons I can't easily pinpoint, torn as I feel between worlds, between traditions, between what others want for me and what I want for myself. What I've just been through and how little it matters now. I am tormented by a need to relive and understand my time in Swaziland, a preoccupation that consumes me at times.

Did I pour my whole self, over two years of my life, into something that was always bound to fail? I doubt it. Tanzanians in Iringa lined up en masse for circumcision because they saw it as the right, responsible, desirable thing to do. Swazis didn't line up because they viewed it with suspicion, didn't see the urgency and considered it an imposition. Could that determination only have been made in hindsight? Sure, we could have done a million things differently. And, yes, problems with the approach should have been diagnosed much earlier. Hopefully in future programs, they will. I'm certainly not the only one who was humbled by the experience. The Nerd Circus that isn't, and never was – the smart, passionate public health practitioners who worked so hard to introduce an untested intervention for the sole purpose of saving lives – also matured, learned a few painful things.

But I also want to leave it behind. Now, I want work that's meaningful, deeply and personally – with women, going back to my midwifery roots. I want to keep moving. Travel – new countries, new cultures, new people, disorientation, assimilation, quick thinking – stimulation of the sort that has always propelled me. I want a real sense of home, of belonging to my own pinprick point on a spinning globe. I want freedom from the unarticulated fear that my life is slipping through my fingers, that every passing year steals more and more of the golden promise of some untapped possibility. I want creativity. I want children. I want beauty. I want to go entire days, weeks even, without asking, 'Where is my place in all of this?' I want to have the courage and the tenacity to dig and dig and dig, as deep as I'm able, to get to my closest approximation of truth and then to have the courage to tell it.

When I left Kibo Hospital almost four years ago, I was afraid of exposing myself as a coward midwife. As a failure. I'd tried to rewrite my narrative so that global health appeared part of the master plan rather than an about-face on a too-bumpy road. I'd tried to reshape myself into something new. Tried to prove that I was smart and able. Hoped permanently to sublimate the sensitive girl within. But now that I've arrived in D.C.? Well, I don't necessarily feel smart and able, but I also don't care as much. I have less to prove. I feel wiser. I feel able *enough*. Now I've lived through a different kind of failure. And I'm still here, still with the chance to recreate myself. The people who really love me never needed me to be, or do, anything other than what I was. I mostly get that now. Never again, I tell myself, will I value a project over people. And even though I'm sticking with public health, a science of populations, I will still seek to know and connect with real individuals, real situations, real stories. That's where my secret strength and intelligence lies. And it's worth something.

My biggest project is now in Pakistan. Our office is based in a megacity, a single metropolis, with twenty times the populace of Swaziland. I have a new wardrobe comprised of long embroidered tunics and headscarves. I watch back-to-back episodes of *Homeland*. I experience my first Ramadan, headachy and thirsty in a hotel with dark, thick, always-closed curtains. I meet women, still girls really, who are courageous beyond comprehension – the first in their families to go to school, working around the clock to care for the mothers and babies in their communities. As one of them told me, 'Yes, I am often afraid when I face an emergency, but I must help these women. I live in such a far-flung place. Out there, emergencies are left only to me and God.'

I fall asleep in my third-floor apartment wondering what it would be like to have Adam with me in D.C. To grocery shop together at the Whole Foods on P and 14th. Adam would love the Saturday morning yoga class at Flow, the studio next door. He could spend hours at the farmers' market by the Dupont Metro station. I miss his eternally sunny glass-half-full disposition, the way he bounces out of bed with a child's energy after just six hours of sleep, the bolstering support of his embrace, his unwavering belief in me.

I see Adam, over and over again, in airports and coffee shops. I am grateful for the hot stab of misplaced recognition as my mind transcribes his face onto that of someone shorter, beakier, or hairier. 'Not him,' I realize, my heart aflutter, reminded with absolute clarity of the size and color of his eyes, the shape of his hands, his stride, the sight of him waiting, one knee crossed over the other. With a blow to the gut, a grip around the throat, I remember, as if surprised, that I continue to love him.

I poll my friends one by one, divide the romantics from the pragmatists. I sit with my Peace Corps friend Gene in a wood-floored, high-ceilinged, fire-placed Logan Circle apartment. I tell him that I fantasize about going back to Africa. 'Does that make me pathetic?' I ask. 'Am I just a Peace Corps volunteer who can't grow up and move on?'

'Not at all,' Gene says, in a statement for which I will forever love him. 'I see you as much more Meryl Streep in *Out of Africa*, classy and gutsy in pleated khaki pants.'

Adam and I still talk most days. He's doing well. He still lives on the Rock Compound. He runs a café downtown where he makes fancy sandwiches and daily specials with organic vegetables he grows himself. We talk about getting back together. He says, 'I won't allow you to break my heart again. No more second place. If we're doing this, we're doing it for good.'

As the temperatures dip below freezing in D.C., I unpack mothballed woolens and book a roundtrip ticket for Johannesburg. I don't exactly know what I'm hoping we'll get out of it. It's only a two-week Christmas break.

He looks different from the man I'd left. I suppose I'm not the same wide-eyed, workaholic American woman he'd fallen in love with, either. I see, in the ledge of his collarbone and the effortful half-smile, that my indecision, my own double-brained bullshit, were betrayals that left indelible marks.

He drives me across the border where a Swazi summer explodes with flapping bursts of white butterflies. The Soka Uncobe billboards are still up along the Malagwane Hill – the attractive avatars professing that a circumcised man is a real Swazi man.

'We should stop at Pick n Pay. I didn't have time to shop before leaving to get you at the airport,' he says.

It's so familiar, so perfectly normal to be here, picking up our groceries at the mall. Pakistan evaporates. D.C. My new life. Adam is parking the car at the far end of the lot when I bump into James, the driver who took me on my first harrowing drive up the Malagwane. He's dressed in a matching red tracksuit and leaning up against his van just outside the entrance to Pick n Pay.

'Sister Laura! Is it really you? Oh, I can't believe it! I am so happy to see you.' And I can truly see that he is. James makes me feel wanted, and welcome, just as he had on my very first day in the Kingdom three years earlier.

Then, once inside, Adam and I spot our old neighbor, Talkative George. He also appears overjoyed to see the two of us. No one mentions the obvious: *Didn't you guys break up?*

'You know how I wound up back here?' he asks, true to his nickname. 'Eventually, I decided that I just wanted to be happy. Either I could be controlled by my pension, or I could control my own life. You know what they say – shrouds don't have pockets! You're here with the person you love. What's more important than that? Are you really going to let a job rule you?'

Is he speaking truth, or is he, like so many who wash up in Swaziland, just avoiding something else? Running from a life that doesn't quite accommodate the oddballs, the less than conventional life choices? A hub for the disenfranchised. Like they say: mercenary, missionary, or misfit? It takes us twenty minutes to force an exit from Talkative George. Same as always.

'I saw Jabu the other day,' Adam tells me as we walk with our groceries back to the car, a cheap import he bought when we sold off the Pajero. 'She sends her greetings. Oh, and she says I owe her *lobola*, a bride-price, because when I asked for clients, she sent me a wife.' I giggle to remember the moody server, my first friend in Swaziland.

Adam stops suddenly. We are standing, facing each other, in the middle of the hot parking lot. I wonder what's wrong. He studies my face for a moment. 'It's so nice to hear you laughing again, angel,' he says. It's true. None of us really laughed much in those final days.

That lazy afternoon, Adam and I climb around the side of Big Rock, up to the granite roof. He packs us some vegetables in olive oil, some pita and hummus. He drops the backpack with the picnic packed carefully inside onto the stone. We look across our bit of Pine Valley before we lie flat like lizards on the hot stone. Impenetrable rock beneath us, we spread our arms wide. We feel the rush of the waterfall. We hear the Zionists chant their eerie blessings across the valley below. Our fingers lace. A stream of sensory memory: a pile of crunching leaves; a foamy lick of seawater; peat smoke in a Donegal pub; a baby's squall; the burning smell of Africa.

Africa.

'Get out of your head,' Adam says. He turns his cheek against the stone, holds my face in his gentle hands. He grins that incredible grin of his. 'Just be here with me. We don't have to think about anything else for now.'

Unbound is the world's first crowdfunding publisher, established in 2011.

We believe that wonderful things can happen when you clear a path for people who share a passion. That's why we've built a platform that brings together readers and authors to crowdfund books they believe in – and give fresh ideas that don't fit the traditional mould the chance they deserve.

This book is in your hands because readers made it possible. Everyone who pledged their support is listed at the front of the book and below. Join them by visiting unbound.com and supporting a book today.

Nabeel Akram
Jessica Alexander
Rachel Auteri
Joya Banerjee
Ruth Boreham
Anna Bosch
Naomi Bouchard
Sara Bryant
Ed Bunker
Lore Businge
Joel Cabrita
Nancy Caiola
Chloe Campbell
Carolyn Carlson
Nancy Comello
Chloe Cooney
Chelsea Cooper
Andrew DiNardo
Cyndy Falwell Pitta

Pamela Faura
Patricia Gomez
Lauren Gradia
Megan Guzman
Eileen Hardin
Natalie Hendler
Bonne Hill
John Hoffman
Heather Hoffmann
Holly Katz
Silvia Kelbert
Jen Kennedy
Megan Key
Sharon Kibwana
Sharon Kim
Amy Kleine
Joanna Knueppel
Fiona Lensvelt
Lindsay Litwin

Thomas Logan
Alan McMahon
Caroline Middlecote
Cyndi Murray
Carlo Navato
Heidi O'Bra
Eric Pavri
Bev Peel
Diana Pietrangelo
paris Pitsillides
Abby Pratt
Presha Regmi
Carolyn Ridpath
Ulrika Rubin
Indira Sarma
Catherine Sassano

Julia Scheeres
Kelly Shimoda
Tracey Shissler
Lisa "Nyamanda Madise" Silvestro
Jessica Smith
Sarah Smith
Deborah Sontag
Elizabeth Swanton
Kelly Taylor
Erica Troncoso
Joris Vandelanotte
Gabriel Vogt
Robyn Wade
Angie Wierzbicki
Emma Williams
Sarah Wingfield

Author's Note and Acknowledgments

Now, almost a decade after the ASI, male circumcision efforts continue in Swaziland (Eswatini). Though many of the challenges chronicled here still thwart HIV-prevention measures there, lessons learned helped neighboring countries successfully expand their own male circumcision programs. Sometimes global health and development projects fail to achieve their goals. Unless we can talk honestly, openly, and with humility about what did not work and why, we miss essential opportunities to learn, adapt, and do better. It is worth noting that in the ten years since the ASI was attempted, the field has changed considerably in positive ways. There is now an increasing emphasis on co-creation between international and national teams as true and equal partners, on developing programs that are designed not just for, but by, those who will benefit from them, on strengthening local organizations to lead, and on addressing entrenched, complex issues with longer-term, systems-minded approaches.

In additional to being bold enough to talk about failure in substantial and meaningful ways, we must also recognize remarkable successes. At the time of writing, PEPFAR is in its fifteenth year of providing lifesaving services to many of the world's most vulnerable people. In 2018 alone, nearly 15 million people living with HIV received antiviral medicines that kept them healthy and prevented them from passing HIV to their partners. By the end of that same year, PEPFAR-supported programs had reached nearly 19 million boys and men with circumcision services across fourteen countries in sub-Saharan Africa.

On a personal note, writing *Those Who Eat Like Crocodiles* has been a labor of love for close to eight years. When I started working on the first messy draft in 2012, I made a number of assumptions about my life that, no surprise, turned out to be laughably false.

Firstly, I assumed that the six-month leave of absence I took to begin writing this book would lead to a departure from global health. At the start of 2012, I was exhausted and disillusioned. Fortunately, life had something else in store. Nearly a decade later, I still work for a global health nonprofit, and with many of the other organizations referenced in this book. These days, I enjoy work that offers a deep sense of purpose, and count many of the 'characters' from this period among my friends, family, colleagues and mentors still. That's why completing this book took so long – it needed to be as true a tale as I was capable of telling, factually and emotionally, but I also wanted to be fair to everyone who was involved in this well-intended project. For this reason, I have changed the names of some places, as well as almost all characters' names and certain identifying characteristics.

Secondly, I doubted that I would have lasting ties to the country now called Eswatini. I consider the Kingdom of Swaziland – the name used in *Those Who Eat Like Crocodiles* because that was the official name until 2018 – both unknowable and beloved. As I describe in the book, the landscape and the culture pulled me in immediately. And didn't let go. In 2013, I purchased the home in Pine Valley where Adam and I lived during most of the time frame of this book. It is my sincerest wish that I have presented the Kingdom both honestly and respectfully. To Swati friends and colleagues, I hope you see some value in the universality of this story, understand why I felt so compelled to tell it, and will forgive any unintended misrepresentations.

Thirdly, when I started writing this book, I had no idea what would happen between Adam and me. As deeply as we cared about each other, I was pessimistic about our ability to sustain a successful relationship across cultures and continents. Thankfully, he has more faith and patience than I do. After a difficult on-and-off year and a half, I moved back to Eswatini at the end of 2013. About two years later, Adam and I welcomed our first daughter. And, shortly thereafter, our second. We were married in Provincetown in August 2018. I owe an unpayable debt of gratitude to him for championing this book unconditionally from the start, despite the substantial personal risk and exposure. Not only that, but he has been the primary parent, the steadfast heart of our family, through two international moves, countless work trips and too many closed-door writing weekends. Without him, achieving the long-held dream of publishing a book would never have been possible.

And this brings me to my final false assumption: that writing a book would be a solitary, introspective task. Part of it was, sure, but really finding the resonant themes and weaving them into a cohesive narrative? Keeping at it rewrite after rewrite, year after year? Well, that took a village. Thank you, Owen Ryan, Bob Forrester, David Watts, Catherine Carr, Katie Peel, Chris Hallman and Mona Hakimi for reading my first terrible drafts, asking smart questions, offering useful feedback and telling me to keep going. Thank you to Julia Scheeres and Catherine Adams for your sharp editorial observations. To

Claudia Ramos and Erica Troncoso, thank you for your talented work behind the camera. Thank you to the team at Unbound for giving new authors and unconventional stories a chance. To my family in Eswatini, thank you for your immediate acceptance and sincere generosity; I am humbled by your fortitude, and I hope what I have written conveys some measure of your strength and grace. To KC, TA and JR, your support has been invaluable. To Mom and Dad, thank you for always allowing me to choose my own way and make my own mistakes, for cheering me along each time I've stubbornly insisted on taking the less-traveled road. It's an example I hope I can follow with my own girls. Lastly, thank you, reader, so very much for reading my first book.